The Last Stack

Entrepreneurism
and the Environment

FRED STENSON

*This book is dedicated
to those who choose
the entrepreneurial path.*

Mission Statement

To preserve the story of Western Research, a frontier environmental company, and to distill from its trials and breakthroughs a wisdom of potential use to all entrepreneurs with dreams of great achievement and a passion for excellence.

© Joe Lukacs, 2000.

CETAC-WEST
Suite 420, 715-5th Avenue S.W.,
Calgary, Alberta, Canada T2P 2X6

Canadian Cataloguing in Publication Data

Stenson, Fred 1951-
The last stack

Includes index.
ISBN 1-55056-782-9

1. Bow Valley Resource Services Ltd. Western Research & Development
Division—History. 2. Desulphurization—Alberta—History.
I. Canadian Environmental Technology Advancement Corporation-West.
II. Title.
HD9718.C34B67 2000   338.4'7628532   C00-910850-5

Printed and bound in Canada by Friesens Corporation.
This book is printed on acid-free paper.
Book design by Cliff Kadatz.

Contents

Part IV: (1981-1992) Going International

Part V: The Shooting Stars

Preface

The mission statement of this book speaks of distilled wisdom, the wisdom gleaned from the experience of Western Research, a frontier environmental company that parlayed a regional success in Alberta into a controlling position in the sulphur species analyzer market worldwide. In my work as a management educator and a management consultant, this type of business wisdom wrought of real-world experience is my stock in trade. It is the material most useful to me in my endeavour to teach the entrepreneurs of tomorrow and to help the entrepreneurs of today.

A very important thing to know in this regard is that business stories are not all created equal when it comes to their value as case studies. Many company stories do not distill down into wisdom, or they distill into a wisdom that is not sufficiently applicable to others to be of use.

The story of Western Research, which I have often used since consulting to the company in the late 1980s, is at the other end of the spectrum: a fine and fascinating case. For starters, very few case studies cover the full life-cycle of a company, in this case over a thirty-year period. What also makes the Western Research case so valuable is that the challenges the company met and conquered in its growth and evolution are the challenges that most small businesses encounter when they seek to grow. The ways by which Western Research surmounted those obstacles were often very astute and are still available to most young companies today. Western Research offered a wide spectrum of services and products in an effort to provide a one-stop environmental source, and this too extends the usefulness of its story. Basically, Western Research had some wonderful values, and a commitment to hard work and problem solving for clients that was consistently placed above the profit motive. This, in the long term, translated into trust and a rock-solid reputation for excellence.

The challenges of entrepreneurship, the shift from service company to products company, the need for new markets created by successful saturation of the local one, the higher risks encountered in the foreign marketplace, the even greater risks associated with moving out of a comfortable niche into the often deadly combination of a new product in a new market, creating a culture, the function of values and culture in the success formula, financing crunches, survival of sustained market downturns, a serious management succession crisis at the end—it's all here, with each chapter lending an inflection point, isolating a business crossroads, where critical decisions were evaluated and taken.

What is also important is that the Western Research story is not exclusively a success story. What small company does not fail, partially if not entirely, along its path? Western Research's navigation into stormy waters and back out of them provides another kind of instruction, as valuable as the moves that brought its success.

Small businesses working in the environmental area will find particular value in these pages, but most small and medium-sized company entrepreneurs will benefit from reading it. At some level, business is business; its challenges, imperatives and remedies are sufficiently parallel for the wisdom to be transferable: a fact upon which the management science is based.

To help crystallize the progress of the book in management terms, each chapter ends with a few questions for the reader. By considering them, by weighing their relevance to your own business experience, the wisdom of Western Research may become yours.

Dr. M. Blaine Lee

Introduction

If there were such a thing as a crystal ball, and if the world unfolds as it should, a look into the twenty-second century might reveal a landscape completely without smoke and exhaust stacks. Maybe the flare stacks will be gone as well. What that would mean is that scientists and engineers, in conjunction with industry and government, would have found and enforced ways of running industrial plants so efficiently that no emissions existed at the tail of any plant to either vent or burn.

The story in this book is about how many of the steps toward such a possible future were taken first in the Canadian province of Alberta. Many of the steps were taken because the government was wise enough to require them. But a surprising number of steps were also taken in advance of the regulations, or in excess of them, either because companies wanted to implement their pollution control strategies on their own timeline, or because companies and individuals in companies genuinely wanted to reduce their emissions and the potential damage they might do.

A catalyst is a chemical that speeds up a desired reaction, and no better metaphor could be found for how Western Research figures into this larger story of how Alberta and the rest of the world learned to deal more effectively with air pollution. Starting in 1965 in the then-small city of Calgary, Western Research became a prosperous high-tech company. In its late-1970s and '80s heyday, it sold high-tech environmental products and services into fifty countries. Keeping oxides of sulphur and nitrogen out of the sky is key to the environmental health of the planet, and Western Research had developed knowledge and techniques for doing that at gas processing plants, power plants and oil refineries that were revolutionary. Few Canadian companies did more to drive sulphur recovery from sour gas toward the absolute limit of 100 percent. As well, few companies were as willing to share the wealth of their knowledge without restriction.

Western Research and Development was a scientific and a business success, and it is the desire of Joe Lukacs, the company's long-time leader, to put that success to one more positive public use. Through this book, he would like to examine and reveal why Western Research was able to succeed where so many other entrepreneurial ventures fail. Out of the complex story of this company and its people, the book will attempt to draw a usable model for entrepreneurial success.

I

The Birth of
Western Research
and Development

*Know what business
you are in*

1

The Birth of Western R&D: The Computer Solutions Company

Pick your market niche well.

The first two characters in the Western Research story are Rod McDaniel and George F. "Bud" Coote. Both were seasoned entrepreneurs and risk-takers by the time they incorporated their fledgling research and development company in 1965.

Rod McDaniel was president of McDaniel and Associates Consultants Ltd., a Calgary-based reservoir engineering consulting firm that he created in 1955. The company was the first of its kind in Canada, and Rod McDaniel left a very good job as Chief Reservoir Engineer with Imperial Oil to start it. He was only twenty-five years old at the time.

By 1965, McDaniel and Associates was a well-known and well-respected firm, the first choice of many in the Canadian oil patch when they needed reserve estimates or company evaluations. It was a big market, fed by amalgamations, divestitures, new bond issues, consolidations, and export and regulatory hearings; also fed by the fact that whenever an oil company goes to the bank for a line of credit, an evaluation of

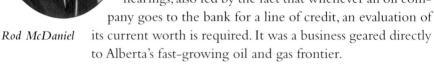

Rod McDaniel

its current worth is required. It was a business geared directly to Alberta's fast-growing oil and gas frontier.

The second figure in the story, Bud Coote, was an entrepreneurial legend on the seismic side of the petroleum industry. Born in Nanton, Alberta, he graduated in civil engineering from the University of Alberta in 1940. He got into geophysical work by virtue of being unable to find an engineering job after graduation. Instead, he caught on with an American geophysical crew doing summer work for Imperial Oil. Imperial decided it wanted its own geophysical department and asked

Bud Coote to be part of it, provided he went back to school to learn that area, which he did at the Colorado School of Mines.

After a few years with Imperial, Bud Coote went out on his own. A first partnership did not work out, but his second venture, Accurate Explorations, with new partner Wes Raybe, did. Accurate was the first company to use the Nodwell tracked all-terrain vehicles for exploration on muskeg. They broke a lot of trail for the Alberta oil patch in '50s and '60s.

George F. "Bud" Coote, his wife, and other family members

Through Accurate, Bud Coote was already involved in a computing company called Computer Data Processing, which was figuring out how to process seismic records with the new technology. Together, Rod McDaniel and Bud Coote decided they needed a second company to explore computer applications on the engineering side. This was Western Research & Development, which they co-founded in 1965.

The computer was still very new in the early '60s. It was only ten years since Remington Rand's UNIVAC computer had accurately predicted Dwight Eisenhower's landslide victory over Adlai Stevenson in the American presidential election, the televised event that gave the general public a taste of how computers would eventually change the world. Since that time, IBM had been using its considerable financial muscle to develop the computer's potential as a business machine.

Despite quite incredible progress–the development of machine memory, disk storage, the use of crystals to achieve miniaturization of circuits–the computer was still far from small or cheap when McDaniel and Coote created their computer solutions company. Computers for individual use were still out of the question.

In the early 1960s in Alberta, there were very few computers, period, and even fewer computer programmers. One of those computers, a huge IBM 1620, lived at the University of Alberta in Edmonton, where a young engineer named Ralph Hughes worked on it, mainly as a sideline, during pursuit of his Master's Degree in Petroleum Engineering in 1961. Hughes took the very first course in computer programming ever offered at U of A. When Hughes completed his degree (in under a year), he came to Calgary to work for Rod McDaniel and Associates. He had been recommended to the company by Bud Coote who'd known him through his nephew for years.

When choosing your market niche, do not be driven by market size alone. Look at the market drivers. Look to your relative strengths.

Hughes' computer experience coupled with his petroleum engineering knowledge was a combination that allowed Rod McDaniel to experiment with the computer age. He put Ralph and another employee, Gerry Knutson, to work writing computer programs for the evaluation of petroleum reservoirs. Together with Cigol (later called Norcen) and Western Union Insurance, McDaniel and Associates rented an IBM 1620 directly from IBM. The immense 1620, with its hundreds of vacuum tubes and its punch cards, was not exactly portable, and Ralph Hughes and Gerry Knutson went around the corner to the IBM Data Centre whenever they needed it. Ralph Hughes also made trips to his alma mater in Edmonton, to employ the somewhat larger brain of the U of A's 1620.

This was the situation that Western Research and Development fit into when it made its quiet entry into the corporate community of Calgary in 1965. Until other prospects presented themselves, it would be charged with finding commercial applications for Ralph Hughes' and Gerry Knutson's software. Western R & D's initial configuration put Rod McDaniel in the President's chair. Ownership was divided 50-50 between McDaniel and Bud Coote.

❖ **What competitive strengths did Western Research have at this time?**

❖ **What were Western Research's chances of succeeding in the computer solutions industry? Why?**

Roderick Rogers McDaniel

Rod McDaniel's father, Dorsey Patton McDaniel, came to Canada from Iowa in 1902 to homestead in the Carstairs region of Alberta. Dorsey's father was a veteran of the American Civil War who had fought for the North while his own brother had fought for the South. In Canada, Dorsey McDaniel was doing very well at farming when his older brother John joined him in 1910 and lured him into ranching. Together they bought the Two Bar Ranch, south of Drumheller, in an area the Indians called The Wintering Hills. The hills often stayed clear of snow in winter and so had been a natural wintering ground for buffalo. In the absence of buffalo, it did the same for cattle and, at its peak, the Two Bar Ranch ran 15,000 head.

From 1900 onward the Canadian open range cattle frontier was badly troubled by a disease called mange. The existing cattlemen's associations and government could not seem to organize effectively to stop the disease and, finally, a group of Alberta's most powerful ranchers, Dorsey McDaniel included, took charge, forming the Cattleman's Protective Association. With the power to force compliance, they set up a cattle-dipping program that put a stop to mange once and for all.

Another of Rod McDaniel's father's public-spirited endeavours was to give Henry Wise Wood the seed money he needed to start the Alberta Wheat Pool.

After the killer winter of 1922 destroyed two-thirds of the Two Bar Ranch's cattle, Dorsey McDaniel changed location, buying the High River Wheat and Cattle Company in the Cayley area south of High River, Alberta (about an hour south of Calgary). Rod McDaniel was born in High River, the last child in the family, and, as he puts it, his father's last hope of a son he could convert into a rancher and farmer. Dorsey used to pack his youngest son with him wherever he went, and, though Rod did not become a rancher or a farmer, he feels he absorbed the kind of stubborn entrepreneurial spirit those early ranchers had.

After completing his petroleum engineering degree at the University of Oklahoma, with exceptional grades, Rod returned to Calgary in 1946. It's a little known fact that, between the end of World War II and the oil find at Leduc in 1947, Alberta was losing population at exactly the same rate as Saskatchewan. All Rod could find to do in Alberta was be a roustabout, at $165 a month. When the Creole Petroleum Corporation offered him an engineering job in Venezuela at three times that, he was gone.

During his stay in Venezuela, Imperial finally hit oil at Leduc, touching off a Canadian exploration and production boom of unprecedented proportions. Rod returned to Western Canada with Imperial and, by 1952, had made Chief Reservoir Engineer for that company: the biggest oil company in Canada. He was 25.

When it comes to why he left Imperial to start his own engineering consulting firm in 1955, Rod McDaniel shrugs. He's not that sure why. Very likely it had to do with the values of independence and entrepreneurism he grew up with. There was no bad blood between him and Imperial over the move, well evidenced by the fact that his first consulting job came from Imperial just a few days after he set up shop. McDaniel and Associates Consultants Ltd. went on to become a rock solid and respected part of the Canadian petroleum community.

Beyond the consulting company he created, Rod McDaniel has been public spirit personified. He has been an active member of several petroleum and engineering associations. His long association with the Calgary Chamber of Commerce included several years on the board of directors and one year as President. As the President of the Elboya Community Association, he successfully lobbied for the creation of Stanley Park, one of the most beautiful parks in all of Calgary. He is an Honourary Life Director of the Calgary Exhibition and Stampede. He has had a long association with the Alberta Conservative Party and was Chairman of its Finance Committee for twenty-eight years.

Rod McDaniel has been a member of many clubs in the Calgary area and saw to it that two of them dropped their rules preventing Jewish membership.

This fair-mindedness also seems to run in the McDaniel family. Rod's father was driving south of High River one day when he saw the Catholic priest standing beside his broken down vehicle at the side of the road. McDaniel was a Protestant, but he stopped and offered the priest a ride to town. In the conversation between them on the way to town, McDaniel asked why those Catholics wouldn't buy the padre a better car. The parish is too poor, was the priest's reply.

"Bull!" said McDaniel.

They continued into High River and McDaniel spent the day going to the homes of every prominent Catholic in town, raising money. In the end, McDaniel kicked in a sum of money too, and Father Bowen had himself a dependable car.

2

The "Wild Hungarian"

Alexander the Great wanted to invade India, but his soldiers were so burdened with booty that they moved very slowly on the march. One day, at dawn, after all of the wagons were loaded, Alexander set fire to his own wagon and to those of his friends. Then he commanded the rest of the army to burn their wagons too. Although a few were unhappy, most of the army was glad to see this barbaric baggage burn away so that they could be warriors again.

—Plutarch

Once Western R & D existed as a corporate entity, it was time to find a leader for it. Rod McDaniel was officially the first president, but managing the company on a daily basis was never part of his plan. What he and Bud Coote wanted was someone to manage the company and be its daily operations leader, someone with a strong technical background who could get his or her mind around a wide range of technical and scientific opportunities, whatever the future might bring.

One of the first names that came up was that of Joe Lukacs, a young engineer currently working for Canadian Fina at the Wildcat Hills gas processing plant near Cochrane, Alberta. Ralph Hughes suggested Lukacs, and he did so for several reasons. First of all, he liked and admired Joe, who he had met and befriended when the two of them were doing their master's degrees in petroleum engineering at U of A. Joe was energetic and always brimming with ideas, "a wild, passionate Hungarian," as Hughes puts it.

After Hughes and Lukacs finished their degrees, both in record time, Hughes went to work for McDaniel & Associates, and Lukacs returned to Canadian Fina, where he had been employed first as a summer student during his undergraduate years and then as a full-time engineer. First at Windfall near Whitecourt, Alberta, and later at Wildcat Hills near Cochrane, Joe Lukacs worked under the tutelage of Dr. Alec Petrunic, a legendary innovator in sour gas processing and sulphur recovery. The two worked hand in hand on frontier problems associated with high pressure sour gas, and sour gas featuring a high CO_2/H_2S ratio. Joe Lukacs's decision to go back to university for his master's was largely so he could study and solve a problem they were having at Windfall with gas hydrates in high pressure sour gas.

Joe Lukacs

That was the other thing weighing in Joe's favour for the Western R & D job: he was a strong engineer. Since escaping Hungary in the revolution year of 1956, he had completed two engineering degrees and worked six years for Fina. He had published a number of papers on sour gas processing and sulphur recovery, some through the auspices of the Canadian Natural Gas Processors' Association. The publications enhanced his reputation as a revolutionary thinker and problem-solver in the emerging art of sulphur recovery from sour gas.

That the Western R & D job would entail research into computer programming applications, something Joe Lukacs had no experience in, was not a fact that overly perplexed McDaniel, Coote, or Hughes. Since almost no one in Alberta did have that experience, the more important criterion was aptitude. Having watched Lukacs master his gas hydrate subject at U of A, under the guidance of Dr. D. B. Robinson, Ralph Hughes could vouch for the man's skills as a thinker, learner, and worker. Important as well was Joe's confidence in his own abilities. He and his friend Dr. Walter Nader, an Austrian professor, often talked about their shared belief that any engineering course at the university could be at least passed given one week of hard work.

None of this was relevant, however, unless Joe Lukacs was interested in a career change, and it was to test that proposition that Ralph Hughes and Gerry Knutson invited Joe in from Cochrane for a discussion in 1965. In a downtown Calgary lounge, the two set about explaining the opportunity, while Joe, for his part, weighed a series of complex financial and loyalty factors against his undeniable interest.

You've got to be willing to burn your wagons, sometimes even with your treasure aboard them.

One of the things he had to think about was security. He was an immigrant after all, lucky enough to have a very good and secure job as an engineer. His wife and he had begun a family: three sons. Joe had already interrupted their household income once to take a leave of absence and return to U of A for his master's, and if that was a disruption, the Western R & D opening was an out-and-out risk: an entrepreneurial flutter with an untried company in an undeveloped, or certainly underdeveloped, area of technology and business.

Then there was the loyalty factor. What had enabled Joe to complete his undergraduate engineering degree at Edmonton was a scholarship from Canadian Fina. The same company employed him in the summers and gave him his first job as an engineer after graduation. All of those opportunities came about because the President of Canadian Fina, Mr. Trajan Nitescu, had a special interest in Joe. Before World War II, Nitescu had been General Manager of Petrofina S.A.'s Rumanian subsidiary. With the coming of the communists, he'd been forced into hiding. Eventually, he and his wife escaped into Yugoslavia, swimming the Danube River. Given that they were then in the hands of the Tito communists, a second escape was required before Nitescu could resume his career as a capitalist and an oilman outside the communist orbit. That path would eventually lead him to the presidency of another Petrofina subsidiary in Canada.

When Hungary was invaded by the Soviets in 1956, it was a bitter reminder to Nitescu of his own post-war treatment at their hands. He wanted to do something to help: hence, the scholarships he provided to Joe Lukacs and another escaped Hungarian student.

Joe Lukacs owed his education and many of the opportunities of his young engineering career to Mr. Nitescu. Others at Fina had also helped him greatly. In his first summer job at Redwater, Herman Leith had helped him gain the confidence that he could work in a new land and in a new language. He owed another debt to Dr. Petrunic, his gas processing mentor at Canadian Fina. At the Windfall pilot plant and, later, at the Wildcat Hills plant that they used as a living laboratory of sour gas and sulphur recovery problems, Joe had enjoyed the opportunity of working with this master scientist, a person of such amazing abilities that he remains a legend. Joe started out as Dr. Petrunic's right-hand man, doing experiments and measurements that the scientist prescribed, and later proceeded to his own studies and papers, which, by 1965, had given him an independent credibility and respect within the industry.

All this, Joe Lukacs would be leaving if he took on the Western R & D opportunity, and he did not take it lightly. On the other hand, the work of a field engineer was beginning to lose its challenge for him. Fina's one field and one plant, and beer with the boys after work, wasn't a combination that was apt to hold Joe in the long term, so why not go now, when an opportunity was awaiting him?

In the end, it was Trajan Nitescu himself who turned the key in the lock. At first, when Joe told his boss about his new opportunity, Mr. Nitescu cautioned him. He warned Joe about the risks associated with a pioneering venture, and he reminded him of the advantages he had at Fina. In just a few years, Joe had become a polished engineer, and a respected one. Computer work would lead him away from those accomplishments.

But Trajan Nitescu also saw that his protégé was leaning in the direction of leaving–so he made it easy for him. "Mr. Lukacs," he said (they were always very formal with one another), "if you ever wish to change your mind and return, your job at Canadian Fina will be waiting for you."

This was a gift of enormous value. The knowledge that he could return was what gave Joe Lukacs the courage to go, and

Mr. Nitescu almost certainly knew that when he made the offer.

On July 15, 1965, Joe Lukacs joined Western R & D as the company's first manager. He rented space above the IBM data centre in downtown Calgary and bought a second-hand desk. Though Rod McDaniel would remain President for several more years, Joe Lukacs was the name people would most closely associate with Western Research and Development for the next twenty-seven years.

❖ *What are the attributes of a successful entrepreneur?*

❖ *How do risk-reward relationships affect personal decisions? Why?*

❖ *How do human motivation and human values affect success?*

Joe Lukacs – The Early Years

When Joe Lukacs is asked to talk about his childhood in Hungary, he is somewhat reluctant, especially if the purpose is to benefit other entrepreneurs by showing them the early makings of a successful businessman. "It was so different, growing up there during and after the war," he says, "that it doesn't have much relevance to the kinds of lives people live here in Canada." Once, when management analyst Blaine Lee asked Joe about his childhood management workshop, Joe produced an overhead that read: "When you are the smallest in your class, when your family is poor and persecuted, when you're a skinny little fart, you try harder."

When the communists took over Hungary after the war, Joe, as a child of only ten, soon saw how the people most willing to give up their own values were the ones who prospered. More independent types like his father and his brother were in trouble.

The Lukacs contract threshing crew in Hungary. Joe, the family accountant, age 12, is seated in front, first on the left.

Joe's father started up various schemes to get ahead, and Joe, though a child, was always involved. One of his earliest memories of this was when his father would lure people out of the city to fish in a pond on his property. Drinking and fishing went together, and Joe recalls lugging giant pressurized soda bottles back and forth to the village to be filled at the local inn. On one such hot and humid summer day, Joe was on his way down the sandy, rutted road carrying as many of the iced-soda bottles as he could bear up under, wearing his customary costume of cheap black shorts and no shoes, when a jeep filled with an American seismic crew roared up behind him. They took Joe by surprise and scared him right off the road into the steep ditch, into a bed of thistles and poison ivy. Regaining the road, covered in dust and scratches, the poison ivy starting to itch, Joe looked after the jeep and acquired his first interest in both North America and the oil industry. He vowed that some day he would be the one driving in the jeep, rather than the one carting payload along the road by foot.

Another family venture was a moonshine still operating in a cellar under the kitchen floor. By virtue of its smell, it was hard to keep a secret and, whenever it suited their fancy, the local authorities would come around to impound it. It then became Joe's and his older brother's job to go in the middle of the night to steal it back. It was only a kilometre, but the still was very heavy, impossibly heavy as Joe recalls. It was the longest kilometre journey of his life.

A third family business was contract threshing. Joe, now all of twelve, was the family accountant. The communists collected an enormous tax on farm produce, and the basis for that tax was the amount of grain harvested. That is, in Joe's case, it was based on his tally of the number of sacks of grain harvested by their crew. The farms were very small, and a farmer's entire harvest might consist of thirty bushels of grain. Of this, he was allowed to keep a couple of bushels per member of his family and maybe another bushel for next year's seed. The rest went to the government. Worse still, the government made no concession for shrinkage. The farmer had to pay in shrunk grain a quantity determined in wet grain, and the result was often that the poor farmers were left with nothing at all.

The farmers would beg Joe to reduce his tally a little, and he was always tempted. But it was dangerous business. The government kept a close eye on the "capitalist" threshing contractors and frequently re-weighed to check the contractor's numbers. If Joe did cheat, and was caught, it would result in his father's imprisonment, maybe even his death.

But finally, Joe took the risk. He reduced the tally of the farmers' grain, which meant that he had to reduce the tally of his father's commission as well. His father was paid in grain, and the secret commission, which Joe's father never knew about, was a little bit of grain that Joe had to make disappear secretly and completely. For this, Joe had an accomplice, a harvest labourer from Budapest, who for a share of the booty, "fenced" the grain. It wasn't until years later that Joe told his father what he had done. His father was shocked.

At school, Joe didn't do particularly well until grades eleven and twelve. For the improvement, he gives a lot of credit to a Jesuit science teacher. The Jesuit organization had been dismantled by the communists, and priests like this one were forced to teach as lay persons in the common schools. The Jesuit took a special interest in Joe and some of his keenest classmates. Every day he gave them a problem, usually a physics problem, that they were to solve by next day. Joe remembers staying up half the night until he had it solved. This and the classics a family friend urged him to read convinced him there was no problem he could not solve if he gave his mind to it.

Joe's dream was to be a nuclear physicist, but the few openings for physics students at the university were taken up by those more in favour with the communist regime. Joe wound up instead taking mining engineering at a university near the Russian border. In his third year, he was transferred to the old and traditional mining university at Sopron near the Austrian border. When the Russians invaded Hungary in 1956 to put down the popular rebellion that year, Joe and a great many other students at his university simply stepped over the border by night into Austria.

But Joe did not stay out. In his refugee camp in Austria, Joe realized he must go back and find his sweetheart, his future wife, Helen, and bring her out with him. He and a friend who had left his fiancé behind returned over the border by night and worked their way deep into Hungary. Joe found Helen and the two of them began the much more difficult journey out of Hungary. All transportation systems had stopped and it was perilous all the way. But they made it.

The decision of where to go from there was all about freedom. Joe's group of students and professors was not happy with the United States. They felt that the United States could have done a lot more to help their country's revolution. At the same time, an English-speaking country did appeal to them, partly because English was a language they had been forbidden by the communists to speak. England itself was not far enough away, so they chose Canada.

For a time, their group was hosted by the University of Toronto, but news of petroleum industry developments in the west lured Joe and a half dozen of his friends to Alberta, where he found his first job with Canadian Fina in a rich new oil field called Redwater. From there onward, Alberta would be Joe Lukacs's home.

Joe Lukacs and his wife Helen arrive in Canada at Pier 21 in Halifax harbour.

When Joe Lukacs looks back at the story of his early life and his final escape from Hungary, he notes an irony. If his early dream of being a nuclear physicist had come true, he would have been swept off to Russia to work on the space program or the arms race. If he hadn't been denied that dream, he would likely have never escaped from the communists until after the fall of the Iron Curtain.

3

Making the Right Connections

The best way to get something done is to start it. —Joe Lukacs

---

In the management workshops that have become an integral part of Joe Lukacs's career, Joe and his team teach clients about the four things a business must have to survive and flourish: market, product (including technology and expertise), financing and sound management. A serious failure or lack in any one area will cause a company to falter or hit the wall. In its fledgling form, at the point when Joe Lukacs took over the management, Western R & D was thin to nil in two of those four categories.

As management expert Dr. Blaine Lee puts it, "The most important of the four is the one you don't have," and in the early years of Western Research, the key difficulty was lack of market. The market for computer software products in Calgary in 1965 was next to non-existent. Everyone was in agreement that the computer was the wave of the future; the problem was that no one considered it the wave of the present. For a new company with limited depth of pocket, future potential was nothing but frustration.

Dr. M. Blaine Lee

17

In 1965, IBM brought out its long-awaited 360 series of mainframe computers. Though this generation of computers was smaller than the 1400 series that had preceded it (because of the partial replacement of vacuum tubes with transistors), the cost was still high. More critical than cost, the average businessman had simply not bought in.

To market a computer program, major preparation of the client was still required. First you had to bring them out of the adding machine age into the computer age, no mean feat. Then you had to convince them that the speed and utility of the computer had a practical, economically feasible application in their business. If you managed to convince them of all that, you still had to train somebody in their organization to use the software, which probably meant bringing another adding machine age person across the great divide into the world of the binary and the digital.

More often, you would wind up doing the computer work for the client at a rate that amounted to subsidy.

In addition to discovering that he was up against a difficult set of market conditions, Joe found out that his personal financial situation was going to be skinnier than he had initially thought. Upon his arrival at Western R & D, Rod McDaniel told him that the usual practice when starting a new venture was to ask the leaders not to draw their whole salary. They would take a portion, whatever they absolutely needed, leaving the rest in the company to help it get started. At the end of the year, they'd split up whatever had accumulated.

Joe learned to program as quickly as possible, and his early contribution to the company's products and revenue was to design a program that would do flash calculations. In his early years at Canadian Fina, Joe was one of three young engineers chosen for a two-year intensive training program. (The others were Jim Campbell and Ed Wishart.) Between 1959 and 1961, they were moved through the entire operation, spending a few months in each department (geology, reservoir engineering, field operation, etc.). Part of this training was that Joe did flash calculations (determining the flash point of a petroleum sample at a variety of temperature and pressure conditions) for veteran Fina engineers like Wally Palmer and Bob

Cunningham. It was basically slide-rule work, and a labourious trial-and-error business. But in the course of it, he had developed a series of equations that would help do the job.

At Western R & D, as Joe became more conversant with the computer, he realized that the computer was uniquely suited to the work of flash calculations, and he set about writing his equations as computer code. In time, he was able to sell this service to some of the gas engineers he knew. Angus Leitch and Jim Richardson were two of his clients. By this time, Joe had three women working for him, punching cards and running programs.

If Rod McDaniel was tough on his young manager in the matter of take-home pay, he was generous in other ways, such as giving Joe a wide-ranging introduction to the players in the Calgary oil patch. Having been part of the local oil and gas community since his return from Venezuela, Rod McDaniel knew everybody. His quick rise with Imperial had set the stage for a successful move into consulting and, by 1965, he had consulted for all the majors (Imperial, Canadian Superior, Chevron, etc.) and was just as well known, and liked, by the rising Canadian stars that would dominate the industry during Alberta's 1970s boom (people like "Doc" and B.J. Seaman).

In Rod's view of things, meeting these people and keeping in touch with them was not socializing, it was business, and toward that end, he challenged Joe to have lunch with someone new every day of the week except Friday. On Fridays, Joe and Rod, along with Ralph Hughes and Gerry Knutson, had their weekly management meeting in Rod's station wagon at the A & W. Over hamburgers they would go over the various contacts Joe was making, and the various possibilities that existed for Western R & D.

Rod McDaniel was also well-connected politically. He was one of a group that was grooming Peter Lougheed and his Alberta Conservative Party to take over the reins of government from the Alberta Social Credit Party. In 1965, the Socreds were in their thirty-first year of continuous power in Alberta, and many, especially in the cities, felt it was time for a change. They could see that Alberta was well positioned to surge ahead economically, and they feared that the Socreds, with their rural base and their go-slow traditions, would hold the province back.

In those days, club memberships were an essential part of Calgary's oil patch diplomacy. Rod McDaniel started Joe Lukacs out with a membership in the Glencoe Club, a family style club on the south side of the Mount Royal hill. Later, when Joe needed access to a more powerful network, McDaniel would help him gain membership in the more exclusive Petroleum Club, the oil patch bastion where the movers and shakers went to lunch and deals were hatched and planned over a sandwich or a steak.

The market pull for computer services was there in 1965, but Western Research had no competitive edge to stay in that market.

—Dr. Blaine Lee

For Rod McDaniel, it was a simple business. People weren't apt to hire somebody they didn't know. He was introducing his manager to the people most likely to give him work. For Joe Lukacs, it was that and more. Up until then, many of his opportunities had come from fellow exiles from Eastern Europe. Now, suddenly, he was being received by Rod McDaniel's circuitry of highly placed friends and associates with an openness he could scarcely believe.

The Alberta oil industry prides itself in its lack of class and pedigree consciousness. There is an almost fanatical belief in ability and hard work. The saying goes that if a person is smart and willing to work, no one cares where they're from or what colour they are. It's a fair system, but it's far from a soft system. What it means is that a newcomer with the right credentials will get a chance, and if he's good he'll reap the rewards of that ability. The reverse is also true: if you screw up, or if you don't work as hard as your bosses do or think you should, you might as well leave town. Although some examples of affirmative action are visible in the industry today, they were absent in 1965. The idea that someone would get a job because they were a Hungarian refugee (a Native, a woman, etc.) was just as out of the question as that they would be prevented from getting a job on any of those counts.

In those early months, Joe was making connections right and left, but it was doing him limited good in his computer solutions business. It all came back to market. Connections would help him sell into an existing market, but connections were not powerful enough to create the market.

An even greater problem was coming from downstairs. To

help sell its new 360 series of mainframe computers, which had cost $5 billion to develop, IBM was giving away programming. Some of the programs it was willing to supply with its mainframes in Calgary were a lot like what Joe Lukacs was trying to sell. It wasn't hard to figure out that you're not going to sell much of something that people can get 100 feet away for free.

Western R & D needed a break, and it got one. Barney Burnett, President of Canadian Superior Oil Ltd. and one of the connections Rod McDaniel had helped Joe Lukacs make, called Joe up with a problem. At Canadian Superior's Harmattan-Elkton plant near Didsbury, Alberta, there was a pollution complaint from a local farmer. Burnett wanted to know if Joe could do the air monitoring and analysis necessary to figure out what the cause of the complaint might be.

If air monitoring was new to Joe Lukacs, sour gas fields and plants were not. He said yes, and, in that moment, Western R & D entered the pollution business.

❖ **Why is relative competitive advantage easier to establish in an emerging market niche?**

❖ **What happens when you have significant competitive advantage but the decision-makers don't perceive it?**

❖ **What could Western Research do to exploit its relative competitive advantage?**

4

The Air Pollution Business In Alberta

One man's problem is another man's opportunity.

The problem Canadian Superior was having with a farmer's complaints at its Harmattan-Elkton sour gas plant was nothing new in Alberta. Ever since British America (BA) put the first phase of its Pincher Creek sour gas plant on stream in 1957, a hostility had been developing between the farm and ranch community and the sour gas industry.

Sour gas is natural gas that contains significant hydrogen sulphide (H_2S), a colourless gas that can be lethal at concentrations as low as 100 parts per million (ppm). That makes it considerably more poisonous than carbon monoxide. At low concentrations, H_2S smells of rotten eggs. At higher concentrations, it disables the human sense of smell.

When H_2S burns, the principal byproduct is sulphur dioxide (SO_2), a choking gas that is also injurious to human health (red, sore eyes and other effects). The greater risk associated with SO_2 is its effect on the environment. It is one of the primary contributors to acid rain.

By 1958, the Canadian gas processing industry had been dealing with sour gas for decades, but at relatively low H_2S percentages. Moving east to west across Alberta, the natural gas accumulations go from shallow and sweet to deep and sour, with the deepest and sourest gas reservoirs being in the Rocky Mountain foothills and the mountain valleys. Another important feature of the deep gas reservoirs is that they are at much higher pressure than the shallow ones.

The first of Alberta's high pressure reservoirs to be produced, and its gas processed, was Shell Jumping Pound in the foothills west of Cochrane. This 1951 gas processing and sulphur plant was Alberta's "sour gas laboratory," and much important information about such things as how hydrates form in high pressure sour gas and the corrosion effects on metals were gathered here and disseminated to the Alberta engineering community.

The significance of BA Pincher Creek was in being the first attempt to process sour gas that was both highly sour (11% H_2S compared to 5% at Jumping Pound) and under high pressure (1,500 pounds per square inch). It was not only the first time in Alberta that this had been attempted, it was the first time in the world.

BA Pincher Creek gas plant, ca. 1960

The impetus to do so was Alberta's decision to allow gas export from Alberta, combined with Canada's decision to allow gas export from Canada. Westcoast Transmission had finished its pipeline to the west coast in 1957, and the first gas went into the TransCanada pipeline to eastern Canada and the northeastern United States the same year. The Alberta & Southern pipeline that would take Alberta gas into the American northwest en route to California was beginning its path through the regulatory labyrinth, but, with the two precedent pipelines already functioning and reserve estimates steadily rising, it looked apt to succeed.

The Pincher Creek gas reservoir was discovered in the early 1950s and was thought to be a giant: 1.7 trillion cubic feet of gas was one estimate. The reservoir had been part of every pipeliner's proposal through the 1950s decade. In fact, the BA Pincher Creek field would prove to be a dud, fractured and inclined to water out, but no one knew that until the field was produced.

Before the BA Pincher Creek plant was built, severe and unusual corrosion problems had been noticed in the field, similar to those Shell had been dealing with at Shell Jumping Pound. Joe Labuda, a Shell engineer at the time, remembers investigating a production tubing failure at Jumping Pound in 1952 that the Shell corrosion experts in Houston had assessed as hydrogren stress-cracking. Shell had continued to research the problem and people like Norm Dunne and Vince Milo had accumulated a good deal of knowledge about it.

In anticipation of the problem at Pincher Creek, British-American poured $1 million into the design of its Stage I plant. But when the 1,500 pounds per square inch gas (11% H_2S) was unleashed into their metallurgical masterpiece, the result was rapid corrosion, worse than anything seen at the earlier sour gas plants. Valves failed all over the plant, some popping off without even being touched.

Elmer Berlie, a future employee of Western Research, was one of the first plant engineers at Pincher Creek, coming over from the Energy Resources Conservation Board. He wanted field experience and, at BA Pincher Creek, he got plenty.

The corrosion problems were solved, often through trial and error, and with a great deal of ingenuity. For example, Elmer Berlie found that the welds throughout the plant were a critical corrosion zone. They had to be re-done, stress-relieved, and radiographed. The hardness of the steel in the welds had be kept low and the carbon-manganese ratio had to be just so.

Hundreds of other modifications had to be made on the fly, as the plant continued to operate and new stages came on.

Meanwhile, in the farming and ranching community around the plant, people became by stages concerned, afraid and finally angry. Everything they were told about hydrogen sulphide was frightening (if you could smell it, that was unpleasant; if you couldn't, that might be lethal) and the plant was upset half the time. They could hardly miss the plant upsets given that the flare would sprout to twice the height of the stack and the ground would vibrate. Besides the rotten egg smell, the lead-based paint on their farm buildings turned rainbow colours, and certain kinds of barbed wire corroded so you could break it with your hands. Even though plant superintendent Martin Bretz had a policy that pollution complaints were to be answered within half an hour, the people of the community were not reassured. Who could blame them?

Elmer Berlie was plant engineer at BA Pincher Creek in the late 1950s.

The situation at Pincher Creek, combined with rapid growth in the number of Alberta's sour gas plants in the late '50s and early '60s, led to several key developments at the industry, government, and community levels. By a circuitous path, it would also lead to the pollution complaint against Canadian Superior Didsbury, and to Western Research and Development's move into the pollution control business.

In the late 1950s, years before the publication of Rachel Carson's *Silent Spring* set the warning bells about world pollution ringing, BA Pincher Creek began monitoring air quality in the area around its plant. Forty-four sulphate testing devices, known as candle stations or, by their appearance, as "bird houses," were installed. When the community proved unwilling to accept BA's finding that there was no serious pollution problem, the Alberta Department of Health got involved. In truth, the candle stations were inadequate to the task of assessing risk to human health. They measured an average level of exposure. The Department's testing apparatus was more sophisticated, capable of providing daily and even hourly readings.

For a problem-solving company, the market consists of problems. Find them and you've found your market.

After its study, the Department of Health insisted that the sulphur stacks at sour gas plants be extended to ensure better diffusion. Otherwise, their finding was the same as BA's: no serious threat to health.

In 1960, the Alberta Department of Health spawned an Air Pollution Branch, and Serge Dobko was hired as the first engineer in charge of air quality control. In 1961, new air pollution regulations were legislated. New sour gas plants had to comply with the emission standards immediately, while the older plants were given five years to make the grade. The same year, the Conservation Board strengthened its standards to bring them in line with the air pollution regulations. The highest economically feasible standard of sulphur recovery was demanded of everyone. The Board determined that standard for each plant.

It cannot be proven that the problems at Pincher Creek led to the creation of the Air Pollution Branch and to passage of the early air pollution legislation in Alberta, but there is a definite relationship between the events. At the very least, the Pincher Creek situation sped up the process by which Alberta's government and sour gas industry combined on an air pollution strategy for the incoming tide of new sour gas fields and plants.

The irony of it all is that, as Alberta became a model of early awareness in the area of sulphur emissions, as its government forced stringent sulphur recovery standards on industry and industry struggled to comply, the people living around Alberta's sour gas plants were, if anything, more upset.

The concerned residents south of Pincher Creek had become suspicious that the government and gas processors were in cahoots and that nothing said by either on the subject of air pollution could be trusted. The result was that Shell Waterton, a major gas plant directly west of BA Pincher Creek at the foot of the mountains, ran directly into a hornet's nest of public controversy when it came on stream in 1962. Shell Waterton, a major field backstopping the new Alberta & Southern pipeline, though definitely as sour and as high pressure as BA Pincher Creek, was shooting for a much higher standard of sulphur recovery efficiency. As well, its designers were able to use the discoveries Shell had made through their operation at Shell Jumping Pound. Shell Waterton was an improvement over previous plants, but that did not prevent local farmers and ranchers joining forces and launching an air pollution lawsuit against both Shell and BA. The suit took years to get anywhere and never did progress in the courts beyond examination for discovery, but in the end the oil companies settled out of court for $750,000.

Focus on the customer. Help your customers solve their problems.

What all of this amounted to was a legacy that other sour gas field and plant operators had to work with, and around, forever after. All the gas plants that backstopped the Alberta & Southern pipeline were foothills trend gas reservoirs: deep and sour. The plants that took the gas and sweetened it to pipeline specification were designed to strip out the H_2S and convert it to elemental sulphur. They were built and operated on a much improved understanding of sour gas and its peculiarities when subjected to cold or high pressure, or the presence of complicating compounds like CO_2. But in the mind of the public, especially the farming and ranching public, the plants were viewed, at best, as hazards.

All of which goes to explain two things of great relevance to Western Research and the direction the company was about to take. First, it explains why the farmer at Didsbury felt he should complain loud and clear to Canadian Superior when a strange odour started to make his wife ill. It also explains why Canadian Superior wanted the problem dealt with thoroughly and soon, rather than casually and too late.

That Canadian Superior called Joe Lukacs at Western Research to investigate the problem was a breakthrough of a different kind. Since the Department of Health began its pollution monitoring at Pincher Creek, it had essentially gone into the pollution monitoring business itself. It was providing a pollution service to the public and to the oil and gas industry, at taxpayers' expense. Indeed, it was already at Didsbury investigating the farmer's complaint. The fact that Canadian Superior called on Western Research to do an independent investigation probably had to do with a growing belief in the industry that the government should get out of that business and let private industry do it.

One of the people who felt most strongly about this happened to be Rod McDaniel. If Western Research could go out to Didsbury, do a good job of sampling and analyzing the local air quality, and perhaps solve the problem, it would be a compelling argument that the Air Pollution Branch of the Alberta government should retire its air monitoring trailer.

From Joe Lukacs's point of view, the government pollution people were more his allies than competitors. Compared to his experience of communist government civil servants in Hungary, he found the Canadian government scientists and technicians a delight to work with. They became his friends. When Western Research appeared on the scene and proved themselves able to do the work up to a high scientific standard, and honestly, Joe's feeling was that the government stepped back almost immediately and let them do it.

As Joe Lukacs prepared to tackle the Didsbury job, the phone rang again and he had his second air pollution job. Shell Waterton wanted him to come down and measure the amount of H_2S and SO_2 in its stack emissions. With the government insisting on a certain percentage of sulphur recovery, the emissions had to be measured. Otherwise, compliance couldn't be achieved or proven. In more ways than one, things were looking up.

Know your market.

❖ **What role can legislation play in market creation?**

❖ **What are the risks of expecting government to create a market for your business?**

❖ **What are the risks when government legislation is the source of the market on which your business relies?**

5

Chasing Plumes at Didsbury: The Ed Hardy Era Begins

Teamwork: assemble your "starting five" with care.

Ed Hardy was not the first person hired at Western Research by Joe Lukacs. The three women working on the computer preceded him. At least Ed thinks there were three. "I wasn't around the office long enough to count them."

Ed was hired to be Joe's first field technician, and the field and the lab were where you could find him for much of the next twenty-five years. For a long time, Ed had an office next to Joe's. "I was never in it," he says. "So finally Joe gave it to somebody else."

What made Ed perfect for the field technician job was his proficiency at gas sampling and analysis, especially gas chromatography, the fast-growing science that would be at the heart of any effort to analyze and measure the content of gas plumes. In a nutshell, gas chromatography is a technique used to separate, identify, and measure organic species like hydrocarbons. For the last twelve years, Ed had been analyzing gas samples for a company called Chemical and Geological Laboratories Ltd., and, during that time, he had pioneered the acceptance of gas chromatography as a method of analysis and measurement. Very few people in Alberta knew more about gas chromatography than Ed Hardy.

The first time Ed Hardy and Joe Lukacs met was at a gas chromatography training session put on by the Southern Alberta Institute of Technology (SAIT) in 1962. They were introduced by Dale White, one of Joe's co-workers at Canadian

Fina who had once worked for Ed at Chemical and Geological. Joe attended the session because of the importance of gas chromatography to the work he was doing with Dr. Petrunic at Fina.

Three years later, Joe still remembered Ed Hardy and his knowledge of gas chromatography, so he gave him a call. The timing was about perfect. At Chemical and Geological, Ed's job was to analyze gas samples, and he'd been doing it for years. Most of the samples came from oil and gas wells or from gas plants, and a great many of them were sour. The technology of the day required that Ed open the stopcocks literally beside his nose with the result that he had his "bells rung" many a time. "Get dizzy, go outside, get some fresh air." Ed felt that his tolerance to H_2S was decreasing with each exposure. In short, he needed a new job.

Initially, Ed Hardy believed Western R & D was a computer programming company and, on that basis alone, he was excited to get Joe's call. He saw computers as the next big technological wave, and he was the kind of person who liked working on the cutting edge of things. When he realized the job would be far removed from computers, and not that distant from what he was already doing, he wanted to investigate the prospect further before accepting. For one thing, he had to confirm that air monitoring and stack testing would keep him out of the levels of H_2S he had become sensitive to. For another, he wanted to ensure beforehand that he was able to work from bottom to top on the enormous stacks now required for Alberta sour gas plants.

In the fall of 1966, Ed Hardy went with Joe Lukacs to Shell Waterton for a day of stack emission testing. Together, they scaled the stack. They sampled and tested the stack gas, while at the same time Ed Hardy sampled and tested the job and his boss. Although, as he points out three and a half decades later, he was never paid for his time that day, Ed Hardy decided he would like the work and his boss well enough to take the job. The different kind of danger associated with climbing ladders and working on catwalks was more acceptable to him than sniffing hydrogen sulphide samples in a poorly ventilated lab. On December 10, 1966, Ed Hardy joined Western R & D.

The Starting Five are the roles you need to fill in your company at the beginning of its life in order to move forward. First, you identify the roles, then you fill them with the right people.

Dr. Blaine Lee

The fieldwork on the Canadian Superior Didsbury air monitoring project fell mostly to Ed Hardy once he was aboard, and he recalls that it was a fairly frustrating business. Even though he was working for Canadian Superior, the Canadian Superior field team wasn't sure they should tell him anything or help him get his work done. Ed had the analyzer in his own car–Joe paid him mileage–and what he needed to do was chase down a gas plume and get his probe into it before it had time to disperse. If the field operators weren't about to tell him when they were flaring gas, it wasn't going to happen.

The field gas itself had interesting peculiarities that Ed knew about because he had tested some of it for the operators back at Chemical and Geological. It was quite sour and, at certain temperature and pressure conditions, sulphur compounds would plug off a well downhole. After unplugging the well, they would flare a little gas to clean out the solvent. That was the ideal time for Ed to catch a sample–if somebody would just tell him when and where the flaring was to occur.

Ed was also having a problem with head office. He wanted to run the analyzer off his car battery, and he needed an adaptor for that purpose. Joe Lukacs didn't want to make the expenditure, somewhere around $8 worth, preferring that he connect to the car battery when required.

Ed argued back that he didn't have time to fool with connecting the battery. The opportunity, if and when it came, would require quick action. Everything had to be up and running in advance.

The two had what Ed Hardy calls "a significant war" about it, perhaps the first of many significant wars they would have on a roughly regular basis for more than two decades to come. "A significant war over eight bucks," says Hardy. "I guess we didn't have much money in those days."

To resolve his other problem, Ed Hardy decided he and the Canadian Superior field operator had to have to have a talk. He went to the field office for that purpose, and once it was clear who he worked for and why he was there, he got cooperation. The plant manager's house was half way between the plant and the farm from which the complaint had issued.

An analyzer was placed in his house until the problem was solved.

Finally, through a combination of Ed's plume-chasing and Joe's investigations of wind and weather patterns relative to the time of complaints, it was proven that the plant was not responsible. That is, the problems the farmer's wife was having also occurred on days when the wind was blowing toward the plant and away from the farm. The woman was having allergic reactions to something on the farm itself.

As for the significant wars, disputes that might have caused a person to quit or be fired in another company, they seldom amounted to much at Western R & D. Joe Lukacs's acceptance of the occasional battle between Ed Hardy and himself was a sign of things to come, an early clue to the kind of "culture" he would help his company to evolve. Joe never liked nor trusted "yes men." He surrounded himself instead with strong-minded individuals, with whom occasional conflict was inevitable. "We'd fight like hell," he says. "Then we'd go have a drink."

Teamwork is differing expertise united in purpose.

❖ *What functional experience is required for the success of a business?*

❖ *What attributes are needed in the first key people added to a business?*

❖ *How does adding people change the role of a successful small business manager?*

Ed Hardy

Ed Hardy is generally considered to be Western Research's Employee #2, after Joe Lukacs. He was with the company for twenty-five years. His ability to design a solution to a problem and then build it made him the ideal person to head up the team of technicians. He was also a top lab man, with experience going back twelve years before Western Research was born.

Ed was born on a farm between Irma and Mannville, Alberta. His father died in 1934 when Ed was five. His family left the farm in 1939 and finally moved to Edmonton in 1942. Being the oldest child, Ed took what work was available. He started out in the Orange Crush plant, washing bottles. The family rented a suite in a house from a man who owned a coal mine. This led to Ed's getting into the coal delivery business. At the age of eighteen, he started in with Zeidler, a millwork company. Ed's job became to quote on major housing projects. If he won the bid, he might wind up designing the cupboards for 500 houses at a time.

While at Zeidler another job came up that linked to an older fascination. Starting

Ed Hardy, age 20

out when he was still on the farm, Ed had built and flown scale-model airplanes, starting with Howie wing gliders. Now, Northwest Industries had an opening in their drafting area for someone to draw airplane parts. Ed applied, submitted drawings, and didn't get the job. It was a sore point, somewhat alleviated when a former Northwest Industries employee came to work at Zeidler. The man recalled Ed's application and the drawings he had sent. The drawings were great, he said. The reason he didn't get the job was his age: too young.

The opening moment in Ed's career with the petroleum industry was a dramatic one. In 1948, he and some buddies spotted a smoke plume on the horizon and followed it to one of the most famous blow-outs of all time: Atlantic #3. The well had just blown out and caught fire. Ed and his friends were there before the police. They crossed on a pipeline bridge and got so close they could feel the tremendous heat.

His first job in the business was with Dowell, a well-servicing company, when he was twenty-two. He looked after the "gun shop," preparing the shape charges that were fired through the well casings. He also learned how to splice cable so that the finished product was the same thickness from end to end.

His longest job outside of Western Research came when he went to work for Chemical and Geological Laboratories Ltd. of Edmonton. For twelve years, he worked in their lab, first in Edmonton, then in Calgary, analyzing gas samples, mostly from the oil and gas patch. He jokes that he lost his hair in a lab explosion at Chemical and Geological. He was cleaning a sample bottle when its frozen valve suddenly gave away. The furnace was around the corner, and the expelling gas reached it in an instant. "The place to be in an explosion," says Ed, "is far away or at the centre. I was at the centre." He put out the fire and took himself to hospital.

Ed Hardy is an inventive, self-taught jack-of-all-trades, and an extremely determined man. Don't dare to dare him; don't tell him he can't. He tells a story of a young man he worked with who was always going on about drumming in a band. Finally, Ed tired of it and said, why do you make such a big deal out of something a person could learn in six weeks? The drummer came in next day with a very good set of drum sticks. He laid them on Ed's desk. If in six weeks you're drumming in a dance band, he said, you can have them. The bet almost cost Ed his marriage. He went straight out and bought a set of drums, drummed both day and night in every spare moment for weeks. Just before his six weeks were up, he made his debut, drumming in an Edmonton dance band. "It doesn't pay to tell me I can't do something," he says.

The Value of Mentors: Rossdale Power Plant

Your starting five do not all have to be employees. As a young company, you really can't afford for them to be.
—Dr. Blaine Lee

As Western Research began to shift gears into the pollution control business, the one thing that seemed likely to stay the same was its focus on the petroleum industry–until, that is, Bud Coote came into Joe Lukacs's office one morning and dropped an *Edmonton Journal* on his desk. There was a tall headline on the front page about air pollution from the city's Rossdale power plant.

"You know something about pollution," said Bud. "Why don't you give these guys a call and see if you can't fix this thing?"

The something Joe knew about pollution had entirely to do with gas plants. At Canadian Fina, he had worked on projects to increase the sulphur plant's efficiency, thus reducing its sulphur emissions. Indeed, this was pollution work, in that it kept sulphur out of the atmosphere, but he knew nothing at all about power generation.

According to Rod McDaniel, who joined Bud Coote in urging Joe to take this on, Joe was anything but jumping at the opportunity. But they kept at him, arguing that it wasn't all that different from the sulphur plants he knew: just a matter of sampling and analyzing the stack gases.

Finally, Joe gathered his courage and phoned Bill Kirkland at Edmonton Power. Perhaps over-stating his level of confidence, he said, "I think I know how to solve your problem." Next thing, he was on a plane.

Edmonton's Rossdale community is one of the oldest parts of the city. You could say the very oldest given that recent excavations in Rossdale have discovered the remains of what might be the settlement's earliest fur trade fort. The community occupies the river-bottom flats between downtown Edmonton to the north and the old community of Strathcona to the south. From Rossdale, you have a fine view of all that is Edmonton: the McDonald Hotel, the Provincial Legislature, the University of Alberta, and, more recently, the High Level Bridge.

Around 1966, various people in Edmonton had started noticing that the Edmonton Power plant at the north end of Rossdale was venting a brownish-yellow plume of gas from its short smoke stacks, not every day but often enough to be alarming. If the wind was from the south, the plume would drift up the north escarpment and into the heart of downtown. Giving rise to the headline that Bud Coote showed Joe Lukacs was the way the yellow plume often drifted up against the *Edmonton Journal* building's south-facing bank of windows.

The Rossdale plant had fairly recently installed two 30-thousand-kilowatt steam turbines and was designing layouts for three more units, for what they were calling their "high pressure plant." The *Journal* had researched the situation and had unearthed the possibility that the brownish-yellow plume could indicate the presence of dangerous oxides of nitrogen.

The *Edmonton Journal* coverage of the problem catalyzed a public outcry, and the City of Edmonton and Edmonton Power were under pressure to come up with a solution, fast. Edmonton Power engineer Frank Battistella recalls that the Government of Alberta had become involved as well and was recommending a single giant stack to replace the five Rossdale boiler stacks, a solution Edmonton Power's engineers thought was ridiculous. It was in the midst of this that Joe Lukacs phoned, a ray of hope from Calgary. He couldn't have timed it better.

Joe's early analysis of the problem told him two things. First, given that nitrous oxide reacts to NO_2 very rapidly in the atmosphere, gas sampling would have to take place directly at the stack mouth to meaningfully express the content of the stack emissions. The second issue was stack height and, to give a solid opinion on that, Joe needed to be able to model the wind and weather patterns in the North Saskatchewan River valley.

What Joe imagined was a two-pronged approach: the first being local and hands-on, and involving field technician Ed Hardy. Together, Joe and Ed had to find a way of sampling at the mouth of the Rossdale stacks. The second matter, the weather modelling, was more theoretical and would take Joe far afield and into conversation with some of the top environmental scientists on the continent.

Part of the deal with Edmonton Power was that Western Research work with Don Stanley, a well-known local consultant who ordinarily handled these kinds of problems for the city. Joe Lukacs recalls that Don Stanley was more than a little sceptical about this Calgary saviour that Bill Kirkland had sent his way. "So you think you know about pollution," was his opening sally. He teamed Joe up with another young scientist, Dr. Bill Oldham, who, according to Stanley, didn't know anything about pollution either.

But Don Stanley also did something that Joe Lukacs recognizes as a major benefit to his own approach to problem-solving. Given that none of them really had the knowledge to deal with the problem, Stanley declared that the way to solve it was to find somebody who did. He got on the phone to Dr. Gus Rossano at the University of Washington, one of the top air pollution experts in the United States. After a brief conversation with Gus Rossano, Don Stanley had Joe on a plane to Seattle.

As often happened in the career of Joe Lukacs, the effect of his personality on that of Gus Rossano soon resulted in his having another in his growing collection of mentors. Gus Rossano had not intended to take on this project—he was too busy—but, after a conversation with Joe, he decided he would.

One thing Gus Rossano could see clearly was the need for an accurate wind and weather model. They could not assess the need for higher stacks at Rossdale without it. Again, Joe would see the value of bringing in the top people in the field as Gus Rossano put him in touch with Larry Faith in Los Angeles and Jim Halitzky, a top weather modeller out of New York. Joe went to New York, and in a New York University wind tunnel, he attempted to simulate the weather systems of the North Saskatchewan River valley at Edmonton.

The contacts made in this way would prove of enormous importance to Western Research, and to Joe Lukacs personally. Joe had only been in pollution control for a few months, and he was already working with the best in the business. His network grew rapidly because of the way top people like Gus Rossano consulted with other top people in other specializations in order to get a job done.

By reaching out and consulting top experts (mentors), a small company can look bigger than it is; it can reach world-class standards of expertise and achievement.

This was a secondary benefit: the knowledge of how top problem-solvers operate. Initially, Joe felt he needed to be the source of knowledge in order to do a job. Now he understood, courtesy first of Don Stanley and then of Gus Rossano, that personal knowledge was not the essential thing. Your ability to solve a problem had more to do with the human resources beyond yourself that you were able to bring to bear on it. Network, in other words, was potentially more important than knowledge.

Obviously you have to be able to understand and employ what the experts were telling you, but that was a gift Joe Lukacs possessed in unusual degree. He was a fast learner and able to get his mind around almost any scientific or engineering concept. He was also, as friend Joe Labuda would comment, "a great implementer."

The other half of the Rossdale problem was the part that would be handled locally. Ed Hardy and Joe Lukacs began discussing, and debating, ways of sampling the stack gas. As Ed Hardy describes it, people could barely spell "pollution" in those days, which meant there was almost no pollution control or testing equipment around to buy. You had to invent it, and then build it.

Joe's first inspiration for the Rossdale sampling project was the use of a hydrogen balloon. As it rose, the balloon could haul up tubing to the mouth of the stack. They could then draw the sample in through the tubing to the analyzer. Ed Hardy was firm in his belief that it would not work. All his experience of flying gliders, remote control model planes, and actual planes suggested to him that the balloon would not take the tubing high enough and would blow over on the ground. But Joe insisted they try it.

In preparation for the test, Ed said he would get all the equipment in place, but beyond that he would have no part of it. When it was set up, he emphasized his non-involvement by walking away about a hundred feet from the launch site. The balloon rose and toppled over. Ed recalls that Joe looked at him across the top of their car with an expression that amounted to acknowledgement that Ed was right–this time.

The next plan was one they agreed on. It involved flying through the plume with a helicopter. No system existed for taking a sample by this method, so Ed Hardy invented one. At home on his ironing board, he made mylar bags and glued heat-sensitive tape to their sides. A few bits of tubing, an old tractor funnel, and brackets with which to attach the gear to the helicopter skid and they were in business, chasing plumes by helicopter.

Devote yourself to solving your client's problems as your first priority, and profits will follow.

Except for a nervous few seconds on each blind pass through the plume, the approach worked. It also solved the Rossdale power plant pollution problem. The analysis showed that the turbines were emitting oxides of nitrogen, but not in amounts sufficient to produce the brown-yellow coloration of the plume. The plume colour was a chromatic, or prismatic effect produced by the rays of the sun on the particulate matter inside the emission plume. As Joe Lukacs put it, "Nobody was killing nobody."

The wind-tunnel modelling in New York also paid off. It proved that the unsightly giant stack extension Edmonton Power had in mind was not necessary. Much more modest extensions would serve to pierce most temperature inversion ceilings, thus keeping the traffic circle and the community free of smoke.

Rossdale was a major success for Western Research. Rod McDaniel and Bud Coote had proven that the company could go beyond oil patch problems in search of opportunities and meet the challenges they found there. Joe Lukacs had learned that a network of experts had the power to bring a small regional company like Western Research up to an international standard of performance. Ed Hardy had demonstrated his inventiveness and dexterity at designing and building pollution sampling and monitoring devices for the company. Western Research had broken out of a dependency on petroleum industry work before a pattern of it had even been established. This was a win-win situation.

The friendship that Joe Lukacs established with Dr. Gus Rossano and other top minds in the American pollution control business had the effect of giving Joe, and the people who worked for him, a confidence that would always characterize the company through its best years. Through those contacts, Joe and company became active in the Air Pollution Control Association, a presence that would one day allow them to open shop south of the border.

For the time being, however, the company business was stack testing, the labour-intensive scaling of sulphur plant stacks for purposes of emission testing, a market guaranteed by legislation in the province of Alberta.

❖ *What are the advantages of using advisors from outside your company?*

❖ *What might be the role of an advisory board or group?*

❖ *For a small private business, why is an advisory board a good alternative to a board of directors?*

7

Stack Testing: Finding and Fitting Your Niche

> **When we heard that Joe Lukacs had a company that was willing to climb our stacks, we were ecstatic. And, I'll tell you, we didn't argue with the price.**
>
> —Elmer Berlie

Three facts about sulphur plant stacks created Western Research's opportunity in the emission testing area.

Number one: the stacks were very tall, from 200 to 400 feet in 1965. Amoco Crossfield and the third Shell Waterton expansion would push the horizon of stack size to 500 feet.

Number two: the height, combined with considerable wind through the Rocky Mountain foothills, and extreme cold in the winter months, meant that nobody wanted to climb them.

Number three, and this was the kicker: the job could not be avoided. The Government of Alberta said the stacks had to be climbed and tested on a monthly basis.

Elmer Berlie, who would eventually join Western Research, saw the whole stack testing saga unfold. At BA Pincher Creek, where Elmer was plant engineer for a couple of years, the concept of stack testing was given a particular Wallenda Brothers quality by virtue of there being no ladder. Instead there were ladder hangers, a type of rung, every ten feet. What you were supposed to do was take two ten-foot ladders, hook the first, and climb it while dragging up the second. Then you hooked the second ladder and climbed it while hauling up the first. Add to that the facts that BA Pincher Creek was one of the windiest places on earth and there was no cage around the leap-frog ladder arrangement, and one can easily understand why no Pincher operators or laboratory staff wanted anything to do with it.

Eventually, when the time came to drill testing ports into the concrete stack at BA Pincher Creek, the contractor had to go to the town's beer parlour to hire a crew emboldened by liquor. By this means, the ports were achieved, but it remained a Pyrrhic victory if no one could be found to climb up the stack and use them.

Market openings can be created by the unpleasantness of the work.

This period of time when plants all over Alberta were getting their stacks ready for compulsory sulphur emission testing led to a startling discovery. A great many of the concrete stacks were found to be rotten, so much so that a couple of bangs with a sledge hammer would punch right through. Joe Lukacs was still working for Fina at this point, and Dr. Petrunic put him in charge of finding out why this was happening. Joe was directed to Dr. Thorvaldsen of the University of Saskatchewan, a scientist who was an expert on concrete.

"Of course you've got a problem," Dr. Thorvaldsen told Joe. "You've got acid gas, air, water vapour–everything you need to cause corrosion." Joe allowed that they hadn't known that, and Dr. Thorvaldsen replied that it was because they didn't know a thing about concrete.

The problem was comprehended, but not solved. Some of the stacks were so far gone that they had to be destroyed. Some like the 250-footer at Bowden's Canadian Oil Companies Limited plant were chopped down like rotten old trees.

Frank Angebrandt, a friend of Joe Lukacs and a very inventive Shell engineer, would one day come up with an even more spectacular solution. When Shell Waterton had a stack problem but did not want to shut down in winter to fix it, Angebrandt designed a steel liner that was raised by helicopter and lowered into the stack from above, all while the plant was running.

When Elmer Berlie moved from Pincher Creek to Texas Gulf Okotoks, he entered a much smoother operating sulphur facility, but he encountered the same employee reluctance to climb the sulphur stack for testing. Elmer recalls with what joy he and other engineers around the province received the news that a crazy Hungarian named Joe Lukacs, with a new company called Western Research and Development, was willing for a price to take the burden of stack testing off their shoulders.

The word spread, the workload increased, and as Ed Hardy says, "The two or three stack tests a year that Joe had predicted we would be doing quickly turned into two or three a week." It was obviously more work than Joe and Ed could handle, and more employees were added. Bill Lewington and Ron Dinsley were the first Western Research stack climbers hired after Ed Hardy. (Another employee was added between Hardy and the two stack testers and that was Gillian Clark. She had taken a year off from her engineering degree to work in 1967 and she spent that year working for Western Research as a technician running programs on the IBM 360. Upon graduation 1971, she returned to Western Research as an engineer.)

Ed Hardy about to hit the road. Packing for overnight was standard practice.

Still it is doubtful that anyone climbed more stacks, or knew more about testing them, than Ed Hardy. The stack climbing might be new, but the concepts of testing and analysis by chromatography were old hat. At Chemical and Geological, Ed had seen every permutation of testing and knew without doubt the dangers of faulty sampling.

A particularly amusing example of this was when an oil-field worker brought Ed a sample at the Chem and Geo lab, boasting that it was a particularly good sample and should lead to an accurate result. When asked why he thought his sample was so good, he said, "I purged it for three straight hours." This probably met with some laughter given that a sample container opened for that length of time would have operated as a mini-separator. The sample was guaranteed to be meaningless.

The routine for a day of sulphur plant stack testing involved an early morning rise and driving out to whatever plant was up for today. Three hundred feet of rope was the average requirement for winching the equipment to the top. Sometimes the plant personnel had the winch and rope in place for you; sometimes they didn't.

Ed Hardy recalls how good for the human memory this work was. "When a 6/32 screw is 250 feet down and half a mile across the plant, it's a long walk." Instead, he would think of every possibility beforehand. Sure-handedness was also necessary, given what a bolt could do to a human on the ground when dropped from that distance.

One of the many jobs Joe and Ed did together was the plant acceptance testing at Petrogas Calgary. There were twin stacks and they spent the day climbing one, attaching sample probes to sample bottles, then going down and up the other stack to start the next test there. In total, the two men climbed the two stacks eight times that day, and Ed Hardy's recollection is that it took eighteen hours.

Once at the sampling port, the pitot tube with the inclined draft gauge assembly attached was moved manually across the space inside the stack. Taking the sampling probe out was another matter because it was hot, as much as 1,500 degrees Fahrenheit. You hoped that the plant would run steady while you were testing because a sudden change in flow would invalidate the test. Worse was a plant upset. If the plant lost equilibrium while you were testing, it would be a full twelve hours before equilibrium could be restored and the test attempted a second time.

After the samples were taken off the stack, the next step

was to head for the plant's lab to do the titrations. Then home, or off to another plant. Sometimes, Ed Hardy was doing more than one plant test per day. He recalls one such day when he put five tanks of gas through his car. During these years, he was putting an average of sixty thousand miles on his vehicle per annum.

Al Brotherston joined Western R & D in 1969 after graduating from SAIT's Aeronautical Engineering Technology course (the same course from which early employee Dave Earl graduated). Al was trained in the art of source testing (stack surveying) by Ed Hardy and took on a variety of other tasks as well. He had a trapline of sulphation monitoring stations around Calgary, tested water wells near the Petrogas plant, and joined Harold Paskall and Robin Rankine when they began testing sulphur plants and needed more manpower. His reward for being a particularly good stack tester was to do lots of it, plus train newcomers in the art.

Company culture grows out of shared values and shared experience.

All the same, Al Brotherston wasn't mad about stack testing. It was often cold and frustrating, and required "superhuman bladder control." When he noticed that the poorest stack samplers, "mostly new engineers," were often given opportunities to do other more interesting work, he fashioned his own plan for getting off the stacks. He became one of the very first of many Western R & D employees to take a leave of absence to go back to school. In 1972-73, he earned his bachelor of engineering, returning to Western R & D for several years thereafter.

Stack testing was always dramatic, a drama composed of height and weather. The wind along the foothills is legendary and a couple of Western Research technicians were once caught at the top of the Shell Waterton stack when wind gusts were clocked at over ninety miles per hour. In the lee of the stack, a little shelter could be found but, leaving it, you would face an accelerated blast. No Western Research employee ever blew off a stack, but many felt they might.

Cold was the other dire working condition. The tests had to be done monthly, no matter the temperature, and this included the winter half of the year when at times it was minus thirty. The snowmobile suit was standard Western R & D equipment.

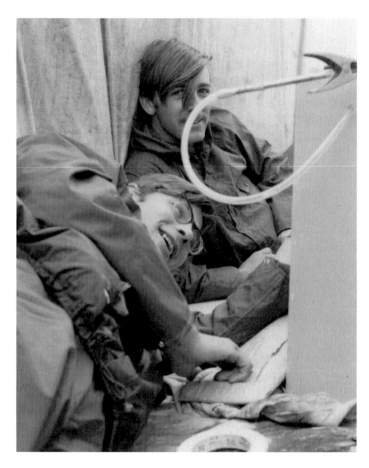

Stack climbing in 1970. Don Stevens and Ron Dimmer.

With time, stack climbing became more than a basic task at Western Research, it became a company rite. Eventually, it would be claimed that all new Western Research employees had to climb a stack as a matter of initiation—secretaries and other office staff included. Others will tell you the rite extended beyond that; that to complete the initiation, you had to pee off the very top.

Western Researchers were the people who braved the cold and wind, who climbed the stacks where other mortals feared to go. Finally, stack climbing became one of the company's principal badges of honour, a key part of the shared culture that at once glued the company together and set its people apart from others.

❖ *Is it possible to manage the creation of a company culture? And, if so, how do you do it?*

❖ *Are some cultures more appropriate to particular corporate strategies?*

❖ *Are some cultures more appropriate to certain industries?*

❖ *What is the impact of a company culture on company behaviour?*

8

A Dream of Automation: The First Financing Crunch

Western Research was a pollution control company ahead of its time. It practised pollution prevention by optimization before there was such a thing as pollution prevention.

—Paul Beauchemin

When you're out of cash, you're out of business.

—Blaine Lee

Western Research and Development's emission testing results were not always welcome news to the people they were working for. Prior to the implementation of testing, sulphur plants had been a kind of a black box that you operated with the instructions given by the design companies. If the plants were operated according to instructions, the designers proclaimed that a certain sulphur recovery efficiency would be achieved: usually 95 percent which was more than enough to meet the standards required of the Alberta industry by the province's Conservation Board at that time.

But then along comes Western Research with its testing program, telling the companies that, in some cases, they were closer to achieving mid-80s than mid-90s efficiency. Ordinarily you kill the messenger in such a situation, but the Western Research team had too much respect within the industry for that. Their results could be duplicated test after test, which meant that the non-complying plants had some work to do.

All along, as Joe Lukacs's company worked at testing stacks, his urge was in one sense to put himself out of business. From his days of working on the reaction furnace and catalyst beds at Canadian Fina Wildcat Hills (the work he had done with Dr. Alec Petrunic), Joe knew that increasing stack heights and improving dispersion of gas plumes was like closing the gate after the horse has run away. The problem and the solution both were to be found in the plant itself, in the reaction furnace most of all, and in the catalyst beds and condensers. At Wildcat Hills, with its CO_2-rich sour gas stream, Dr. Petrunic had, after long study, extended the length of the reaction furnace to give more time for the complex reactions to complete themselves. It was this type of study and problem-solving that Joe Lukacs longed to do at the plants for which he was working, even if it meant that his pollution control business at the tail end of the plant might one day no longer be needed.

Joe was not alone in this type of thinking. Way back in 1963, he had received a visit at Wildcat Hills from a Shell engineer named Joe Labuda. A chemical engineering grad from Queen's, Labuda was working at Shell Jumping Pound which was not far from Wildcat Hills. Having read one of Joe's papers on gas hydrates, he decided to take the short drive over the foothills to meet the author.

Labuda and Lukacs hit it off and found that they had many complementary ideas about sour gas processing and sulphur plant operation. For a time, the two and another Shell engineer, the inventive Frank Angebrandt, had a tradition of meeting at an east Calgary Hungarian restaurant to indulge another shared passion, which was Hungarian strudel. Over lunches of soup and strudel, the three solved many problems and hatched many plans. Joe Labuda remembers one discussion involving the plugging up of pitot tubes during sulphur plant testing. He came up with the scheme of purging the tube after each test, something that would eventually become standard practice at Western Research and an essential part of the design of the Continuous Stack Emission Monitor, Western Research's first commercial instrument.

Perhaps because he was born at Creighton Mine, practically at the foot of Inco's infamous Sudbury smokestack, Joe Labuda was no fan of oil companies that dragged their feet on reducing sulphur emissions. Believing it was possible to reduce those sulphur emissions all the way to zero, he viewed the sulphur stacks as "monuments to poor process engineering." He looked forward to plants that would operate without them.

In the late 1960s, Joe Lukacs and Joe Labuda would meet again in a more formal capacity at Shell Waterton, where Joe Labuda was the project manager in charge of the plant's third expansion. Joe Labuda had already suggested to his superiors at Shell that the way to go for sulphur plant operation was automation, but there was no way they were going to take the lead. He was told to wait and let someone else come up with it. Then they would buy it.

Act on market pull. Successful products and services come from knowing your clients and answering their needs.

In 1968, when Joe Lukacs looked at the tail gas emission results for Shell Waterton, he told them, "You've got bigger problems here than SO_2 monitoring. You have to go back to the plant and find out what's going on in there." Together, the two Joes, Labuda and Lukacs, came up with a plan for studying Shell Waterton's plant performance. Joe Lukacs remembers how advanced Joe Labuda was in his thinking about sulphur plant automation. He was imagining a closed-loop feedback approach to plant process control long before the idea was generally embraced by the industry.

For Joe Lukacs, this adventure in process control was a return to the work he had started with Dr. Petrunic at Fina: going step by step through the sulphur plant and analyzing the gases at each stage. If you know how the gas composition has changed from point A to point B, you can begin to deduce what chemical reactions happened between the points, and why.

It also made great business sense. If you tested a company's stack and told them they weren't getting the results the government required, they might dislike you for it. But if you went on to say that your company could test their plant and find out where the inefficiencies were coming from, you went from hated messenger to knight in shining armour.

Either because sulphur was a saleable product (usually not) or a pollutant that had to be removed, sulphur recovery was essential to the processing business. His own instincts and the wise counsel of his various mentors in the international pollution control business gave Joe Lukacs every reason to believe that the present sulphur recovery standards were only the beginning. He expected to see the government push the sulphur efficiency requirement into the high nineties before long.

Most plant design companies liked to say that 95 percent efficiency was a ceiling that could not be breached, and the operating companies liked to hear that because it saved them the expense of trying to go higher. But Joe Lukacs and Joe Labuda, and others on the cutting edge of the science and technology involved in extracting sulphur, knew it wasn't so. Not only could they go much higher, they could probably do it at a price the industry could afford.

While Joe Lukacs strove to achieve higher sulphur recovery efficiencies through process control, Joe Labuda worked toward applying the latest tail gas clean-up processes toward the same result. The third expansion of the Shell Waterton plant, the one that Joe Labuda oversaw, was the first use of the sulfreen tail gas process in Canada.

From Ed Hardy's point of view, this branching out by Western Research into process control was another prime example of "Joe's never saying no to anything." Ed's part in the process control work at Waterton was helping decide where the sample ports should be placed throughout the sulphur plant, and how the sampling would be done. He soon realized that the probe had to extend fairly deep into the pipe because sulphur had a tendency to condense along the walls.

The other problem was getting reliable samples that represented the process flow at that point. If, in the course of removing the sample, more reactions took place, the sample would be flawed and the analysis false. What was needed was a way of quenching the sample, preventing further reactions, and, over time, the solution found was to rapidly dry the sample. The water content made a sample reactive. If it could be dried, the reactions could be stopped. Knowing this and coming up with a means of doing it were major Western Research innovations.

Besides giving Western Research a chance to study the process inside the sulphur plant, Joe Labuda made another major contribution to Western Research by introducing Joe Lukacs to scientist Robin Rankine. Joe Labuda met Robin Rankine when he was canvassing for the Trudeau Liberals in Calgary North. One of the houses he happened to call upon was Robin Rankine's, and they got talking about what each of them did for a living. It came out that Robin Rankine was working on a PhD in physics at the University of Calgary and was not at all happy with the direction his advisor was trying to take his thesis in thermodynamics of particles. It sounded as though he was ripe for some other opportunity.

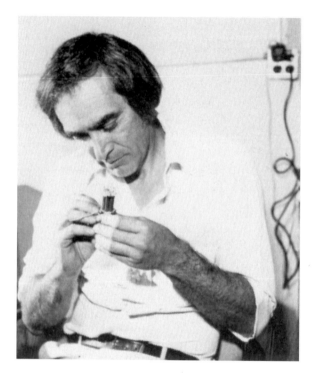

Robin Rankine, Western Research's first scientist, inspecting an ultraviolet lamp

When Joe Lukacs began to do process work at Shell Waterton, it recalled to him how poorly understood the modified-Claus process was. He was greatly excited by the prospect of using his company to improve that understanding, but realized he would need top scientists to accomplish it. When Joe Labuda told Joe Lukacs about meeting Robin Rankine, Lukacs got on it immediately. He called Rankine up and arranged an interview. Joe Lukacs soon realized Rankine was a man of uncommon intelligence who could help him in the frontier study of sulphur process, and he offered him a job in October, 1968.

"I told him, I have no idea what I'm going to do with you but I want to hire you," says Joe.

When Robin Rankine joined Western Research, he had no specific gas processing or sulphur plant knowledge or experience. Joe Lukacs decided to use Shell Waterton as his finishing school. He assigned Robin to Waterton, to work alongside Ed Hardy and Bill Lewington. In all, Rankine would

Rod McDaniel

Joe Lukacs

Petro-Canada Wildcat Hills (formerly Canadian Fina),
where Joe Lukacs worked prior to Western Research.

*Petrogas Balzac
with its twin smokestacks:
double the trouble
for stack testers.*

*The stack
climber's
view down.*

*The view up one of the
Petrogas Balzac stacks.*

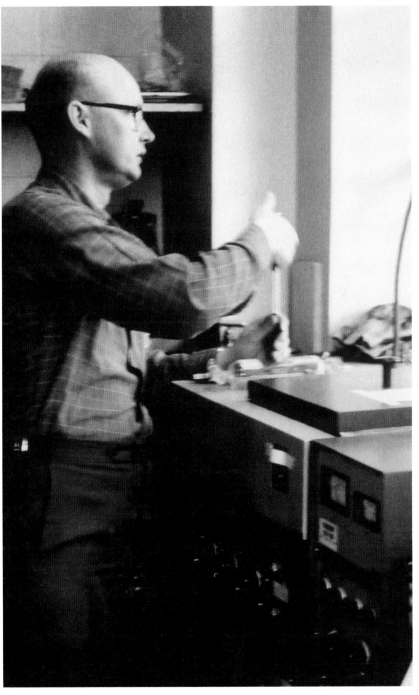

*Ed Hardy operating a gas chromatograph in the original
Western Research laboratory.*

Sulphur: the "gold" that Western Research mined.

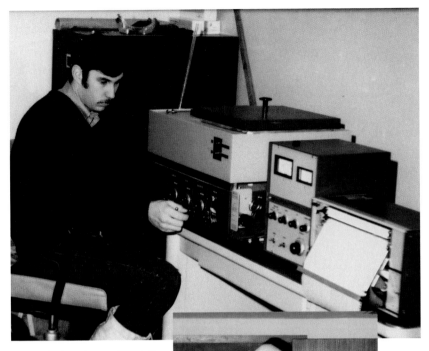

Dave Earl testing at HBOG Edson, 1970.

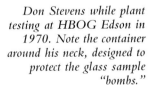

Don Stevens while plant testing at HBOG Edson in 1970. Note the container around his neck, designed to protect the glass sample "bombs."

The Shell Waterton gas processing and sulphur recovery plant: where so many Western Research breakthroughs were made.

*The Air Pollution Control Association (PNWIS Chapter) convention in Calgary, 1971.
Joe (centre) helped organize. His mentor Gus Rossano (2nd from left) attended.*

*Ed Hardy (centre)
demonstrates a
model of the
Continuous Stack
Emission Monitor,
the first Western
Research product.*

Hugh Hicklin (l.) And Calvin Price study wind currents, ca. 1972.

spend six months at Shell Waterton that year, and the fruits of his study would eventually revolutionize not only Western Research but sulphur recovery itself.

The on-going work of stack testing was also, in the eyes of everyone who had to do it, an area in need of technological breakthrough. Running up the stacks to test them every month may have been the company's bread and butter, but no one would miss it if a method could be found to replace it. The solution had to be automation and the natural question was, could there be an automated system that could do this testing? Also, could it be done on a continuous basis?

Such a plan had several exciting possibilities attached to it. If emission gases could be continuously monitored, that amounted to a continuous read-out of plant performance. If you could tell what the sulphur plant was producing as emissions, you could take that information back to various points along the train and make performance-improving adjustments. In other words, it would relate directly to the testing they had begun to do inside the sulphur plant.

Joe Lukacs and Ed Hardy were already thinking of how an automated stack emission analyzer might work, and how it might be built and installed.

With all these exciting developments taking place, and with the employee base up to ten people and more growth on the way, it was hard to see Western R & D—from the inside at least—as anything but an emerging success story. But, from the point of view of its business backers, the picture was not as rosy. Bud Coote was already gone. The further Joe ventured into processing and pollution work, the further he moved away from Bud Coote's areas of interest and expertise (i.e., seismic). In addition, Bud was tired of all the cash calls that the growing business required. Rod McDaniel took over Bud's 50 percent "for the losses." At about the same time, Joe Lukacs was given a significant share position in the company as an incentive.

But as he looked at his R & D company, Rod McDaniel was not all that pleased either. Sure, Western Research had work, in the air monitoring and stack testing area. The initial contacts with Edmonton Power had led to more utility and urban air pollution testing, both in Edmonton and Calgary, and now there was the Shell Waterton contract to do process study and control work. But, in studying the numbers, Rod McDaniel could not help but conclude that Western R & D was making more money for its equipment suppliers than it was for itself.

Into this mix, Joe threw the ideas that he was nurturing. Why not make Western Research an instrumentation manufacturer and marketer? With his knowledge, Ed Hardy's practical design sense, and Robin Rankine's high scientific input, Western had the beginnings of a team to pull that off.

Rod McDaniel considered it, and could certainly see that was the direction to go if Western R & D was to become a financial success, but he also knew developing instrumentation was a long and expensive business. McDaniel had to ask himself if he had enough enthusiasm about such a venture to justify the major investment. He was not sure that he did. As Rod McDaniel puts it, "What we needed to develop was an automatic system so we could improve the efficiency of the plants. We needed to develop the instrumentation and it was going to take a lot of money. If we put that money in, I'd have to live with it, and I was more interested in the area I was already in." Rod McDaniel went looking for a buyer.

At this time, Bow Valley Industries, the Seaman brothers' wide-ranging Calgary oil company, was growing rapidly through acquisitions. Looking for a solution to the Western R & D financing dilemma, Rod McDaniel went to Doc and B.J. Seaman in early 1969. He knew the brothers well. He started out curling against Doc in Calgary rinks. He also wrote the report on the Seaman brothers' first oil well back in 1956.

The Seaman brothers were interested in Western R & D because it seemed to fit with their 1967 acquisition of Flamemaster Ltd., an Edmonton company. Flamemaster manufactured furnaces and heating equipment, and Doc Seaman thought that the development of instrumentation for Western

R & D might serve some of Flamemaster's needs as well. B.J. Seaman remembers that the Western Research purchase fit with a desire BVI had to diversify into pure science. The research and development initiatives promised results throughout the company, while presenting attractive tax write-offs.

The deal by which Bow Valley Industries took over Western Research and Development was designed to happen in two stages. In the first stage, as of February, 1969, BVI acquired 50 percent of Western R & D. Western Research could then get on with development of its first instrumentation products, backed by the deeper pockets of BVI. According to Don Thurston, who became BVI's liaison to Western R & D, the plan was for BVI to take over the remaining 50 percent at a later date. The price of the remaining 50 percent would be paid for by earnings, so that the more Western R & D made in profit, the more the other owners would get for their share.

During the following year, however, certain realities led to the deal for the remaining 50 percent being consummated more quickly. First, some of the partners felt too much money was flowing out of Western Research to Dominion Instruments, an Edmonton company put in charge of inventing a flow-measuring device for the continous stack monitor. It was thought that Western R & D would do better by buying Dominion Instruments, but Rod McDaniel, for one, was cool to the idea of pouring that kind of money into a company he was only luke warm toward at best.

Joe Lukacs also had reservations about continuing as a minority owner of the company. The tying of profits to the price BVI would eventually pay for the remainder of the company was in direct opposition to how Joe believed the company should progress. They were in a product development and scientific R & D mode, and were unlikely to produce high profits for some time. The value of his share in the company was more likely to decline than grow if he took the company in the direction and at the speed he believed it should go.

In the end, these forces contributed to Bow Valley Industries' buying the remaining 50 percent of Western R & D in early 1970. From that day forward, Western R & D became a wholly owned subsidiary of BVI.

If you want to grow and create real wealth, consider giving up some control in return for capital, complementary skills, and leverage.

Finally, everybody got what they wanted. Rod McDaniel got out of a business he didn't want to be in. Bow Valley Industries got a company with instrument manufacturing potential, which it could apply elsewhere in its family of companies. Western Research got its chance to grow and change in tune with the growing and changing marketplace. But the fulfilment of the latter two ambitions would be full of challenges. Progress would be slow, and at times completely uncertain.

❖ *What is the impact on a small business if the owners go out after equity funding too early in the company's life?*

❖ *What is the result of going after equity funding too late?*

❖ *How do you determine the right time to go after new equity?*

❖ *What should you look for in new equity? (That is: is all money of equal value?)*

Doc, Don and B.J. Seaman

The story of how the Seaman brothers, Doc, Don, and
B.J., went from small-town Saskatchewan roots to being
the kingpins of a multinational corporate conglomerate is one
of the great business sagas in Canadian history. Back in
Rouleau, Saskatchewan,
their father Byron, Sr.
was in contract road
construction for the
Municipal District. Doc,
the oldest son, went to
war before the age of
twenty. Serving as a
bomber pilot over Eu-
rope, he was wounded
through both legs and
still managed to bring his
plane home. Doc had
started his engineering
degree at the University
of Saskatchewan before
the war and he finished
it afterward. While Doc

had been away, both B.J. and Don
had started their engineering
degrees, also at U of S. The three
brothers graduated within a few
years of one another.

*The Seaman brothers,
(l. to r.) B.J., Doc and
Don. They acquired
Western Research in
1970.*

After university, Doc Seaman got into the seismic business
with a share in one seismic rig. When there proved to be
more contracts than his one rig could serve, he convinced his
brothers to gather up every cent they could call upon and
buy another. This was the origin of their early company, Sedco.

As he gained the capital to do so, Doc started acquiring
other businesses. He and his brothers got into drilling, slim

holes and even water wells at first, while they put the capital together to buy their first oil well-drilling rig. Where able, as oil well drillers, they looked for contracts that gave them a piece of the action in lieu of cash.

The acquisition or conglomeration approach to growth was the Seaman modus operandi for many years. In 1959, they swallowed Ralph Will's drilling company, Hi-Tower, a larger company than themselves. The resulting company took the name Bow Valley Industries Ltd.

Western Rockbit, Cardwell Manufacturing, Flamemaster, Western R & D, Alcon, Syracuse—the acquisitions kept on coming until the Seaman brothers were major international operators, known and respected worldwide.

The Western R & D acquisition seemed a little out of the Seamans' ordinary orbit. Don Thurston, whose job it was to take on some of these companies for BVI and oversee their business practices, thinks the attraction might have been the upsurgence of air pollution initiatives about this time. Air pollution work was coming on fast and having a company like Western R & D at the forefront of that work added "sex appeal" to the BVI portfolio.

II

The R&D Explosion:
Western Research
Develops Its Product Line

*To achieve success in business,
you need vision,
perseverence, and courage.*

1969-1975

9

Alberta: A Leader in Pollution Awareness and Control

Know the driving forces within your market and within your society.

The story of a company is in many ways the story of its marketplace, and also the story of the governments that regulate that marketplace. The close of the 1960s, the start of the 1970s, was a time of considerable change in the market for environmental science and technology—what Western R & D in its own language had been calling "the pollution control business."

In a fairly quiet fashion, the Province of Alberta had been leading Canada in air pollution legislation and regulation throughout the 1960s. The most basic reason was that Alberta had the majority of sour gas in the country and had begun exploiting that resource to meet the growing gas export market since the late '50s. To ensure that sour gas production and processing were done safely, with proper conservation and minimum pollution, the Alberta Social Credit government had put in place legislation and regulatory guidelines that were quite advanced for their time. Air pollution was not something that most jurisdictions were even thinking about in 1961, but that was the year Alberta's Air Pollution Branch piloted the first air emission regulations through the provincial legislature. Alberta's Energy Resources Conservation Board was recognized as one of the most progressive conservation authorities in the world. Progressive is of course a relative term, and the rest of the country, and the continent, would catch up.

Air pollution did not become a world *cause célèbre* until the United States decided to move on it. In the last half of the 1960s, it became an American political plus to be an environmentalist. Democrat Edmund Muskie began pushing for federal air pollution legislation at the committee level in 1967 and, as he focussed his long-range sights on a run at the presidency, pollution and a clean air act were major planks in his platform.

The sitting Republican president, Richard Nixon, was just as surely not an environmentalist. He considered the whole environmental movement a radical fad. But when it became clear to him that, at the very least, environmentalism was a politically popular fad, he decided he must spike Muskie's guns by supporting it. With the approval of the president, the 50-page Clean Air Act passed Congress in 1970.

Beyond politics, the Clean Air Act was legislation whose time had come. Levels of urban and industrial air pollution had risen unchecked for the first two-thirds of the twentieth century. Scientists were turning up disturbing evidence that this pollution was more than a smoke problem and an eyesore. Human health was at risk and possibly the health of the planet.

The effect of the American Clean Air Act, and of environmentalism's general movement into the popular culture, was to spread the concern through the classes and to the corners of the United States. The influence of the U.S. Clear Air Act also extended beyond America's borders. In Canada, and in Alberta where most of Canada's oil and gas production was located, the public began to ask their governments for greater protection against the pollution threat, and the governments responded.

As usual, Alberta moved quickly. James Henderson, the Minister of Health in the Social Credit government under Premier Harry Strom, brought forward a flurry of environmental legislation, starting in 1970 with the passage of the Environmental Conservation Act. In 1971, Mr. Henderson introduced a Department of the Environment Act by which the first provincial environment ministry in Canada was created. A Clean Air Act and a Clean Water Act were also introduced. In the first months after the passage of the Department of the Environment Act, James Henderson served as both Alberta's Minister of the Environment and its Minister of Health.

Things were also moving on the federal level. The Canadian government announced national air quality objectives for five major air pollutants as defined by the National Clean Air Act in 1971.

Changes in government often mean changes in regulation. The effect on companies dependent on regulation for their market can be positive or negative.

Interestingly, although the Alberta Social Credit government, and Health and Environment Minister James Henderson in particular, initiated the legislative changes in the environmental area in 1970 and 1971, a totally different government would be the ones who acted on and enforced the new regime. Peter Lougheed had won the leadership of the Alberta Conservative party in 1965, and, in the Alberta election two years later, he and five other Conservatives won their way into the Alberta legislature. In a 1969 by-election, caused by the retirement of former Premier Ernest Manning, the Conservatives won again, electing William Yurko, a chemical engineer. Heading into the election year of 1971, the 36-year unbroken rule of the Social Credit party in Alberta was in danger.

Ironically, given that Alberta would see two major oil booms in the 1970s, the election of 1971 was fought on what might happen to Alberta if the oil industry left the province. Of late, Alberta had been losing its prominence in the petroleum industry, as attention turned to the new girl on the block: Alaska's massive Prudhoe Bay discovery. Peter Lougheed's election attack on the Socreds featured much about the government's failure to diversify the provincial economy away from oil.

When it finally did come to pass, the Progressive Conservative victory of 1971 was classed as an upset. The Conservatives won a majority, with 49 seats, and Peter Lougheed was sworn in as premier on September 10, 1971. He would remain as premier until his voluntary departure in 1985.

As Peter Foster pointed out in his book *The Blue-Eyed Sheiks*, Peter Lougheed, as premier of Alberta, was surprisingly cool toward big oil. Simply put, he understood the arithmetic of the multinational corporation. The oil majors, headquartered in the United States, and running branch plants in Alberta, served different masters than the average Albertan. As a result, Peter Lougheed's version of progressive politics would not necessarily support the oil industry at every turn, and this included the party's stance on environment and pollution. Perhaps for this reason, he and W.J.Yurko, who was named the new government's minister of the environment, took up the Social Credit environmental legislation as if it were their own. They became strong promoters of pollution control.

> We, the Alberta Government, recognize that there must be a balance between the desire to not upset the natural state of our land and water, and the job opportunities created by petroleum, timber, coal and other mineral and natural resource developers. If we are forced to lean in one direction or another, it would likely be toward conservation rather than development. —Peter Lougheed, 1971

> We, the Alberta Government, will watch EPA action closely and always lead where possible. We wouldn't under any circumstance sanction standards in Alberta less stringent than those set by the EPA for the United States or those set nationally in Canada.
> —W.J. Yurko,
> Alberta Minister of the Environment, January, 1973

This was the context as Joe Lukacs and his Western Research team adjusted to their second life under Bow Valley Industries ownership in the early 1970s. It was not lost on Joe that most of the changes and omens of the new decade seemed likely to play in his company's favour. Because of his American mentors and his growing involvement in the American-based Air Pollution Control Association, Joe was aware of the U.S. Clean Air Act movement and other developments at the U.S. Environmental Protection Agency level, often before they became news. Watching the country with the most automobiles and the biggest industrial machine move fast toward greater environmental awareness and tougher regulations, Joe understood that Canada would likely be influenced by that momentum. If Alberta did move to higher levels of pollution control, it could mean major openings for Western Research in the monitoring, testing, and process control areas.

In 1971, Gerry Gainor of Gulf Canada, Lloyd Bellows of the Energy Resources Conservation Board, Elmer Berlie and Joe Lukacs organized the first Alberta conference of the Air Pollution Control Association's Pacific North West International Section (PNWIS). It was held in Calgary with record attendance: more than 700. It was by far the largest environmental conference in Alberta's history. Joe Lukacs chaired the event, and he and the other organizers were successful in convincing Minister of the Environment Yurko to give the keynote speech.

Professional organization membership is a powerful means of networking, marketing, and staying on top of changes in your industry.

At this point, Bill Yurko had not been environment minister long and he used the opportunity to deliver a detailed description of the stricter environmental controls his government was about to impose on industry. The Government of Alberta would, he said, "continue to encourage development of the province's natural resources," but would do so "based upon a new formula of environmental awareness." All enterprise would soon be required to "adequately monitor each of its pollution streams and report the details to government on a periodic basis." Industry should expect to be required to "increase its on-site monitoring facilities with frequent written and automatic reporting to government."

Another of his statements that must have caused unease for those who were having difficulty meeting current emission standards was: "It will be the government's policy to impose pollution source standards of such initial severity as to prevent the need for revision of the standards at frequent intervals."

Further to that, Bill Yurko told the PNWIS group that, from now on, a company's emissions were going to be public knowledge and that the public was going to be encouraged by government to get involved in the setting of regulations. What's more, no one should get the impression that the regulations were to be anything but stringently policed.

All of this must have been music to Joe Lukacs's ears. On-site monitoring facilities with frequent reporting meant more work for the air monitoring and stack emission testing group at Western Research, plus a market for the emerging continuous stack emission monitor. Tougher emission standards for sulphur plants meant a big increase in the market for the new plant testing and optimization squad. The new government was institutionalizing the demand for services that only Western R & D was providing in Alberta. Perhaps more importantly, it was creating a government and regulatory environment that seemed likely to welcome any new technology Western R & D could create to automatically control and optimize sulphur plants.

Another feature of all these changes, although it may not have been in the company's thinking to any great extent in 1971, was the possibility of opportunity outside Canada. If Western Research could establish and maintain a scientific and technical edge, there was every reason to believe the company would be able to expand its business wherever there was pollution and the political will to combat it.

❖ *How might Western Research have better capitalized on the opportunities available at this time in history?*

❖ *How can a company take advantage of market momentum?*

❖ *Significant opportunity invites competition: what competition is likely to emerge for Western Research in the coming chapters?*

10

The Western Research Culture

I got a better education than I would have going to school, simply because Joe said yes we'll do it and we had to find a way.

—Ed Hardy

What Western R & D had experienced leading up to the company's acquisition by BVI in 1969 and 1970 was a classic financing crunch. The company's ambitions were bigger than its wallet. Joe Lukacs knew much of what he wanted to do and build, and research, but he could do none of it unless an entity with deep pockets was willing to back him.

Many a company dies because the entrepreneur refuses to give up total control.

Given the old aphorism that you can choose to own 100 percent of nothing or a smaller amount of something, Joe traded his interest in the company for an opportunity to grow and realize his dreams. As soon as he had that chance to grow, he bolted from the starting gate and the company went on an amazing growth and development ride for the next five years.

Engineer Paul Beauchemin joined the company in October, 1969. He became head of the consulting group and, after four years, left the company to start an independent bookstore on Vancouver Island. The month of his departure was February, 1974. This period of time provides an interesting window on Western R & D's growth during the period. Paul reckons there were fifteen people working for the company when he started and about fifty when he left–more than three–fold growth in just over four years.

The company added a little bit of everything: scientists, stack technicians, CSEM technicians, pilots, meteorologists, air monitoring technicians, lab workers, accountants, biologists, manufacturers, modellers, programmers. As Joe Lukacs puts it, "We exploded."

In this period, Western R & D essentially completed its package, becoming a full-spectrum environmental company. But it was also more than that. The company's researchers, and the plant testing and optimization work they were opening up, gave Western Research a scientific profile that was unique. Instead of dealing with noxious emissions from the stack mouth out, the company's sulphur doctors traced excess emission problems back through the sulphur plant, finding and solving them at the source.

Paul Beauchemin

One of Joe Lukacs's favourite management concepts is "the starting five." It means that a company needs a strong starting player in each of several key positions. Once it has them, it is able to go forward. Until it has them, it is blocked.

Joe Lukacs was the leader, and there was no disputing that. He led by example and insisted he would not ask of anyone what he was not willing to do himself. What he looked for in his hiring were people who could do things he could not do, people who would extend the company into areas he could not take it himself.

Ed Hardy was an early source of strength in the stack testing, manufacturing, and lab areas, with the jack-of-all-trades ability to pitch in wherever needed. Hardy was like basketball's "sixth man," a player so multitalented that he can come in and shore up a weakness or bolster strength in any area.

Paul Vetro (who started with the company in 1970) managed the air monitoring group, principally Ron Dinsley (1968) and Joe Brigan (1969). Robin Rankine (1968) was the scientific inspiration, the research idea man, working alongside key implementer Harold Paskall (1969). Bill Lewington (1968), Al Brotherston (1969), Ron Dimmer (1969), Don Stevens (1970), and Gord Tallin (1971) were the technicians who carried out much of the work that Paskall and Rankine prescribed. Chemist Dan Violini (1970) ran the chromatograph tests on plant and stack samples, and engineer Chris Harvey (1970) supervised and crunched the numbers. Dave Earl (1969) worked with Harold Paskall pioneering the calibration techniques that were basic to accuracy in all the company's testing. Paul Beauchemin (1969) led the consulting group, including bio-scientist Hugh Hicklin (1970). Elmer Berlie (September, 1971) became a one-man sales force.

A leader is someone whom others will follow.

With all this horsepower, the company began to move fast and Joe Lukacs let it go as fast as it could.

During these years of growth and heady innovation, the Western Research culture took shape, an unusual shape to say the least. If you look to the world of computers for a metaphor, Western Research was definitely more Apple than IBM. In Calgary terms, it was one of the new-growth, new-generation Canadian companies as opposed to the bureaucratic, blue-suit American majors. It was energetic, frenetic, volatile, and a little arrogant. At times, it was outrageous, and a bit proud of being so. It had a work hard/play hard ethos that was extreme on both ends.

The roots of the culture were set in the early days, when the company was imprinted with the values and personalities of its founders and first employees. Joe Lukacs's immense energy, fertile imagination, and omnivorous social instincts made for a company that moved fast, worked hard, and employed a vast network of experts and contacts. The more confidence Joe acquired as a leader, the more firmly these traits and practices were embedded into the company spirit. Joe also injected flamboyance and enthusiasm, practically daring his people to be as individual as he was.

Personality is the *X* factor of leadership, the thing you cannot teach or artificially create, and Joe Lukacs had it in spades. The image of their leader racing through the plant with his white lab coat flapping, talking, joking and laughing, cursing and yelling, is embedded deeply in the memory of everyone who worked for Western R & D. The recollection of former employees tends to begin with Joe Lukacs and the open, positive, informal atmosphere he created for them to work in.

Joe Lukacs was a rebel and a maverick, albeit a polite and well-socialized one. If he hadn't been, he would quite probably have remained in Hungary to face the dismal music of oppression. Having escaped, he was hardly likely to build a company hamstrung by strict rules of decorum and orthodox corporate behaviour.

When Joe hired people, he was looking for a mixture of traits like the ones that motivated him. Obedience only irritated him, and he was far more comfortable with employees with whom he could argue, ones he could trust to be honest. He was looking for driven people with an urgent need to solve problems, ones whose competitive urges would keep them from doing slack work. When it came to managing, Joe's mentality was sink or swim. He outlined what he wanted people to do, and he left them to do it. The self-starters thrived. They loved the lack of supervision and meddling from above. The ones who weren't self-starters crumbled and soon departed. Joe called it a "self-cleansing system."

What Western R & D employees did in their off hours, how polite they were, when they came and went, how many cocktails they had at lunch, weren't things Joe Lukacs cared much about as long as they produced. Some of the employees couldn't help but put such a free-wheeling system to some abuse, but even these recognized the bottom line. They worked, and often worked extra, in exchange for their liberties.

Joe Lukacs did not always understand what his own management style and practices were. Rather, he was feeling his way by instinct. One example from the early years was a complicated evaluation tool he used to assess job candidates, an elaborate form that claimed to be able to quantify the process of employee selection. He recalls he was quite proud of it. Then one day, Ralph Hughes asked him, "That test of yours? Did you ever take it yourself?" Joe hadn't, so he did, and he failed. That was the end of that. In hindsight, he knows he

A company's culture bonds it together, fosters healthy internal competition, increases loyalty, and generates enthusiasm.

71

made up his mind about employees almost instantly, by instinct. That would remain his most reliable means.

As the employee group built up, the culture of the company grew with it. What developed was an ethos that was hard working in the extreme. The indefatigable Ed Hardy trained the crew of technicians in his own hard-working image, requiring of them the same precision and endless hours that he demanded of himself. "Everybody had to go through Ed," he recollects with a smile. Scaling sulphur plant stacks was the initiation, a test of courage, endurance, and chutzpah. At the end of the day, you played just as hard as you worked, and because your schedule was too unpredictable to plan anything, you usually played with the same people with whom you worked.

The word "family" crops up often in people's memories of the company, and it is fitting. They were a family in all the usual ways: friendship and fondness, occasional jealousy, furious battles, and fierce loyalty when challenged from without.

In many ways, Western R & D prided itself on eccentricity. A co-worker's colourful attributes would be described as though they belonged to the teller by extension. For example, here's a paragraph from the monthly staff newsletter under the heading "Professional Development":

"Douglas Leahey has been named to the Standing Committee on Scientific and Professional Matters of the Canadian Meteorological Society. And Larry Peters has become a consistent winner of the Most Popular Car award at the Circle Eight Speedway demolition derbys. His latest entry: a facsimile police cruiser, complete with the red bubble gum machine on top and Royal Ukrainian Mounted Police (RUMP) on the sides."

Nor was Larry Peters the only racer of automobiles on staff. Stack surveyor Denver Smart also competed. Pilots were a dime a dozen. There were also several mountain climbers.

Another somewhat unusual employee at Western R & D was technical editor and report writer Ben Gadd who joined the company in November, 1972. Chris Harvey recalls that Ben Gadd made enormous improvements in the company's report writing by asking such probing questions as, "What the heck does this mean?" An ardent geologist and naturalist, Ben Gadd went on to a strong career in writing and teaching. He is author of the well-known *Handbook of the Canadian Rockies*.

Loyalty was another feature that Western R & D fostered from the top down. Joe Lukacs hated to fire people or lay them off. He would not do so for mere screwing up. In fact, Joe seldom punished mistakes at all, believing that the hurt pride of the person involved would be sufficient to prevent a repetition. He recalls a dilly of a mistake that someone made while working at Canadian Forces Base Suffield, something about driving an army tank without permission. The army considered the error grave enough to warrant the person's dismissal. Joe investigated, thought it an honest mistake, and told the army he would not comply with their wishes. He did not fire people for mistakes he might have made himself in the same situation.

Shared values make for effective teamwork and a strong company culture.

When the employees of Western R & D understood this fully, their response tended to be a flowering of loyalty just as dependable and powerful.

If all this is beginning to sound like a daily love-in, let it be known that few companies knew the level of acrimony that Western R & D also achieved on an alarmingly regular basis. It was inevitable in the sense that you cannot choose to hire people of maverick personality, inclined to strong and stubborn views, without controversy. Battles were frequent, and conducted with passion. A fist fight once broke out at the Christmas party, though actual physical violence was rare. Joe Lukacs's style of managing this chaos was to allow it up to a point in the belief that, to a certain level, the venting of anger and frustration was healthy. He held that his job was to prevent it from going any further, "to stop people hurting each other or themselves."

It must also be said that Joe's statesmanship in this regard sometimes faltered when he was one of the principals in a battle. After coming to Western Research from New York University, Dr. Douglas Leahey and Joe would often engage in loud, spirited argument in the company hallways. Finally, Joe asked Douglas to join him in the office for a serious chat.

"Douglas," he said, "you and I enjoy these battles that we have. But others are complaining. When they hear us, they think the company is falling down around their ears. I'm afraid we're going to have to stop."

Don Thurston, Bow Valley Industries' liaison to Western R & D provides an interesting viewpoint on all this. It was Don Thurston's job to take Western R & D in hand after the acquisition and make sure that it was a "well-run company" in the normal sense of that phrase. He recalls that initially his coaching was seen as unwanted interference. Only after he made clear that he wasn't going away, and wouldn't settle for anything less than top-quality budgets and bookkeeping, did he and Joe get over what he calls their "difference in style." In his opinion, Joe Lukacs could not have created–nor have been pleased by–a company without controversy. Joe liked argument and emotion, people speaking their minds. It was how he operated and what he understood best. In the heat of the battles, he would often be seen to smile as if to say, "Now we're really getting somewhere."

Once Don Thurston was satisfied with the way Western R & D was doing business, he stepped back and let Joe Lukacs take the company where he wanted it to go. In this, he was influenced by something Rod McDaniel had said. "Joe's a thoroughbred," was the comment. "You've got to let a thoroughbred run." Joe and his company were lucky that Don Thurston understood this and ran interference for them with the BVI board.

When Joe Lukacs looks back to Western R & D during its key years of innovation and growth, what impresses him most is the teamwork. The employees would "fight like hell," but, when the chips were down, they would always band together and meet the current challenge. A complaint during this period was that Joe never turned anything down. Paul Beauchemin remembers sitting beside Joe during meetings with prospective clients. When he heard what Joe was committing his department, to he would kick Joe under the table to try and get him to stop–to no avail. The "never say no to anything" strategy prompted Ed Hardy to leave a note on his boss's desk that read, "Everything is easy for the person who doesn't have to do the work."

But there was little incentive for Joe Lukacs to reject any opportunity because his team always seemed to manage to solve whatever it was.

❖ *How is leadership shared?*

❖ *What was the leadership style at Western Research at this time?*

❖ *What are the strengths and weaknesses of this leadership style?*

Sheila O'Brien

Sheila O'Brien is known to the Canadian petroleum industry as the dynamo senior vice-president of NOVA Petrochemicals. A little known fact about her career is that her first job after a B.A. from the University of Calgary was with Western Research and Development in the summer and fall of 1969.

Sheila O'Brien

Working in the Western R & D office, Sheila was a chart reader, reading and logging marks on paper tape that were the basis of the government-required air analysis reports. She and the others were always aware of what Joe Lukacs was doing because his style, in her words, was "management by shouting." He shouted to them, he shouted on the telephone, he probably shouted when he talked to himself. The effect was that everyone was in on everything. In those days, Joe wore his signature white lab coat, with an array of pens and pencils in the breast pocket. When he walked, always at top speed, the coat flapped around him like Superman's cape. Sheila recalls that the office always smelled like burned coffee because Joe insisted on making his own special Hungarian brew in his office. The machine sputtered, sizzled, boiled over, and burned on a regular basis. The only person who partook of the Hungarian coffee with Joe was visitor Elmer Berlie. Elmer was not yet a Western R & D employee at this time, but liked to drop by when he was in the city from Okotoks. The beginning of such a visit was always the same. Joe would cry, "Elmer, Elmer, Elmer!" Guiding him into his office for coffee, he would yell, "Come in and feel yourself ... at home!" And everyone would laugh.

Sheila O'Brien looks back with some horror at how she and the others made fun of Joe. They teased him, they mimicked his accent, they laughed at his antics. Joe's characteristic way of ending a phone call (if, for example, he was talking to Rod McDaniel) was, "Thank you, Rod. Thank you, bye." "Rod" would sound more like "Rud." Sheila, for the amusement of her friends, would go around saying, "Thank you, Rud. Thank you, bye. Thank you, Linda. Thank you, bye." She was a ringleader, and it probably all went way too far, adversely affecting her work and that of others. On a particularly good day, they could get Joe to come out of his office holding his head in both hands, crying, "You girls, you drive me crazy!" Nonetheless, when noon rolled around, they would most often repair en masse to a restaurant for lunch. Lunches tended to be long, liquid, and hilarious. If the standard of work declined in the afternoon, Joe would severely bawl them out, and they would accept it as their due. The work would be redone, improved, without quarrel.

On October 30, 1969, Sheila O'Brien left the company for a lengthy and low-cost journey across Europe, as was traditional at the time for 21-year-olds. When Sheila looks back on her time with Western Research, she recalls a giddy happiness. Partly it was being 21 and full of joy anyway, but she knows that a lot of people would go to work and have that joy diminished. Hers was amplified. "I couldn't wait to get to work," she recalls.

When Sheila O'Brien returned from Europe the next year, she needed a reference and went to Joe Lukacs with no certainty that he would give her a good one. She was not at all sure she deserved a good one. She had often been out of control, and pushing her co-workers to similar extremes. Possibly, she should have been fired. But Joe was happy to give her a reference, and what he said was that Sheila O'Brien had a great deal of drive and spirit. She needed the direction of a strong leader but would be a great employee if she got that direction. The fact that Joe saw this potential in her, and conveyed it in a positive reference, greatly helped Sheila O'Brien on her way.

11

The First Western Research Product: The Continuous Stack Emission Monitor

A board of directors is a valuable resource. When Bow Valley Industries acquired Western Research, I was amazed at the power and experience on the BVI board. I made use of them to help Western Research grow. —Joe Lukacs

Bow Valley Industries bought the first 50 percent of Western Research because of the company's potential in instrumentation. The remaining 50 percent went to BVI in 1970 because of the time and the expense involved in developing such a product line.

The first Western Research instrument was the Continuous Stack Emission Monitor (CSEM), and it was seen initially as the solution to the often frigid and always arduous monthly task of testing stack emissions at sour gas processing plants. The Western Research personnel who experienced stack testing in the early years–basically everyone who was physically capable–were unanimous in their desire to see the job automated out of existence; hence, the popularity of the CSEM development project. The great irony, as you will see as you read on, is that the CSEM, though enormously successful, didn't put an end to manual stack testing at all. In fact, it provided more concrete reasons for doing it.

In the years of the CSEM's evolution, practically everyone at Western Research became involved to some degree. Just about every employee with a scientific, engineering, or technical bent takes credit for some bit or piece or idea or procedure that became part of the final instrument.

The original idea for a continuous stack monitoring device came from Joe Lukacs. His conception of it and his belief in it started the evolutionary wheel in motion. Joe and Ed Hardy took the next few steps together, imagining, discussing, and drawing images of how such an instrument could do its work mounted high on a sulphur plant stack. Their years of sampling and stack testing gave them a strong basis of tricks and procedures to build into the instrument's concept.

The biggest difference between the stack testing they were already doing and the CSEM revolved around the word "continuous." The gas chromatograph took several minutes to analyze a gas sample and that disqualified it as a technology for the CSEM. The newer and faster analyzers were based on infrared technology and the CSEM started out with a Leeds and Northrup infrared analyzer at its heart.

After BVI bought the first 50 percent of Western Research from Rod McDaniel, the CSEM went onto a faster development track, an important aspect being to find an inventor who could tackle part of the design. Ed Hardy suggested an Edmonton-based inventor named Ed Adams, whose company Dominion Instruments designed, among other things, delicate equipment for hospital use. In his days with Chemical and Geological in Edmonton, Ed Hardy had employed Ed Adams to maintain his equipment.

Joe Lukacs liked what he heard and was soon on the plane to Edmonton to talk to this inventor. They struck a deal, and Ed Adams got to work on the design of a device capable of continuously measuring the flow of gases up the plant stack. Once the flow was known, and the gases were analyzed into percentages, the quantity of each gas could be computed. From there, you could calculate the mass of sulphur emissions, and all on a continuous basis. The flow-measuring device was called a Differential Pressure Cell (also called a "pitot flow"). Essentially, it was a diaphragm sensitive to changes in pressure.

During the next several months, as Ed Adams did his work and was paid for it, Western Research's combined ownership decided too much money was flowing out of the company to Dominion Instruments. As McDaniel associate Ralph Hughes puts it, "The only company making any money on this was Dominion Instruments. If we were ever going to make money, we needed to own Dominion Instruments." As it turned out, Dominion was potentially for sale, but Rod McDaniel was not interested in making the kind of financial outlay needed. Instead, the second half of Western Research was sold to Bow Valley Industries and Dominion Instruments was purchased under that arrangement.

After Ed Adams produced his prototype of the DP Cell, Ed Hardy modified it (created a second prototype) suitable for manufacture. Paul Beauchemin, a young engineer who joined the company in September of 1969, recalls the quality of Ed Hardy's workmanship. "Ed was an amazing builder of quality items. When he put an instrument together, every wire was exactly the right length. It was beautiful hands-on work." Some of the other aspects of the CSEM that owed to Ed Hardy's workmanship were the sulphur knock-out and the cabinet design.

Something Ed Hardy likes to mention about the early CSEM is the welding of the aluminum. The best aluminum welder in Calgary was a self-taught man whose hobby was racing stock cars and motorcycles. His welding expertise also made an important impact on the CSEM.

The first working CSEM was built directly on the stack at the Hudson's Bay Oil and Gas plant at Edson, Alberta. Ed Hardy and Don Stevens put it together *in situ*. Right on the stack, they bent tubing, connected the devices, and assembled the cabinet; they made it work. As Don Stevens remembers it, there they were a hundred feet in the air on hands and knees, building the first mass-based, continuous emission monitoring device in the world.

The same team of Ed Hardy and Don Stevens built the second CSEM at a newer HBOG plant called Kaybob. These were the only two CSEMs ever built around the Leeds and Northrup analyzer. In the interval between the construction of the first two and the next one after that, Ed Hardy went to the United States and discovered the Dupont analyzer, which was based on ultraviolet light. The advantage of UV was that it could operate in the higher temperatures found in many sulphur plant stacks, which the infrared analyzer could not. Seeing the advantage immediately, Ed cancelled an order for more L & N analyzers. Henceforth, until Western Research had a UV analyzer of its own, CSEMs would be based on the Dupont device.

Other early CSEMs went to Shell Waterton, Shell Jumping Pound, and Texas Gulf Okotoks.

It is important to remember that, in these early years, the CSEM was a work in progress. In the Western Research lab, which had by now moved into a rented space near the airport, Robin Rankine headed up a group that, as one employee put it, "played around with a bench model of the CSEM, trying to make it work." Joining him in this was Robin's University of Calgary friend, physical chemist Harold Paskall. Robin had lured Harold to Western Research in April of 1969. Later, technician Gord Tallin worked on CSEM development with Robin and Harold. Gord came to work with Western R & D in February, 1971.

When the patent was eventually taken out on the CSEM, it bore the names Ed Hardy, Joe Lukacs, and Robin Rankine. During the period of its development, one part of the instrument was patented by Shell, for which Western Research paid a royalty.

Now that Western Research had the CSEM, it needed someone to sell the instrument into the gas processing industry, someone who had knowledge of sulphur recovery from natural gas and also had a lot of contacts in the industry. The person Joe Lukacs set his sights on was Elmer Berlie. As plant manager for Texas Gulf Okotoks, Elmer knew how sulphur plants should work. He was a student of the art and was used to explaining its intricacies to junior engineers and operators. When it came to contacts within the industry, Elmer was flush. Either from the Conservation Board, or from Pincher Creek or Okotoks, or from the Canadian Gas Processors Association, or his involvement with various safety initiatives, Elmer knew just about everybody there was. But was Elmer Berlie available and willing?

It turned out he was both. Texas Gulf Okotoks, called "Elmer Berlie's Stainless Steel Plant" by some, was almost too smooth-running. There was little challenge there any more for Elmer. In the end, he accepted Joe Lukacs's job offer, with the proviso that he be able to travel to Russia first and honour a commitment he had made to give a United Nations-

Elmer Berlie

sponsored talk. Joe agreed to that, and Elmer Berlie joined Western Research in September of 1971.

Selling the CSEM was by no means a slam dunk. Very few could fail to see the efficacy of a continuous stack monitoring device to track emissions, but many were doubtful it would work. It is possible that a few others didn't want their emissions monitored that closely. The doubts about the CSEM were somewhat justified. At the beginning, no two CSEMs were alike, and there was a problem keeping them in calibration. It doesn't take much to turn plant operators against something new. They like what they know and, when some new-fangled thing comes along, pushed upon them by their engineer or by management, their first tendency is to stand against it. If the innovation malfunctions, all the more reason to dispense with it.

To get over this credibility hump, Elmer Berlie came up with the idea of leasing the device to those who were not quite willing to buy. This, as Ed Hardy points out, had a double advantage. It got the device out there where the operators could get used to it and, when it malfunctioned, they called for Western Research to come and fix it. If they had owned it, there might have been a tendency to leave it broken, resulting in a further loss of faith.

The other great Western Research advantage that Elmer Berlie had to sell, along with the CSEM, was the flying technicians (a story dealt with in detail in the next chapter.)

If one looks at where the earliest CSEMs went, it tended to be to the plants where Western Research had the greatest credibility: the plants where the company was doing the most work, particularly sulphur plant process work. HBOG Edson and Kaybob, and Shell Waterton were perfect examples. Western R & D was working with them already, trying to get their plant efficiencies up. The CSEM was not only a way to check emissions; it was also a way to check continuously on the functioning of the plant. In time, the second function of continuous monitoring would be at least as important as the first.

Joe Lukacs often speaks of the value of the Bow Valley Industries Board of Directors as a source of wisdom to which he had access after the acquisition by BVI. Initially, he and BVI liaison Don Thurston locked horns over issues of paperwork and control. Thurston was insisting that Western Research shed a little of its cowboy, laissez-faire image in favour of playing the game of business by the same rules as everyone else. In time, Joe would accept this need and make it part of his own management style.

When looking for investors for your company, look for smart money. Smart money can bring quality management, and it's free.

A similar growth occurred in Joe's understanding and appreciation of the BVI Board of Directors, people like Doc and B.J. Seaman, and Harry Van Rensselaer. Often the advice of these mentors was of the briefest kind, but no less valuable for that. With respect to the new CSEM, Doc Seaman's cryptic comment was, "Double the price." He felt Joe was not factoring in the true cost of its long development. Western Research did double the price of the CSEM as instructed, and the only effect of the change was increased revenue. Looking back, Joe is fairly sure this Doc Seaman insight turned the tide on the CSEM, guaranteeing its success as a product.

Over time, Elmer Berlie and his capable group of sales technologists succeeded in leasing or selling CSEMs to nearly all of the Alberta sulphur industry. The need to lease declined as the device improved and faith in it became widespread. Then the Government of Alberta intervened in a way that guaranteed the CSEM would be around for a long time. Impressed by the new invention, the Alberta government's environment department made continuous stack emission monitoring mandatory, the first jurisdiction in the world to do so. The continuous emission monitoring standards that existed elsewhere in the world were for monitoring of the composition of tail gas. The true uniqueness of the CSEM and of the Alberta regulation it prompted was that they were based on an analysis of *both* composition and mass. Although a very few sulphur plants met the standard some other way, usually by gas chromatography, the new regulation came very close to compelling the industry to buy Western Research's CSEM.

Know your market. Grow from a position of strength.

Back when the Alberta government had made stack emission monitoring compulsory, Western Research jumped in on the market created by the regulation. This time was different. By coming up with a brand new technology, continuous stack emission monitoring, the company had given the Government of Alberta an idea for regulation that they could not have had before the technology existed. From the government's point of view, continuous monitoring of composition and mass was simply better, for the citizens and for the environment, and they got behind it with a regulation. In other words, Western R & D had created its own market driver.

But here's the irony. The regulation requiring continuous monitoring of the plants' emissions *did not replace* the mandatory stack emission tests as some at Western R & D had been hoping. The periodic manual tests were retained in Alberta as the standard means of regulating plant emissions. The calibration of the CSEMs was to be set according to the manual tests, based on the government's belief that one could not be reliable without the other. In the end, both forms of testing became mandatory.

For Western R & D, this was a boon. The employees may have quarrelled with the fact that, as a group including CSEM maintenance technicians, they would be climbing more stacks not less, but the fact was the company was also doing more business: manual stack emission tests *plus* monthly calibration and maintenance of the CSEMs. The situation could hardly have been better if Western R & D had written the regulations itself.

Emblematic of how quickly the company was growing at this time, the first ever issue of *The Monitor*, Western Research's monthly staff newsletter, dated February, 1973, recorded several important staff additions. Michael Beamish, a University of Toronto graduate in electrical engineering and business administration, arrived in December, 1972, to head up the Product Design and Manufacturing Department. John Budlong, a design engineer, was hired to assist him. Ben Gadd, technical writer and editor, arrived in this period as did Geoff Sams, an electrical engineer from England. Linda Biswanger, the only woman in Paul Beauchemin's engineering class at the University of Alberta, hired on as a chemical engineer and mathmatical modelling specialist.

In charge of instrumentation, Mike Beamish's challenge would be to standardize the CSEM. From now on, the CSEMs would cease to be slightly eccentric individuals. They would be manufactured clones. As Beamish puts it, "That was the secret to making money."

Mike Beamish

In June, 1973, Western Research and Development sent a contingent to the Air Pollution Control Association's 66th annual meeting at Chicago. Joe Lukacs was by now a director of APCA and remained a firm believer of the value of belonging to organizations like this one and the Canadian Gas Processors Association back in Alberta. Elmer Berlie, Mike Beamish, Ed Hardy and Paul Beauchemin rounded out the Western R & D team in Chicago, and a working model of the CSEM, complete with miniature stack, was a major feature of the company's booth. The booth was adjudged one of the top three at the show, and its distinguished visitors included the U.S. Environmental Protection Agency's representative. Upon coming home, Elmer Berlie was quoted as saying, "At a time when the Americans are taking over everything, we're actually moving into the U.S. instrumentation market."

The CSEM, now called the Model 710, was up, running, patented, standardized, and exported–all in under five years. What it meant to the company was the chance to shift onto a higher plateau of growth and revenue. Service companies are by their nature low margin operations. A product manufacturing company, on the other hand, can parlay its product's uniqueness into greater profits, partaking in the general profitability of its industry.

But as for any idea that the company was now bound for riches, the size of the market suggested not. The genius of the CSEM, its ability to continuously analyze for percentage composition of SO_2, while at the same time calculating its mass, was a market drawback outside Alberta. Alberta was the only jurisdiction in North America that required such a sophisticated analysis. For the rest of the North American market, the CSEM was too loaded. Cheaper non-mass monitors could do the job their governments were asking be done. Mike Beamish, for one, believed that Western Research should nurture the small but sound Alberta market rather than get too carried away with foreign expansion plans.

For similar reasons, Western Research was also smart enough not to get out of service. Air monitoring, weather modelling, stack testing, plant testing, and other kinds of consulting amounted to stable core work. The services that were demanded by regulation were economic safeguards against recessions in the cyclical petroleum industry. Compared to that, the sale of products would fluctuate in exact accordance with the ups and downs of the industry.

By having both products and services, Western R & D was laying the groundwork of a company that could both grow in the good times and survive the bad.

Especially if a product is designed to help meet a regulation, it can be too sophisticated for its marketplace.

❖ *What benefits and advantages did Western Research gain by becoming a products company?*

❖ *Does a products company have special advantages if it was originally a service company?*

❖ *What strategic value did Western Research retain by keeping its service component?*

12

The Flying Technicians: A Service Innovation

> *Dick Cooper was a great flyer. He should have been in the war.*
> —Peter Dale

Finding an innovative way to serve your clients brands your company and builds customer loyalty at the same time.

The idea of flying the technicians to remote sulphur plants to do maintenance on the Continuous Stack Emission Monitors came from Ed Hardy, who, among his many other talents, was a flyer. His recollection is that he started flying for the company almost as soon as the first CSEMs were up at the Hudson's Bay Oil and Gas plants at Edson and Kaybob. Both places were far enough away to require a long day of driving plus work, or an overnight stay. Tired of his 60,000 mile per year driving habit, Ed proposed renting a Piper Cherokee as a means of accomplishing the necessary CSEM calibrations and repairs.

Joe Lukacs liked the idea from the start. Taking to the air was the right image for a company marketing itself as leading edge. As well, same-day airborne maintenance was a powerful antidote to the fears and reservations of the more conservative plant engineers and operators. If there were problems with the CSEM, help could be winging its way toward you in no time. When Elmer Berlie arrived in 1971 to sell the CSEM, the flying technicians proved an excellent marketing tool.

The only problem was that Ed Hardy was too valuable to the company in other ways to have him spending all his time flying to remote plants to service CSEMs. Among other things, he was soon assigned to the building of the revolutionary

REM plant testing trailer (Chapter 16). Clearly a replacement flying technician was needed, but where were you going to find one? The CSEMs of this vintage tended to be sufficiently unique, one from another, that the technicians couldn't simply rely on a checklist of standard procedures to maintain or fix them. You needed a bit of what one tech-nician called "haywire mentality," not to be daunted by the maze of interrelated devices that made up a CSEM–plus, of course, you had to know how to fly.

A temporary solution was to rent technician/pilot Johnny Evans from an-other company. At the same time, Ed Hardy was put in charge of interview-ing in search of someone who could do the job from within the company. The first man he found for the job was Jim Hill. Like a few other Western Research alumni, Jim came out of the SAIT's Aeronautical Technology course. The SAIT program qualified you to maintain rather than to fly planes, but Jim had picked up a flying licence to go with it. He also had some prior experience with an instrument com-pany, all of which qualified him to be Western R & D's next flying technician.

Jim Hill, flying technician

As Ed Hardy had done, Jim Hill rented the airplane that he used. When there was a big maintenance job, requiring a bigger crew, both Ed Hardy and Jim Hill would rent planes. Later, John Anderson and Larry Peters also did flying technician work for the company, renting planes as needed.

Larry Peters was from Prince George, British Columbia, and had graduated in chemistry from the University of Calgary. He had a reputation at Western R & D for eccentricity, endurance, and daring-do. He was known as the man you sent in when the job was the most difficult and the conditions least bearable. In such situations, he thrived. Something else that he contributed to the company was the occasional rental of an old International 3/4 ton 4 x 4. When an air pollution trailer needed to go halfway up a mountain, this impossibly rough vehicle was the only thing around that could put it there.

At university, Peters had distinguished himself by wearing a pair of World War I flying goggles in lieu of the usual visor-type mask during lab experiments. After a sulphur experiment blew up in his face, he went around for a month with yellow cheeks and pink racoon eyes. Once at Western R & D, a half bottle of rocket fuel was left over after a project. Larry took it home, mixed it with gas, and tried it out in his sluggish lawn mower. The mower performed beautifully, he said, virtually roared like a lion—for a half hour before expiring in a plume of smoke.

The first Western Research flying technician to own his own plane, and perhaps the best remembered of Western Research's flyers, was Richard Cooper, who joined the ranks in May of 1974. Dick Cooper was originally from Britain, and he traces his ability to face and fix the oddest of the CSEMs to the fact that nothing in his post-war British home had been bought new. He and his father were forever repairing broken home appliances, or plumbing, wiring, and painting. It eventually became second nature to build and repair things.

Ever a restless type, Dick exhausted the possibilities of Britain by the time he was twenty-one. He dispensed with school early on and raced and repaired stock cars until he could no longer afford it. He had also learned to fly but could find no opportunities in that area. Finally, he followed a pretty girl to Mexico, which, in a long, shaggy-dog way, led to Montreal, back to Britain, back to Montreal, and out to Calgary, where his English travelling companion was established as an educational TV producer.

In Calgary, Dick started out as a car mechanic at Bert and Jack's. In his spare time, he got a commercial pilot's licence. As the airlines were not hiring, he followed a lead to Western Research, which was said to be looking for another pilot for its CSEM flying technician squad. Richard Cooper was as if designed especially for the job. He got it and was soon flying to several northern plants in Bow Valley Industries' Cessna 206, which Western was sub-leasing.

Richard Cooper is an entrepreneur to his very core, and it didn't take him long to ascertain that the people owning the plane were the ones making the money in this arrangement. He approached Joe Lukacs with a scheme by which he, Dick, would become that person. The arrangement made sense money-wise to Joe, and Dick went out and bought a venerable 1948 Luscombe for $6,000. The choice of plane had everything to do with the fact that $6,000 was the sum the bank was willing to loan Dick for the venture. The Luscombe was a two-seater monoplane with a maximum air speed of 100 miles per hour.

The deal was that he would be paid by the hour to fly, plus his regular technician's wages. He would make the plane available to Western R & D seven days a week. "By modern

standards," he says, it was all illegal. But nobody seemed to bother us. It was only quasi-wrong."

Richard Cooper with his Cessna 190

Richard Cooper looks upon himself as having nine cat lives to spend. He used them up at Western Research and, when they were gone, so was he. One example from the Luscombe period was a flight to the Whitecourt area. As he passed Red Deer, he came upon a deep cloud bank that he would either have to fly below or above. As it seemed to extend to the ground, he chose above. "I was pottering along, fat, dumb and happy," he recalls when he realized that he was not allowed to fly on top by Canadian regulations and would soon have to declare his position to the folks in Edmonton. Rather than submit to this, he thought he would take her down through the cloud and "hopefully sneak below the radar."

What this meant was flying by instrument, which he admits neither he nor the plane were equipped for. After about a thousand feet of descent his wings had huge accumulations of ice on them. He brought up the power to arrest the descent, and the air frame began to shake. A stall seemed imminent and his legs were jelly. It kept on like that for another fifteen minutes of descent and, in the end, he was using full power and a high air speed just to keep it in the air. Fortunately, there was a little daylight between the bottom of the cloud and the ground when he broke out, and, with the rise in temperature, the ice began to burn off. Rather than continue, he decided he must go straight home and spend a little time in the bar.

Before long, Richard was responsible for about ten plants and fifteen pollution trailers. What it meant in the Luscombe was six to seven hours of flying and another seven or eight hours of technician work per day. He was getting very tired, almost falling asleep flying, and he determined that he had to get a plane that had more speed. What he wanted was a Cessna 185, the modern bush plane of the day, but he didn't have the cash to swing it. What did come up for sale was a 1948 Cessna 190, a romantic old tail-dragger with a radial engine, available in Lethbridge for $12,000. This Dick could manage, and he bought it. It came with a pick-up truck full of spare parts, including a spare engine, which to this day Dick uses as the base of a coffee table in his home.

Thinking of the Cessna 190, Dick Cooper remembers many a time that he was flying when all the other aircraft out of the Calgary airport were on the ground. His reasoning: "When the aircraft was in the air, it made money. When it was on the ground, it made none." The Cessna had more size inside so that Dick was able to fly crews to plants for purposes beyond

CSEM maintenance and air monitoring. Now they could fly in for CSEM installations as well, plus monthly manual stack surveys. Dick became part of the team on these occasions.

Dick had only owned the Cessna 190 for two days when he had his first cat life adventure in it. He and John Anderson had gone to Amoco Whitecourt for what they estimated would be a five-hour job. When they arrived at the gravel airstrip just outside of Whitecourt around 10 a.m. it was thirty below. There was no hangar, of course, and Richard was somewhat concerned about starting back up at the end of the day.

When they got to the plant, a series of problems caused a plant shutdown, and they were forced to wait around. It wasn't until 10 p.m. that they finally got away.

The method of travelling to and from the town's air strip was by rented car. The fellow who rented the vehicle drove it out to the strip in the morning and, when they finished at night, they were simply to lock the keys in the car at the airstrip and leave it there. Dick's only hope of getting his plane engine to start was to use the nice warm car battery as an auxiliary. Even with the car battery helping, the cold-soaked Cessna took a long time to start, but it finally did.

With plane engine running, they ran the car back to its parking spot and locked it up with the keys inside according to plan. They jumped into the plane to take off and saw that both fuel gauges read empty. Not good. Either they'd sprung a leak, or someone had syphoned their gas, or the fuel gauges didn't work. But they couldn't leave without knowing which it was.

Dick was very reluctant to turn the plane off so, leaving it running, and with John Anderson holding the brakes, he got out and climbed onto the wing. The prop was spinning and blowing the minus thirty air onto him with lord knows what wind-chill effect. He was able to discover that there was indeed fuel in the tanks. Time for take off.

By now, it had been black dark for many hours, plus there was a deep layer of ice fog, all of which meant IFR or instrument flying. Dick was not at this time an IFR pilot, which technically meant they shouldn't go, but they did. Before long, they were in thick ice fog and flying completely by instruments.

Dick was maintaining a climb to 3,000 feet and feeling very confident. At 3,000 feet, he turned right on a heading for Calgary, checked his instruments, and saw that they read that he was still climbing straight ahead. All the instruments were frozen.

Inside a cloud without instrumentation, you've got about twenty seconds before becoming totally disoriented. Luckily he broke out above the cloud before this happened. At the very least, he now had a horizon by which to control the aircraft, but his compass was among the frozen instruments. Direction had he none. He tried for various radio navigation aids but got nowhere, and what they finally flew by was John Anderson's astral navigation skills, achieved in a two-week course. The heater behind the seat was by no means a match for the weather, and they were very cold, but otherwise they felt good about their situation.

Eventually, a wonderful glow came up through the ice fog. It was Calgary, and they asked air traffic control to put up some runway lights at full brightness. They could just make out the line through the fog. They made their approach, landed, and parked the plane. They went home to bed after a long but ultimately satisfying day.

The terror didn't come until the next day when Dick went out to the airport to take another flight. He checked his oil and discovered that it had gone from its normal capacity of five gallons down to half a gallon during the previous night's flight. The vent off the crank case had frozen, pressure had built up, and the oil had all been pumped overboard. When they had landed, they were no more than ten minutes away from a total and final engine seizure.

There were many such death-defying adventures. Once while flying with Randy Hauer to Fort St. John, the turbulence got so bad that the two very heavy tool boxes behind their seats lept in the air and swapped ends. Had either box hit them on the head, it would have spelled curtains.

Another time, the engine stopped when Dick was over the trees between Rocky Mountain House and Edson. There wasn't even so much as a road to land on. He went through the usual menu of emergency procedures, changing fuel tanks, turning the fuel pump on, checking the mags, cycling the prop. Nothing. When he was only a thousand feet above the ground, he prepared to land in the trees. The final thing one does is shut down the fuel as protection against fire when you hit the ground. As he moved the mixture control, starving the engine, it came to life. By moving the control back and forth, he was able to get home. Later, when he pulled the carburetor off to see what was going on, he found a hole in a brass float controlling the fuel level.

Yet another time, coming home from Fort Nelson in disgusting weather, a combination of snow and no cloud clearance had forced him to fly along the road south toward Whitecourt. As the hills rose into the cloud, he was forced lower and lower until he was beneath the tree tops. Some unexplainable instinct suddenly told him to get out of that cut, and he rose and circled the plane. At that exact moment a Cessna 210 came roaring up the highway from the other direction. If Richard had continued on, instead of circling, they would have met head on.

Not all the adventure happened in the air. Early on, when Richard Cooper was still flying the Luscombe, he headed out for Whitecourt but was forced by fog to land at Edson. To get from Edson to Whitecourt meant driving east toward Edmonton quite a distance and then northwest again to Whitecourt. It was a long drive, but he rented a small car and did it.

When he finally arrived at the Whitecourt plant, he got some good luck in the sense that the maintenance job on the CSEM was less difficult than expected. In just two hours, he had it fixed and was ready to go. It was late afternoon on Friday and a young man's fancy turned to the fastest possible way of getting home. Dick had heard that there was a forestry road from Whitecourt to Edson that would cut off all that driving back south and west again. He decided to try it.

It was early spring and the road was gumbo, the gumbo that only veterans of the Swan Hills-Whitecourt area can really appreciate, the kind that turns your boots into pontoons of mud in a minute. The gumbo is also very slippery, and, about fifteen miles out, Richard started to spin out on an incline.

He went off the side of the road and down a bank. He was stuck tight.

Remembering that he'd passed an oil rig a mile and a half or so back, Richard started to walk. It was drizzling. He had on regular shoes. They were soon enormous with gumbo. Finally arriving at the camp he'd seen, he found that everyone had left for the weekend. There wasn't a soul around. But there were a few trailers and, more importantly, a few trucks with winches. The trucks had no keys in them, but they were not locked either, and Richard soon had one running.

The trucks had been parked off the road, and Richard found he could not get up the incline onto the road. The truck would just dig its way along the steep incline but could not climb. He got the first one stuck and started up a second one. Same difference. The trailers were on the other side of the road, and Dick got an idea. He would carry the truck's winch across the road and hook onto one of the trailers. He would haul his truck up with the trailer as an anchor. They were mechanical rather than electrical winches so he had to put the vehicle in gear and set the power-take-off. Amazingly, it started to work, the truck started to climb, the only problem being that the trailer began to climb too. The truck went up one side of the incline and the trailer went up the other until the two met in the middle of the road. Dick unhooked the winch and started for his car.

Near the car, he got the truck stuck, but close enough so that he could reach the car with the winch cable. He set the winch in motion, pulled it up out of the mud, got it jammed three times, and had to take it apart. But, finally, he was able to winch the car out of the ditch and onto the road—albeit facing the wrong direction. In the end, he drove the car three miles in reverse before he found a place to turn around.

Back to Whitecourt and onto the main road he went. All things considered, he didn't mind taking the long way to Edson.

Eventually Western Research's growth, and the increasing remoteness of several of its plants (Rainbow Lake, Shell Simonette, Sturgeon Lake, Fort Nelson, etc.), would mean a need for more flying than Richard Cooper could do. A partial solution was found in Larry Peters, who had purchased Richard Cooper's venerable Luscombe after he'd switched to the Cessna 190. Larry made a deal with Western Research similar to Richard's, and flew short hauls and trips where the client wasn't in too big a hurry. Dan Violini remembers flying in the Luscombe with Peters. If they were near a highway and flying into the wind, they couldn't keep pace with trucks on the ground.

Finally, Richard Cooper bought a second airplane, an Aztec, and Paul Fuller was hired to fly it. Fuller was strictly a pilot and was employed by Cooper rather than by Western Research.

The Richard Cooper era at Western R & D ended in February, 1978. He, Larry Peters and Randy Hauer were living in an old farm house west of Calgary that they affectionately called *Rancho del Ghetto*. They decided one day that the company owed them a holiday, and they jumped in the Cessna and headed for California. Their idea was that they might even start a new business of some sort when they found a warm place.

They finally found the warmth they were after in southern California, but the state's tax regime put a business out of the question. They worked their way back up the west coast and

This venerable Luscombe was owned by Dick Cooper, then by Larry Peters – both of whom hired it out to Western Research.

wound up landing in Victoria to clear customs. It was February and flowers were coming up. Richard hadn't realized there
was any place in Canada with mild winters like this. Upon
arrival in Calgary, he submitted his resignation, with the intention of returning to this glorious place where flowers grew
in February.

On Vancouver Island, Dick went on to found Cooper Air
Inc., a very successful charter company, based out of Patricia
Bay, not far from the Victoria airport.

Dick Cooper's departure didn't end the flying technician
era at Western R & D, but it signalled the beginning of the
end. Not long after, Paul Fuller convinced BVI that it needed
a plane of its own. For a while, the company leased him a
Piper Aztec, but then, somewhat to Dick Cooper's long-
distance chagrin, BVI bought a turbine-powered Cheyenne
II from Corpac Canada. It was the first turboprop Paul Fuller

Paul Fuller, pilot

had ever flown, but he made the adjustment rapidly, so rapidly that the Cheyenne logged 200 hours in the air in its first two months of operation for BVI. It was a great airplane, as Paul Fuller recalls. It was easy to fly; it could carry a big payload; and it had loads of power. But, in another sense, this was a plane perhaps too good for gravel air strips and gumbo. Over time, the Cheyenne was used less and less for rough northern work. It did most of its flying between cities, often carrying the Seaman brothers to appointments in the United States.

With some reluctance, Western R & D gave up flying its own people in 1982. At that point, one of the company's most colourful eras came to an end.

❖ *How does a company benefit from repeating its company stories and compiling its history?*

❖ *How does a service attitude impact customer loyalty?*

13

The Air and Water Doctors

Focus on solutions, not on problems.

Paul Vetro

As Western Research grew, it took on an ever-wider spectrum of projects under the general umbrella of pollution work. The early job at Edmonton Power's Rossdale plant would, over time, parlay into major consulting work with all of Alberta's coal-fired and gas-fired power generators. Good relations with Edmonton Power after the successful Rossdale job led to urban air pollution work, both in Edmonton and in Calgary. The early involvement with air monitoring led to contracts for plant site selection and other aspects of the first environmental impact assessments. Much of this work was grouped into a category called consulting services.

Air monitoring and consulting services were the parts of the company that showed Western Research's face to the world, and they often served as forerunners. Once the air monitoring and consulting teams had made contact, the instrumentation and process analysis bunch was seldom far behind.

Air monitoring was by far the earliest of these involvements. Along with stack testing, air monitoring was the first pollution work Western Research did, beginning with Ed Hardy's "plume chasing" forays at Didsbury and his and Joe Lukacs's baptism by yellow smoke at Edmonton Power's Rossdale plant.

In January, 1971, Paul Vetro was given management responsibility for the lab, stack surveying, and air monitoring. He recalls that air monitoring had between eight and ten trailers then: a few at the Petrogras plant north of Calgary, one at Shell Waterton, and one at Shell Jumping Pound. Ron Dinsley, a SAIT electronics graduate, ran the air monitoring group. He and Joe Brigan were the principal technicians, later joined by Calvin Price and Dan Violini. (Dan Violini started with the company in October, 1970, after finishing a chemistry degree at the University of Calgary. He started out in stack and plant testing but moved to the air monitoring group, replacing Calvin Price, in 1972.)

Dan Violini

The system of trailers was supplemented by any number of "bird houses," so called because they were square boxes, grey, with louvred sides, which sat atop fence posts along country roads. The bird houses were a simple system of monitoring average concentrations of total sulphur and SO_2. Each one contained two jars with bands of filter paper tied around them. One band contained lead acetate, which reacted with all sulphur species; the other contained lead peroxide, which reacted only with SO_2. By lab testing at the end of each month, you could determine the average quantity of total sulphur and SO_2 to which the bird house had been exposed.

Averages checked monthly are not a sufficient defence against the problems of H_2S and SO_2 pollution. H_2S in particular is most dangerous when its concentration spikes above safe levels for even short periods. That was where the trailers came in. The measuring devices in the trailers tracked the concentrations against date and time, on a continuous basis.

Dan Violini likes to point out that a lot of the technology that enabled Western Research to become an industry leader was not invented by the company. It was acquired and was well used. In the air monitoring area, the American EPA and Alberta environmental regulations led to three generations of ambient SO_2 gas analyzers in five years. Prior to 1970, the

Leeds and Northrop and the Davis wet chemical analyzers were the vogue. Both were cumbersome and expensive. In 1970 the much better Philips 9700 analyzer was introduced, and it quickly replaced everything else. In 1972, Philips came up with an improved version called the 9755. In 1975, pulsed fluorescent analyzers were developed for SO_2 and H_2S, and that technology is still in use today.

Also within the magic window of 1970 and 1975, a new generation of gas chromatographs came on the scene with programmable ovens, capillary columns, and more sensitive detectors. The Hewlett Packard GC became Western Research's standard and enabled the company to reach high levels of precision and accuracy in its gas analysis.

Back-stopping all the testing Western Research did, be it stack testing, plant testing, or air quality testing, was accurate calibration. As Dan Violini puts it, "If it moved, we calibrated it." In this area, Violini makes special mention of Harold Paskall and Dave Earl. In the Western Research lab, the two developed calibration techniques that were truly revolutionary. Paskall had designed a scale of extreme accuracy and sensitivity upon which samples in thin glass flasks could be weighed. When they had a sample measurable to the parts per million level, they could feed it to the gas chromatographs and calibrate them with confidence.

The pitot tubes for stack testing were calibrated in the Southern Alberta Institute of Technology wind tunnel. This was near the beginning of a long relationship between that institution and Western Research.

In air quality monitoring, the calibration system devised by Paskall and Earl involved pencil-sized permeation tubes. Samples of SO_2 or H_2S under pressure in the tubes would permeate out at a known rate over time. This, plus sensitive weighing, provided another accurate basis of calibration.

The importance of this cannot be over-emphasized. Without accurate calibration, all you have is numbers. The fact that the numbers Western Research produced could be trusted was the basis upon which the company's reputation was built.

Another early step forward for the air quality monitoring side at Western Research was the use of telemetry. Once the trailers could be connected to the plant control room by telemetry, plant engineers and operators could instantly and continuously monitor the levels of hydrogen sulphide and sulphur dioxide in the area surrounding their plants.

The move to telemetry began at Waterton in 1970. Hugh Hicklin, a master's degree holder in bio-medical engineering from the University of Alberta, had possessed his amateur radio licence since 1937. With Western R & D, this ham radio aptitude was put to use in the first air waves connection between a monitoring trailer and a plant control room. The air monitoring station was a few miles east of Shell Waterton on the Pincher Creek-Waterton highway, and between the station and the plant was a large hill. On that hill, Hugh helped set up a relay station, a beam antennae facing west and east. They set up a monitor and recorder in the Shell control room and thus put Shell in contact with its air monitoring trailer. The telemetry systems that followed soon after mostly used telephone lines as a means of connection.

Ron Dinsley

In 1971, Shell Waterton put in an order for another five trailers, at a cost of $100,000. To put the size of the order in context, it doubled the department's revenue that year. These new trailers also used the telephone lines as the means of getting information back to the plant.

Ron Dinsley and Joe Brigan were the telemetry experts at Western Research. The Petrogas plant at Balzac just north of Calgary was required to have a sophisticated system of air monitoring. Dinsley and Hicklin set up a monitoring station on Nose Hill above the city and Ron Dinsley and Joe Brigan did the telemetry back to the Petrogas plant.

Eventually, all trailers would be connected to control rooms in this way.

The air monitoring group tended to be the front line when it came to relations with the community. If farmers or others in a community were mad at the local gas plant over pollution, and they saw some technicians pull in and start setting up a trailer, it made a certain obvious sense to tear a strip off them. The idea that Western Research was a middleman inside a triangle of community, processing company, and government did not sell that well in the community. They tended to look at who was paying whom and draw their own conclusions. Particularly in the Waterton area, the air monitoring technicians came in for this type of flack on a fairly routine basis.

To look at it from their perspective, the farmers and ranchers were mainly unlucky to have their surface rights and leases sitting atop petroleum-bearing structures. They didn't own mineral rights, and so were not going to share in the general economic upsurgence that the government predicted the oil industry would bring. Basically, they had been living in one of the most environmentally pristine places on earth, and, given that emissions are and always will be a result of processing and flaring, their Eden was less perfect with the coming of the wells, the pipeline compressors, and the plants.

Then there was barbed wire. The standard barbed wire that the ranchers had been using for years was not up to the corrosive power of acid gases in the air, and, when ranchers found that they could break the wire with their hands in some severe cases of air pollution, and were losing about ten years of wire life in less severe cases, it was pretty natural to ask: what's this doing to my livestock and me?

In response to the barbed wire question, Joe Lukacs added steel corrosion coupons and six strands of different kinds of barbed wire to the Western Research bird houses. These were weighed periodically to quantify the corrosion loss.

Pincher Creek-Waterton wasn't the only place where the public didn't want the air emissions that went with industrial progress. Joe Brigan remembers going out to check a trailer in a farmer's yard in northern Alberta and having the farmer come out of his house wearing a gas mask.

But the truth was that the sophisticated continuous air

monitoring trailers and the monitoring of them by telemetered information to the control room were the greatest advances in community safety since the high pressure sour gas processing plants had come on stream in Alberta.

Even given this level of sophistication, the air monitoring system at Western Research was not complete with trailers, telemetry, and birdhouses. The missing component was an understanding of how local wind and weather patterns moved or dispersed the emissions from the plant outward. This was particularly complex down at Waterton, where the fierce Chinook winds came over the mountains with incredible velocity. The effect was termed "downwash," and it made a mockery of the idea of extending stack height to guarantee dispersion. To entirely understand it, Joe Lukacs had to resort to the same tools and network he had used to understand weather patterns in the North Saskatchewan River valley for the Rossdale project.

Douglas Leahey

He headed for the wind tunnels of New York City, to his favourite weather modelling expert James Halitzky.

Through talking to James Halitzky, Joe Lukacs became aware of a young professional meteorologist named Douglas Leahey. Douglas Leahey was from Pugwash, Nova Scotia, and he had completed his doctorate in diffusion meteorology at the New York University with James Friend and James Halitzky as his advisors. At that time, Douglas Leahey was working as a research scientist at NYU, but he was finding the opportunities for a Canadian in the United States somewhat limited. Joe Lukacs liked the idea of having a PhD meteorologist in his company, and he arranged to meet Douglas Leahey in Montreal for an interview. Douglas describes the interview as "intense," and the result was a letter of offer from Robin Rankine, which Dr. Leahey accepted. He joined Western Research in January of 1972.

With the hiring of Douglas Leahey, Western Research was in the position of being the only company in western Canada with a PhD meteorologist on staff. This made an enormous difference to the credibility with which Western Research's meteorological work was regarded. Douglas smiles when he notes that, not long after, Eugene Kupchenko of Alberta Environment hired dispersion meteorologist Randy Angle for the Alberta government.

Douglas Leahey's first boss at Western Research was Paul Beauchemin, who headed up the consulting group at the time. Paul was a fairly young engineer, a graduate in Chemical Engineering from the University of Alberta, and he found it more than a little intimidating to be in charge of a research scientist. Douglas recalls that Paul didn't like to give him orders and that, sometimes, Joe would go to Paul's office and yell what he wanted Paul to instruct Douglas to do. Douglas's office wasn't far away so the effect was to get the information to him immediately without compromising Paul's authority over his department.

Douglas Leahey found the air monitoring effort at Western Research to be of a quite professional quality. Ron Dinsley's air monitoring group was doing a good job. But the presence of Douglas Leahey meant that any report on the suitability of a plant site or on the dispersion from a stack had a much higher level of science behind it. One of the early contributions he remembers making had to do with tracking the source of high SO_2 readings at the Petrogas air monitoring trailers. By weather modelling, Douglas was able to prove that the main incinerator stacks at the plant were not the source of the SO_2; it was coming instead from their well flares. This was an easier problem to deal with, and Petrogas was well pleased with the discovery.

Another Western Research service that Douglas Leahey was able to enhance was consulting on stack design. Before he arrived, these reports had been very simple and the price charged very low. By adding sophisticated weather data, Douglas put out a better product for which the plants were willing to pay handsomely.

In the fall of 1972 and during the following winter, Douglas would be involved with the air monitoring group in doing

Reputation, image, and network are what get you through the door into a new market; delivering quality and solving your customers' problems are what keep you there.

air pollution impact studies on all existing and planned power plants in Alberta. Joe Brigan remembers holing up in schools, and at the University of Alberta, and even at the provincial legislature, with the sampling probes hanging out the window. He was collecting data with which Douglas Leahey's meteorological squad could create air pollution models.

Also in that time period, Western Research was involved in a background air monitoring study for Syncrude.

Another substantial contract that would involve Douglas Leahey in his first years in the company came to Western R & D from the provincial government: a source and emission study of pollution in Calgary and Edmonton. This was one of many environmental initiatives sparked by Environment Minister William Yurko in the years after the Lougheed provincial election victory of 1971. The two-year project involved both helicopter and ground monitoring of Edmonton and Calgary pollution sources. It occupied a great deal of Gillian Clark's time, and when it was completed, the company newsletter described Gillian as having to be led away mumbling. "It's done. They like it," were the words of her mantra. Douglas Leahey published a paper based on this work, one of 80 papers he has delivered and published over his career.

Gillian Clark

The Western R & D consulting group was in a sense the company's SWAT team. Hugh Hicklin recalls that you always went to work with a packed bag because you didn't know when you might have to drop everything and go. He remembers one emergency where he and several others had to head toward Red Deer to contain a well-site oil spill caused by a broken dyke. The Western R & D team took on a load of treated straw bales at Red Deer and continued to the site where they soaked up the spill before it reached a nearby stream, all in the black dark of a moonless night.

Another time, Hugh Hicklin was off to Fox Creek where a small spill of condensate was being blamed for problems in a nearby recreational lake. After considerable canoeing and testing, they were able to conclude that the lake had a blue-green algae growth, occasioned not by petroleum but by lack of circulation in the lake.

In the summer of 1974, Hugh Hicklin, Frank Cullen, and Gord Brown were charged with finding out the effect on

North Saskatchewan River fish of heated water released into the river by the Clover Bar power plant. Hugh Hicklin does not remember this project fondly because the river was extremely high and the job required them to cross the current repeatedly. The staff newsletter reported the event as follows:

"The North Saskatchewan River, home of Edmonton Power's Clover Bar power plant and millions of

Hugh Hicklin (foreground) and Calvin Price.

insect larvae is now perhaps the most studied-by-WR&D water body in the world (next to Lake MacDonald out by Petrogas). Gordon Brown, Hugh Hicklin and Frank Cullen have been going back and forth across it near Clover Bar in a little boat. They're measuring the river's depth and temperature to see what happens to the river when Clover Bar dumps warm water into it. One conclusion is positive: according to Gordon the fishing just below the warm water outfall is fantastic."

Another part of the consulting group's earliest work was the bio-assay, better or more commonly known as "the fish test." The idea came to Western R & D from the United States, through the Air Pollution Control Association, long before it was required by provincial legislation. As with many aspects of legislation in Alberta, Western Research was pro-active rather than reactive.

The concept of the fish test is that water effluents from operations such as sulphur plants could be tested for their quality by determining how well fish could live in them. Bio-assays come in two types: static and dynamic. In a static test, you take a water sample, fill an aquarium with it, then add oxygen and fish. The generally acceptable standard was referred to as "LC50-96" which meant that 50 percent of the fish must be alive after 96 hours. The dynamic bio-assay differed by virtue of using a cage rather than an aquarium and placing it directly into the water stream or body being tested.

The first fish tests Western Research conducted were of the dynamic variety. At Shell Waterton, the fish cage was placed directly into a water discharge. Hugh Hicklin recalls another early bio-assay of Nose Creek below the Petrogas plant at Balzac. Nose Creek is a tiny meandering stream that flows into the Bow River in northeast Calgary. It isn't very big at the best of times, and Hugh Hicklin remembered much difficulty finding a place deep enough to submerge the cage.

That the water quality in some of the plant ponds was not the best, to start out with at least, is evidenced by one interview subject who sighed, "Those poor fish." However, like the coal mine canaries, the trout might die but they did not lie. It was a simple and effective test of the water that the plants were releasing, and, in practice, fish testing resulted in much better protection of streams and aquifers in Alberta.

While part of the consulting group was busy with these kinds of assessments, much of Paul Beauchemin's time was taken up doing studies of electrostatic precipitators in Alberta's coal-fired power generation plants. The purpose of ESPs in coal-fired power plants is to keep the ash formed by the combustion of coal from entering the atmosphere. The ESP assembly in a typical plant is an enormous piece of a equipment (100' x 200' x 100') in which huge plates of steel hang vertically with vertical wires hanging between them. A high voltage electrical charge applied to the wires imparts a charge to the particles of ash, which causes them to stick to the grounded steel plates. By striking the plates, the ash is knocked off into a hopper from which it can be collected and removed.

The problem the Alberta power companies were having was that Alberta's coal is low in sulphur. Low sulphur coal ash lacks the electrical properties to work well in an ESP, and the result was too much fly ash getting into the air. Paul Beauchemin's job was to run pilot plant experiments at the various coal-fired facilities and hopefully find a solution. The pilot plant was 1/10th scale, about the size of a fifth-wheel trailer, and experiments required that the testing team stay at the test site often a week at a time.

Although these chapters speak of this group or that group as if they were well-defined entities within the company, the truth was much less formal. Though an attempt was made to use people where their expertise was most applicable, in times of crisis (and crisis was more typical than exceptional), a departing crew would press-gang whoever was handy for whatever job. The ESP testing crew at Sundance, Wabamun, and Forestburg was anything but a set group. To test what came into the pilot precipitator and what went out, five or so people were required.

The revolutionary aspect of this work was the experimentation Paul and his group did to combat the low sulphur coal. They injected SO_3 into the stream to raise the sulphur content, a subject upon which Paul would eventually deliver a paper to the Air Pollution Control Association. To help with the work, Joe Lukacs found the foremost North American authority on ESPs, an American named Dr. Harry J. White. He was elderly by this time, and Paul flew down to consult with him first in Portland and later in a Monterey, California, nursing home. Paul would arrive, blueprints in hand, to sit at the feet of this expert, another example in action of Joe Lukacs's faith in mentors.

Another problem Paul Beauchemin and his group tackled in this period had to do with the gas-fired power generation systems in the province. To reduce the NO_x emissions from the boilers, they changed the way the boilers ran. By reducing the peak flame temperature, they were able to reduce NO_x formation. This too was pioneer work, and more papers resulted. For Paul Beauchemin, it was the beginning of a career-long association with the Air Pollution Control Association. After Paul Beauchemin left Western Research in 1974, the ESP studies and the NO_x reduction work was carried on by Dr. Roger Mellor, who had joined the company in 1972.

Paul Beauchemin's departure from Western R & D was recorded in the January/February, 1974, newsletter in these words:

"Good 'ol Paul Beauchemin, who has been with WR&D since the time when it consisted of only nine people, is leaving us. When Paul arrived in 1969, Western Research was located in the Bradie Building–to which we shall return again shortly–and the lab consisted of a large closet in the Bamlett Bldg, two blocks away. We also had a bit of storage space under the stairs at the Western Union Building next door. The company consisted of Joe Lukacs, Al Brotherston, Ron Dinsley, Robin Rankine, Gloria Miller, Harold Paskall, Ed Hardy and Gill Earl. Paul started in the monitoring section, graduated to stack surveys and wound up in charge of consulting services. He left at the end of January, headed for Courtenay, B.C. to open a bookshop called the Laughing Oyster."

Speculate in assets; invest in people.

A startling thing that has to be remembered about the work that Paul Beauchemin's (and Dr. Mellor's) consulting group did in the first half of the 1970s is that most of it was not required by regulation, not yet. The regulations would come in time, requiring plant selection studies and full-scale Environmental Impact Assessments (EIAs), as were already being required in some jurisdictions in the United States. But the fish testing and much of the early work done for the power generation plants on fly ash from coal, and on NO_x emissions, was voluntary, a subject we will return to later.

By hiring environmental engineer Paul Beauchemin, meteorologist Douglas Leahey, biologist Gordon Brown and bio-medical engineer Hugh Hicklin, Joe Lukacs had anticipated the trend toward government-required Environmental Impact Assessments almost to the moment. Not too surprisingly, when the Alberta government required an Environmental Impact Assessment for the first time in its history, in

1975, Western R & D was the company called upon to do the job.

The project was a fertilizer plant that Cominco and CIL were intending to build in the Carseland area southeast of Calgary. A group was objecting to the placement of the plant, the Government suggested a study be done, and Western Research was asked to do a report. The problem was that the companies and the Government wanted the report *in four days*, including the up-coming weekend. The location wasn't far from Okotoks, and Elmer Berlie had already studied the lay of the land for safety and environmental reasons while managing the Texas Gulf Okotoks sulphur plant. Elmer was in charge of the CIL/Cominco study, and he was assisted by Gordon Brown, Hugh Hicklin, and technical editor Ben Gadd. Eventually, EIAs would become Gordon Brown's career, but his memory of this first one is of how very cursory it was. No actual field data was collected and the information on wild-life was from a variety of literary sources. Meanwhile, Ben Gadd played in a band on weekends and was by no means thrilled at having to work. There was almost a mutiny, as Elmer Berlie recalls. Nonetheless, the report was filed on time and it did, in the end, pass the test of a review by the Environmental Conservation Authority.

Given what environmental impact assessments would become, the feet of shelf space they would one day occupy, this first step seems a bit comical. But Western Research was there ahead of everyone else. The work the company had already done (such as bio-assays) would become standard practice for EIAs. In many other ways, the company would play a considerable role in developing the protocols and methods by which assessments advanced in thoroughness and scientific validity.

❖ *What advantages did Western Research have with respect to the emerging Environmental Impact Assessment market?*

❖ *How did Western Research's comprehensive package of environmental services help it as a products company?*

❖ *When working in air quality monitoring or the preparation of EIAs, the environmental company is solving problems for more than one entity. Who are the entities whose problems must be solved before the company has done its work?*

14

Becoming the Sulphur Doctors

At Western Research in the early years, we had no golden-haired R&D group—either that or everyone was in it.

—Joe Lukacs

The previous chapter on the air monitoring and consulting groups shows that Western Research was a company that worked beyond the boundaries of the oil and gas industry. But many of the company's key developments, particularly the ones that took it into the realm of being a product company, did come from the petroleum industry, and not from the whole industry but from one small sector of it: sulphur recovery from sour gas.

Sour gas processing and sulphur recovery were Joe Lukacs's specialties long before his affiliation with Western R&D. As the Alberta government put in place its legislation requiring higher sulphur recovery efficiencies, Joe had a natural urge to go back and apply his old and new knowledge to improving the operation of sulphur plants. The other very important factor, perhaps more important, was that sour gas processing was the only major industrial producer of sulphur emissions in Alberta. Because Alberta had the densest concentration of sulphur plants in the world, it was natural that there be a government and public concern about the H_2S and SO_2 emissions given off by them. As we've seen, the regulations controlling those emissions, and the consequent efficiency requirements the plants had to meet, were the market drivers behind much of Western Research's growth and development. As those regulations stiffened in response to greater world awareness of pollution, regulations became the driver behind a different kind of development in the company: scientific breakthroughs that fed into revolutionary instrument development.

Industrial pollution can be handled in two ways. Either you control the dispersion of your polluting emissions, by plant site selection and building ever higher stacks, or you go back inside the plant and figure out how to control the process so that pollutants are limited or not created in the first place. Obviously, the latter is the better solution, but, as of the late 1960s, there was limited ability within the sulphur recovery industry to do that.

This is where Western Research first donned the white coat and declared itself a sulphur doctor. While doing stack surveys for plants that were failing to meet the efficiency standards set for them by the Alberta government, Joe Lukacs made a claim. He told the plant engineers that the problem of low efficiency was back in their sulphur plant and that he and his company were capable of fixing it.

In truth, Joe was one of the few people in the industry who could make this vast claim because of the work he had done with Dr. Petrunic at Canadian Fina, and his own master's thesis work at University of Alberta. With Dr. Petrunic, he had studied the reaction furnace. They considered the COS and CS_2 formation in the furnace at the head end of the sulphur plant and learned to extend the furnace to allow the reactions to reach completion.

One aspect of this work was use of the Karl Fisher method for measuring the water content in high pressure H_2S. It took forever. The belief that there had to be a better way was what propelled Joe Lukacs back to university for his master's. He developed the chromatographic technique for measuring H_2S and water together, and for measuring COS/CS_2 and H_2S/SO_2 ratios. This work and the sampling techniques Western Research had developed for stack testing at sulphur plants were the structures on which the company would build its techniques for testing plant performance.

The first plants to give Western R&D a shot at living up to Joe's claims were naturally the ones to which Western Research

Product and service diversity helps a company stay flexible, a good defence during market downturns.

was best known and/or the ones having the most problems. This is how Western Research came to enter the sulphur plants at Shell Waterton and HBOG Edson.

At Shell Waterton, Western Research was very much among friends, including Joe's old strudel companions, Joe Labuda and Frank Angebrandt. The goal at Waterton was to achieve sulphur recovery in the high nineties and, as they studied the plant's process, the two Joes and Frank Angebrandt were fulfilling a dream they had shared for several years.

The situation at HBOG Edson, into which they were invited next, differed considerably. Edson had a severe problem with their catalyst, and they were asking Western Research to diagnose it and find a solution. Sulphur plants of this period were basically a reaction furnace followed by one or more catalyst beds. Most of the conversion of sulphur (approximately 60%) took place in the furnace and the next most (another 20-25%) at the first catalyst bed. The results gained in subsequent catalyst stages were smaller and decreased with each bed.

The problem at HBOG Edson was catalyst life. At worst, new catalyst at Edson would last as little as three weeks; six weeks was considered a good run before the catalyst was deactivated and had to be changed out. Catalyst isn't cheap, and HBOG also suffered production losses every time the plant had to shut down to change out the catalyst. The company was desperate for a solution.

To have any hope of solving the problems in either plant, Western Research had to be able to sample at various points along the sulphur recovery process. This alone was a major undertaking. Though there were sample valves available, they didn't trust what came off a side valve as being what was actually inside the plant. There was too much potential for further reactions within the samples that would render them false. Also, it became clear that samples taken along the side wall were different from those taken in the centre stream. They started to achieve better samples when they took them in centre stream.

Another problem was how to quench the sample, or in other words prevent it from undergoing further reactions that would turn the sample into a false sample. Sulphur dioxide, hydrogen sulphide, and water, the principal constituents of a plant's gas stream, are ever ready to react with one another, so getting a sample without further reactions was a formidable problem. Perhaps the greatest breakthrough in the sampling process was learning to dry the sample. This proved to be the key to quenching the sample (preventing further reactions). Various drying agents were experimented with, and the best was found to be phosphorous pentoxide (P_2O_5). The sample was drawn through a tube packed with P_2O_5 powder on its way into the sample container.

Another important principle was using relatively unreactive glass instead of metal wherever possible throughout the sampling and analyzing processes. The glass flasks, or bombs, used for the sampling were specially commissioned from University of Calgary gas blower Duncan Lindsay. They were of extreme thinness, with glass stopcocks at each end. Plant testers drew their samples into them.

Chris Harvey, an English engineer who had worked for the Atomic Energy Authority and Celanese at Clover Bar on his way to Western Research, was an early member of the plant testing brigade. He describes the sampling process this way: "Inside the plants we'd be climbing all over the sulphur converters to the sample points with a can around our necks containing the glass bombs packed in foam. Then you'd get your mitts off and take a sample."

Chris Harvey

Still another key to good sampling was getting all the samples within a compact timeframe. Gas passes through the entire sulphur plant in a matter of seconds so it is imperative that the samples be taken within the same brief period of time. This was accomplished by the whole crew going out to the different sampling points at once.

In the plant lab or wherever the testing crew was situated, the samples would be sucked out of the bomb with a hypodermic needle and injected into the gas chromatograph for analysis. This delicate operation was often Dan Violini's task. The chromatograph columns were another place where the sample could undergo further reactions and be falsified. Robin Rankine built and conditioned a series of chromatograph columns and each plant test served as the test of his latest design and procedure.

The chromatography results had to be read first, and then the analysis had to be calculated. The reading amounted to counting "bumps" or "peaks," which the testing crew often did together. Everyone also pitched in on the analysis, which were drawn-out hand calculations.

Don't be afraid to hire people who know more than you do.

What Chris Harvey remembers about these times was how innovative and inexpensively practical the Western Research test team was and had to be. For example, he remembers measuring molten sulphur streams from the condensers with a cheap little saucepan and a stop watch. It was, as he recalls, a reasonably accurate method of measurement.

For Western Research, amazing breakthroughs were made at Shell Waterton and HBOG Edson. The result of having physicist Robin Rankine participate in the six months of testing at Shell Waterton was, according to Joe Lukacs, that he came back knowing "more about the sulphur recovery process than anybody in North America." This was an enormous turning point in Western Research history, and Joe Lukacs recollects it this way:

"Robin Rankine is singlehandedly the smartest researcher I've ever met in my life, the brightest when it comes to diagnostic analysis. There's no problem Robin can't solve. I knew a lot about sulphur plants. My interest was in process, what went on in that vessel. But when Rankine came back, he knew much more than I did. From then on we built on his knowledge. I built a team around Rankine. With his understanding of the sulphur plant, we got into building an instrument that controlled the sulphur plant: the closed-loop control system."

Richard Cooper in his most familiar environment: the cockpit of a plane.

The white coat lectures the red coats.
Joe Lukacs in his trademark white lab coat addresses his red-coated seminar team.
Left to right, the red coats are: Jerry Smolarski, Graham Latonas,
John Jackson, Al Niven, Frank Cullen, Randy Hauer, John Sames,
and Len Edwards.

On the company blazers were the company crests:
(left) the Bow Valley Industries crest, designed by Don Binney,
and (right) the Western Research crest, designed by Joe Lukacs.

Elmer Berlie models the blue blazer with company crest
at the Amsterdam seminar of 1981.

Another aspect of company branding: white coveralls in the field to support Western Research's "Sulphur Doctors" image. Peter Dale takes a sample during a plant test.

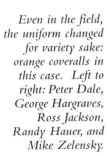

Even in the field, the uniform changed for variety sake: orange coveralls in this case. Left to right: Peter Dale, George Hargraves, Ross Jackson, Randy Hauer, and Mike Zelensky.

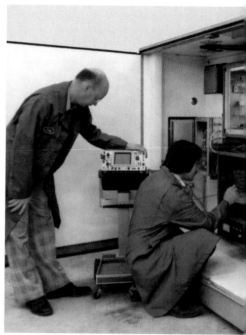

Dave Marion poses with the SO_2 analyzer, one of a family of analyzers based on the air demand analyzer.

Ed Hardy (l.) and Dennis Hniden, putting the finishing touches on an analyzer in the manufacturing department.

During the second oil price boom of the 1970s, Western Research went to Melville Island in the Canadian Arctic to do a fog study.

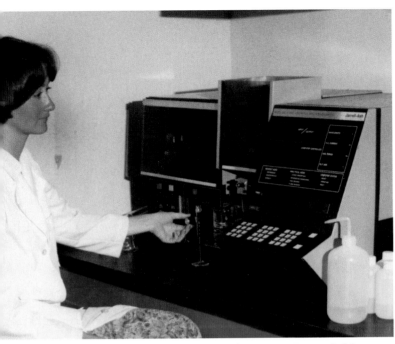

Lori Anderson working as a technician in the Western Research laboratory.

Jackie Hudson, of Air Quality Monitoring, was the first woman hired by Western Research to be a full-time field technician.

Jackie Hudson on a stack test.

Sampling from a flare in the old Redwater oil field.

*Plant testing: Mike Zelensky (l.)
and Bob Hensley.*

*Plant testing: Bob Hensley (l.), Mike
Zelensky (centre) and Peter Dale.*

*Liz Cole in the
Western Research laboratory.*

*Close-up view of the
Western Research lab.*

*Seeking a solution for
the Redwater field
odor problem led the
consulting group at
Western Research to
invent a family of
waste gas incinerators.
(Len Edwards with
the match.)*

Bill Wong, stack testing in the '80s.

Pan-Canadian's Morley gas plant: Western Research got Transport Canada approval for a green (rather than a candy-striped) stack.

Ed Hardy fondly remembers the Waterton period. He and Robin Rankine got on well because of how their abilities complemented one another. Robin's strengths were theoretical and analytical; Ed had experience and mechanical skill. When they combined their skill sets, there wasn't much the two couldn't accomplish. Like most of those interviewed for this book, Ed Hardy marvels at the capacity Robin Rankine has to take on a problem and solve it. "Robin is an unusual guy," says Ed. "If he didn't know something, like electronics, he'd learn it."

Another complementary pairing was Robin Rankine with Harold Paskall. Here again, Robin was the idea man, the theoretician. What Harold Paskall brought to the pair, when he joined the company in 1969, was his knowledge of chemistry and an amazing thoroughness and meticulousness. His precise calibrations ensured that the data was correct. You could say that Robin invented and Harold made sure that none of it got lost. It makes sense that it was Harold who did much of the writing and publishing concerning what the team accomplished.

Involve your research people in your operations work. It will result in more motivated, practical, results-oriented research.

To the quest for sulphur plant optimization and automation, the goals that Angebrandt, Labuda, and Lukacs had been thinking toward for years, Robin Rankine brought a new dimension. The group's thinking to date had been that either nitrogen balance or H_2S/SO_2 ratio should be the basis upon which automated control of the plant was achieved. Robin Rankine was not satisfied with either. He believed the answer was air demand, and, in the extension of that idea, the solution would eventually be found.

After its victorious debut at Shell Waterton, Western Research went on to successfully solve the catalyst problems at HBOG Edson as well. They discovered that the catalyst was being deactivated by the process stream, causing the plant to produce "black sulphur." In some sulphur plant designs, a portion of the inlet stream (also known as the acid gas stream) is by-passed around the reaction furnace. It is then mixed with hot process gas from the reaction furnace before entering the first catalyst bed. At Edson, the acid gas stream had been put into the process stream at a hot point. When the cold gas hit the hot gas, polymers of sulphur formed. These polymers, building up on the catalyst and giving it the appearance of black lustrous glass beads, also deactivated the catalyst. The solution was to extend the by-pass so the feed gas was heated by a cooler stream of gas off the reaction furnace. This solved the catalyst life problem and kept the plant from producing black sulphur at the same time.

This was a very exciting time for Joe Lukacs. Western Research had taken on its first two plant process jobs and had been successful in both of them. What was even more exciting were Robin Rankine's discoveries at Shell Waterton and the way they pushed back the frontiers of knowledge on the modified-Claus process. Joe was anxious to push that knowledge as far as it could go, into products that might one day fully automate and guarantee optimized operation in sulphur plants all over the world.

All this occurred at the same time that ownership was changing over to Bow Valley Industries and accounts in part for Joe's enthusiasm for the change. If BVI would go along with Western Research financially, the new knowledge really could be parlayed into the changes Joe Lukacs, Robin Rankine, and Harold Paskall foresaw.

Then, in 1971, the Lougheed Conservatives came to power. The new government, through its Department of the Environment, established new, and much tougher, ambient air quality standards for the province of Alberta, effective January 10, 1973. New sulphur recovery efficiency standards were imposed such that the plants with the highest output of elemental sulphur (1,000 to 4,000 long tons per day) would have to achieve 97 to 99 percent recovery of their sulphur.

The regulations completed the puzzle. In the next few years, they revolutionized how sulphur was recovered from sour gas in Alberta. Tail gas clean-up units became the norm. Stack gases were continuously monitored. Ground-level concentrations were continuously monitored, and the results were telemetered to the control room. Closed-loop process control went from being a science fiction notion to being a fact that more forward-thinking companies wanted for their plants.

All in all, the new Alberta regulations provided a market for every sulphur plant optimization scheme and tool Western Research could think of and invent.

❖ *What were the advantages for Western Research of cycling technologists through the Research and Development testing program, and research scientists through the day-to-day operations and plant testing?*

Air Cooler Testing

In the late 1960s, Western Research became involved in air cooler testing. The fin/fan air cooling systems at Alberta's gas plants were often designed in Houston for Houston conditions, and, in Alberta, they tended not to work. Testing the coolers as a first step toward redesigning them was an awful job, one the plants were happy to farm out. As with stack surveying, Western Research took on the unpleasant chore, and most everyone working for the company got involved. As Joe puts it, air cooler testing was the company's "cash cow" in this period, and it paid for a lot of the company's research.

The task consisted of laying out a grid of thermometers above and below the cooler. Underneath, it might be twenty below zero Fahrenheit. On top it might be 140 to 170° F above. The people doing the tests were like monkeys climbing back and forth between temperature zones. Ed Hardy's description of the work was "walking out on all those one inch things with those fins sticking out all over, placing thermometers." Paul Beauchemin remembers the enormous temperature change, how one minute your shoe soles would actually be melting and then suddenly your problem would be that you were freezing.

Given the unpleasantness of the work, it isn't surprising that a major panic ensued when suddenly an entire day's findings went missing. The readings were all on a single page and no matter where they looked, they could not find it. One theory was that the page had been sucked up into a fan and sliced to pieces. A second idea was that the sheet of paper must have fallen off the cooler. Preferring the second hypothesis, Robin Rankine got the brainwave that all they needed to do was drop a second sheet of paper off the same cooler and see where it went. After an argument about the practicality of Rankine's scheme, the second sheet was dropped and followed. It floated this way, was sucked over here, and blown over there. It finally came to rest almost on top of the lost page of cooler readings.

Another amusing moment on the air coolers, remembered by Ed Hardy, came the day Joe Lukacs decided to get some concrete evidence of how the air currents were flowing across the coolers. The system he struck upon was to light flares and run back and forth across the coolers with the burning flares while someone took pictures. After Joe had done much of this running around on the coolers with the flares, and after he had burned up most of the flares he had scoured half of Alberta to find, he asked Bill Lewington, who had the camera, whether he was getting it all.

"Oh," said Lewington, "was I supposed to be taking the pictures now?"

15

Little "R" Big "D"
The IRAP Project

Western Research couldn't afford the R in R & D.

Richard Kerr, ca. 1975

In 1970 and 1971, Joe began hiring people for his new research initiatives. In February, 1970, Dr. Roger Mellor, a Ph.D. in chemical engineering and fuel technology from the University of Sheffield, was lured into the company from Toronto, where he had been in charge of a computer control system for the manufacture of glass. In November, 1971, Richard Kerr, a Ph.D. physicist from the University of British Columbia was also added to the team.

One of the main R & D projects undertaken in this period was an in-depth study of the modified-Claus sulphur recovery process. To support this work, Joe Lukacs was successful in getting funds from the National Research Council's Industrial Research Assistance Program (IRAP). This was the project that would take Robin Rankine's new understanding of the kinetics of the modified-Claus process and elaborate upon it. Richard Kerr headed up the research team. Robin Rankine and Harold Paskall naturally remained closely involved.

The success of this project, and the excitement of the team of researchers, is evidenced by a memo Robin Rankine sent Joe Lukacs on September 21, 1972:

"In connection with the NRC Industrial Research Assistance Program, the Research Group has concluded a series of experiments which give strong indication that we can develop a 100 per cent sulphur recovery process."

This was both exciting news and news the industry was in no way ready for. Most sour gas plant operators were still reeling from the government's push to get recoveries into the high 90s.

As Don Stevens describes it, the study of the modified-Claus was an on-going exercise more than it was a specific event. Most things the company did in these years amounted to a study of modified-Claus, and the plant optimization testing provided a steady stream of reliable analytical data for use in the company's research. Harold Paskall's IRAP-supported study of the process chemistry in the reaction furnace was another example.

Still another piece of R & D machinery created during this time was the SCAT. The acronym stood for Standard Catalyst Activity Test and, with it, Western Research was able to carry out tests for plants and catalyst manufacturers at a very sophisticated level. The researchers found out things about catalyst that the catalyst's own manufacturers did not know. Don Stevens recollects that Robin Rankine, Ron Dimmer, Dave Earl, and he built the first model sulphur plant for catalyst testing and that it was a real Rube Goldberg device, but it got great results. Later, Richard Kerr and his group would refine that early design. Also in the catalyst testing vein, Stevens remembers Emira Farag, a master's degree chemist hired in 1972, spending entire days at Western Research putting catalyst pellets in a drill press and measuring the pressure it took to crush them.

One of the basic steps in the modified-Claus study was the building of a laboratory model of the sulphur plant. This was accomplished by Robin Rankine and Harold Paskall. A related initiative that followed was creation of a mathematical model of the sulphur plant. Robin Rankine and Richard Kerr worked on this together. Linda Biswanger (later Van Gastel) did the computer programming. Eventually, with this tool, test data from the plants could be plugged into the mathematical

When the opportunity arises to access government funding to support your research, make sure it is research you would have done with or without government funding.

model and the necessary changes computed. Nothing like it had existed in the world before. When computing caught up with it, it would become the basis of Western Research's computer program simulation of the sulphur plant (called Sulsim).

Again, the telling of this story may give the impression of a research and development department within Western R & D that was well defined and cloistered away from the hurly-burly of the company's other business. Nothing could have been farther from the truth. People from all over the company's operations were grabbed to help with the R & D experiments, often, as Ron Dimmer recalls, on weekends. Discussion of the projects was non-stop and everyone felt free to make suggestions.

Linda Biswanger (Van Gastel), above, and Gillian Clark were Western Research's first two women engineers.

The flip-side was that the research scientists were often called upon to support other aspects of the company's work. In fact, plant performance tests carried out by Ron Dimmer, Don Stevens, and others were thinly veiled experiments. The data collected was used both to solve the operating company's problem and to test the R & D scientists' latest theory. It was sometimes a bone of contention between Joe Lukacs and Robin Rankine that research was so driven by project demands. At a larger company, research might have meant years of failed attempts to produce a single breakthrough. At Western Research, you were inventing against the clock, and there was no time for failure. The result was considerable stress and a surprisingly high success rate. Failure, as Ed Hardy puts it, is a word that doesn't fit well within research anyway. "What seems like a failure just means you have to take a different road to success."

❖ **What does the statement that Western Research "couldn't afford the R in R & D" mean?**

❖ **Under what circumstances might a small company engage in extensive research?**

❖ **What are the risks for a small company in investing heavily in research?**

16

The Air Demand Analyzer

At Western Research, failure was never an option.
—Don Stevens

The idea of a closed-loop, automated system (an analyzer) capable of controlling and optimizing the sulphur plant was never far from anyone's thoughts at Western Research, and, in the early 1970s, the company began to close the distance between itself and that goal.

One of Robin Rankine's initiatives during this period was Analytical Flow Ratio (AFR), a system for calculating sulphur plant performance and testing rates of emission. Initially, the problem he set out to solve was how to test emissions in plants that had a very low velocity of air up their stacks. To measure stack emissions, you must measure both the quantity of SO_2 and the velocity up the stack. The standard method of velocity measurement only worked where the velocity was greater than twenty feet per second. For the plants that had a stack velocity lower than this, Western Research had been computing velocity in a very primitive way. That is, they had been shooting a fire extinguisher into the bottom of the stack and using a stop watch to time the puff out the top. What Robin Rankine came up with was a way of computing stack velocity by measuring the rate of flow of materials through the sulphur plant. This was AFR.

A related development, also based on Robin's theoretical knowledge, was the Recovery Efficiency Monitor (REM), the first attempt to continuously control a sulphur plant's process at optimum efficiency. REM began with taking a plant's tail gas and calculating the carbon to sulphur ratio. This was done in the laboratory by introducing pure oxygen so that all the sulphur species were oxidized to SO_2 and increasing the heat to 1700 degrees Fahrenheit. The quantity of sulphur (from SO_2) was computed with an ultraviolet analyzer and the quantity of carbon (from CO_2) was computed with an infrared analyzer. The result was the carbon to sulphur ratio in the tail gas. Western Research's sister company Dominion Instruments came up with an analog computer capable of combining this information with an analysis of the acid gas stream entering the plant that would calculate the efficiency loss through the plant.

The first sulphur plant REM was housed in a fold-down tent trailer. It was built by Ed Hardy, Don Stevens, and Dave Earl, under Robin Rankine's guidance, and was tested at Shell Jumping Pound. When the first REM was destroyed in an accident, a second one was built in a much larger trailer. Dr. Roger Mellor joined the development team for the testing of this prototype, which took place primarily at Chevron Kaybob. When the REM was doing what it was supposed to do, measuring the efficiency loss across the sulphur plant, it was taken to Shell Jumping Pound where a marketing demonstration was staged.

In the end, the potential customers were simply not impressed enough with the sulphur REM to buy it. It was adjudged to be too cumbersome and expensive. As some at Western said, it was easier to run the sulphur plant than to run the REM.

Meanwhile, Dr. Mellor went to work on yet another REM, this time for determining the mass balance in power generation plants. Its goal was the reduction of NO_x emissions. Another trailer was constructed and equipped, this time with a PDP-8E computer, and testing took place at both the Rossdale and Clover Bar Edmonton Power plants. NO_x emissions were lowered by reducing heat and oxygen. Reducing the oxygen also improved efficiency. The NO_x REM was not an attempt at continuous optimization. Test results were studied, recommendations were made for controlling the air/fuel ratio, and the plant process was altered accordingly by the operators.

Though the sulphur REM did not result in a marketable system, it was a wonderful proof of Ed Hardy's theory as regards failures. Within this system, which could never be successfully sold for use in the field, were concepts and actual devices that would in the longer run find their way into Western Research's world of ideas and marketable products. Dominion Instruments had begun work on a UV analyzer for the REM. When Robin Rankine saw it, he was challenged to go away and build a better one. The result was a brand new UV analyzer which was an improvement on the Dupont Model 400, which the company had been using for its CSEM. The optics were better, and so were the electronics: modern analog electronics versus vacuum tubes. Henceforward, all the company's systems were built around its own UV analyzer at a considerable saving in cost.

To achieve success in business, you need champions with vision, perseverence and courage.

Robin Rankine's work on the REM soon translated into another new concept having to do with excess air demand in the sulphur plant. It was the theoretical basis for the Air Demand Analyzer (ADA), which was probably the most successful of all Western Research instruments. The ADA would eventually do what the REM had not been able to do cheaply or automatically enough.

The third advance that can be traced back to the REM has to do with teamwork. A strong group was emerging within the company that was able to imagine, create, test, and manufacture entirely new systems. Ironically, that group gained enormous confidence from its "failure" on the REM, confidence that buoyed it up in the drive for the next product development: the ADA.

For years, the rule of thumb for controlling modified-Claus plants had been to shoot for a tail gas H_2S/SO_2 ratio of two to one. What Robin Rankine came up with, a breakthrough that would enable the company to build its closed-loop analyzer for sulphur plants at long last, was a new equation for controlling air in the plant, which also took into account the plant's recovery efficiency: an equation that would tell you if the plant was running with excess or deficient air.

The ADA analyzer was the instrumentation outgrowth of that algorithm. If it could be made to work, it would be a method of controlling plant performance *and* would greatly simplify the analytical task of testing and maintaining performance.

Again, Joe Lukacs was able to convince his federal and provincial government funding sources of the importance of the work on the ADA. Since the acquisition by BVI, Joe had been reinjecting, on average, 15 percent of the company's annual revenues into R&D. Even granting that this 15 percent included government grants, it was still a substantial R & D commitment for a small and growing company. Acquiring government support was basically a matter of communication. With his flare for the dramatic, Joe was able to reduce any scepticism the funders might have had and to fire them with his own enthusiasm. The simple truth was that the ADA, the CSEM, and improved knowledge of modified-Claus, were all contributors to improved sulphur plant efficiency, which translates into lower sulphur tonnage going into the atmosphere. Some of the technologies were adaptable to other industries like pulp and paper and power generation. All in all, governments and other scientific research funding agencies would have had a hard time justifying it if they had chosen not to fund.

Perseverence and courage come into play in the early days of commercialization, when the market is most inclined to doubt you.

Like its predecessor, the REM, the ADA was long in gestation, prototype-building, and testing. The ADA was built in the same trailer as the last sulphur REM and it utilized the PDP-8E computer last used for the NO_x REM. The computer controlled the valves that determined the air mixture in the reaction furnace, the critical determiner of the sulphur plant's efficiency. Linda Biswanger and Geoff Sams (with whom Dr. Mellor had worked in Toronto) were both involved in the real-time programming of the computer.

The grant money ran out before the ADA was ready to roll, and much of the final development and testing were done with the company's own cash. The final step was the testing of the prototype at the Saratoga sour gas processing plant at Coleman in Alberta's Crowsnest Pass.

Pressure of another kind was added to the ADA development process when Don Stevens went out and sold two in New Brunswick. Two new sulphur plants were being built for Irving Oil, and Western Research was asked to bid on the stack monitoring system. During the process of making that bid, Don Stevens happened to mention the ADA to a representative of the engineering company. This Bechtel representative, Bob Klett, was very interested, and he asked Don to submit a bid to supply this new ADA system. Even though Western Research did not have a product design as yet, Don worked with Mike Beamish and with Robin Rankine to come up with a price. A CSEM proposal was adjusted and submitted as an ADA proposal.

When Bob Klett saw the bid, he was intrigued by it. He phoned Don Stevens and asked if Western Research was really serious about this bid because, if they were, he wanted it.

As promising as all this sounds, the ADA project came within an inch of being stopped in 1975. The problem, oddly enough, began with increases in the world price of oil during the winter of 1973-74. This was the first OPEC inspired "oil crisis" whereby OPEC succeeded, under the leadership of Sheik Yamani, to increase the world price of oil from a paltry $3 per barrel to four times that. This good news was only good if you could get that price and, in Canada, the price was pegged at a much lower rate as a subsidy to Canadians and industries in Canada. To the oil-producing province of Alberta, this meant a subsidy by Alberta to the population centres of Ontario and Quebec.

Peter Lougheed was determined to force Ottawa to raise the Canadian price toward the world price, based on the indisputable fact that natural resources belonged to the provinces. Pierre Trudeau and his federal Liberals were not entirely against raising the price of oil and gas, but wanted to tax back much of the increase at the federal level, which Lougheed, in turn, said they had absolutely no right to do. When this battle resulted in both the federal government and the Alberta government taxing the same oil price increase, the drilling industry headed for the borders, and the share value of Canadian oil companies plunged.

In 1975, Bow Valley Industries' shares lost half their value. Because of the attractiveness of the company's prospects, particularly offshore in the North Sea, the Seaman brothers felt uncomfortably vulnerable to takeover. Through the BVI family of companies, the directive went out: cut costs.

Right at that exact moment, Western Research did not look all that great to the BVI board of directors. Under the guise of R & D, the company had been spending a lot of money on instrumentation, which in the gloomy atmosphere of 1975 looked more like a haemorrhage than a sound investment. Don Thurston, as the BVI liaison in charge of Western Research, was getting a lot of heat.

There came a fateful day when Don Thurston marched over to Western Research and Development to tell Joe and the leaders of his research and instrumentation development group that all their R & D must stop. That day stands out in a lot of memories, including Thurston's. "I can hardly remember an event in my business life as pivotal," he recalls. He knew that when he enforced this rule, and he fully intended

Leadership proves itself in times of crisis

Joe Lukacs and Don Thurston

to, Western Research would never be the same. Joe Lukacs loved the scientifically innovative side of the company he had built. He wasn't likely to stay if that side were removed. The other bright lights on the R & D team would probably follow him out the door.

A company's culture sustains it across financial crises and market downturns.

When Don Thurston told Joe the news, he got the reaction he expected. Joe said that he would not stand for it. If the R & D were stopped, he would quit. But Joe Lukacs showed what a team player he really is. He asked Don Thurston to meet with some of the people most involved in the decision they were weighing.

In this meeting, several speakers put forth their best arguments why the R & D program at Western Research should be allowed to continue. Mike Beamish explained how convinced he was that the ADA was a winner. Robin Rankine asked Don Thurston to consider the distance they had gone down the road toward the ADA analysr, and to compare it to the distance they had yet to go. Likely, the ratio was about 7 to 8. Another $50,000 and they would have a product for which they already had contracts. If instead, BVI stuck to their guns and killed the R & D, short of the commercial development of the ADA, they would have nothing to show for the money they had sunk.

Don Thurston was finally convinced.

He went back to the BVI board and fought successfully to save Western R & D's instrumentation development program. Back at Western Research, he put the delivery of the first ADAs on a strict schedule, and even remembers nailing up some of the packing crates himself to meet that schedule.

In the end it was a wonderful turning point for the company, which entered a period of profitability that lasted into the 1990s.

With the crises of 1975 behind them, and with the company officially ten years old and counting, Western Research and Development, and all its staff, had a lot to be proud of. Soon they would have two very strong instruments on the market in the CSEM and the ADA, both of which represented an industry-leading understanding of how sulphur plants worked. The consulting services group, the stack surveying, and air monitoring groups were all industry leaders. The plant performance testing and optimization squad had a routine that was approaching clockwork.

Western Research and Development had truly come a long way.

❖ *What creative approaches will help a small company afford to do research and development?*

❖ *What determines the proper balance between the R component and the D component of R & D?*

❖ *What was Western Research doing at this time to create a brand image?*

III

Western Research and Development: The Product Company

Pick the best people you can.
Give them a good home.
Treat them well.
They will adopt the business as their own.

17

A Time of Transition

Hanging onto your best people during a downturn is smart business. If you let them go, you are spawning your competition. —Joe Lukacs

Don Thurston's decision to allow the Air Demand Analyzer's development to continue was a definite turning point in Western Research's history, one of the most important to date. But it was never as simple as Bow Valley Industries giving its blessing and Western Research charging forward on the path to glory. Facing the disastrous collapse of its share value, Bow Valley wanted major cutbacks from all its companies, including Western Research, and if the savings weren't going to come from the instrumentation development side, they had to come from somewhere.

Perhaps no one knows this side of the story better than accountant Terry Crooks, who came on board to replace Noel Llanos on April 1, 1975. Up to the time Terry came to the company, Western Research had maintained a delicate but reasonable financial health. Suddenly, coincident with his arrival, the company started to bleed red at an alarming rate. This was part of the situation that brought on Don Thurston's directive to shut down the R & D, and this was the situation that Western Research had to turn around quickly in the days and weeks that followed. When Terry Crooks sat down with Don Thurston, Joe Lukacs, and the Western Research middle managers, what they set out to do was nothing short of a complete restructuring of the company.

One of the first things to go was Dominion Instruments. The Edmonton subsidiary was essentially closed down. The next target was the communications problems within the company. The splitting of the company between a downtown office and a distant northeast lab was seen to be the cause of various problems, and the solution found was to move the downtown portion of the company to join the others near the airport. Joe Lukacs and Elmer Berlie both liked the downtown situation for the ease of networking it afforded them, but the consolidation was more of a directive than a choice. They headed northeast with the rest.

Lab and Field, and Air Quality Monitoring also came in for their share of restructuring. Elmer Berlie and Ron Dimmer were asked to re-examine the pricing of their services and to determine the profitability of each. At some point in the process, Terry Crooks recommended that Lab and Field be sold to Ron Dimmer for a dollar. The suggestion wasn't taken very seriously, despite its having some sound thinking behind it. As Terry saw it, it was an area with a low cost of entry and low margins. It seemed destined for heavy competition, price wars, and unprofitability. But many others were just as certain that these services were key to the marketing of more profitable aspects of the company: instruments and air monitoring being two obvious examples. There was also the fact, Ron Dimmer points out, that Lab and Field was carrying on its budget the salaries of several of the company's scientists.

The support of your investors often comes down to shared vision and shared values.

All in all, Ron Dimmer took the unprofitability charge as a personal challenge, and he bet a case of Crown Royal with Terry Crooks that he could deliver a net profit of $100,000 from his department next fiscal year. At the end of the fiscal year, it was there in black and white and Terry Crooks had to deliver the whisky.

The old bedrock of stack and plant testing was still the way that Western Research got into plants, solved problems, and made friends. The excellence and likability of its technicians, engineers, and scientists took over from there.

As for R & D, there was widespread support for the instrumentation initiatives within the company. The instruments were seen as the place where the company had the most room to grow. Here, Thurston and Crooks focussed their energies more on gaining control of the flow of expenditures, short of curtailing or stopping them.

Richard Kerr, ca. 2000

The dark days of 1975 were not, however, without cost. To retain the development of the Air Demand Analyzer, other cuts had to be made. For the first time in its history, Western Research faced lay-offs. Joe Lukacs genuinely hated this because of his loyalty to his employees and his personal faith in them. They had all worked hard. But with Bow Valley shares dropping to half their value and cutbacks and layoffs happening all over the greater company, Joe could hardly keep Western Research exempt.

Among those who were let go were chemists fairly recently added to Richard Kerr's research team. Although it did not change his positive view of Western Research, and the exciting work he and the other researchers were doing there, the situation did motivate Dr. Kerr to seek opportunities elsewhere. He decided he would rather not be exposed to the cyclical vagaries of the consulting business any longer. In 1976, after initiating a major incinerator study at Western Research, he left to join Alberta Energy Co. Ltd., as supervisor of research and development.

These days, Dr. Richard Kerr is chief engineer for Canadian Occidental Petroleum Ltd. He belongs to any number of important boards and councils, among them the Advisory Council on Science and Technology for the federal Minister of Natural Resources, and COURSE, a body that advises the Alberta government on R & D funding in the energy area.

Looking back at Western Research, Dr. Kerr remembers best the way people worked, right up to 24 hours a day, not because of management coercion, but simply because they wanted to. They wanted to find out the answers and were not willing to wait for another day. It was a motivated group.

Although the company's buoyancy and optimism must have sustained some damage from the events of 1975, it was not like Joe Lukacs to stay with his head down for long. The main thing was that the ADA was going to make it, and that the team he had assembled over the first ten years at Western Research would emerge from the mid-1970s slump largely intact. The ADA was more than just a new product or tool, it was for Joe a dream come true. He and his friends, the brightest young engineers of their day, had dreamt of automating the sulphur plant before Western Research even existed, and now his company had done it. They had a closed-loop analyzer capable of assessing and adjusting to changes in the plant as they occurred.

Joe was on the verge of going out and doing what he liked best, which was to convince the unbelieving world that little Western Research had produced an instrument that could

Paul Vetro, Don Thurston, and Robin Rankine, after the ADA was saved

compete head-to-head with the best that mighty Dupont had to offer. What's more, with enough bravado and foot speed, with his team of crack engineers, scientists, and technicians behind him, Joe Lukacs believed Western Research could be David to Dupont's Goliath, driving the giant from at least this small corner of the field.

❖ *What problems are associated with starting and stopping an R & D effort?*

❖ *What impact does a leader's faith and determination have on success?*

❖ *What are the weaknesses of a large, established company?*

❖ *How can you favourably differentiate yourself from a large, established company?*

18

The Sulphur Seminars: Giving Away the Western Research Advantage

Recognize the power of branding

In the pivotal year of 1975, a drying up of government funds was added to the general malaise of intergovernmental feuding and slashed share values in the Canadian oil patch. The various funds that Western Research had tapped for the modified-Claus study, the mathematical modelling of the sulphur plant, and the catalyst research were no more and, though it might not have been exactly what management felt, the official line was that it was time Western Research stood on its own two feet.

But before the money ran out, Joe Lukacs was able to score one final grant, a two-year Energy Resources Research Fund (ERRF) grant listing seven goals that Western Research would seek to achieve with the money. The first goal was to compile the results of all the studies and testing the company had done to revolutionize the understanding of the modified-Claus sulphur recovery process and gather it together into a book. Other important uses of the ERRF funding would be to research incineration processes toward development of a recuperative tail gas incinerator (and a whole family of waste gas incinerators, as it turned out) and to study the feasibility of producing electric power and sulphur from high H_2S (90%) gas.

Harold Paskall

143

Dr. Bob Ritter, former dean of engineering at the University of Calgary, was secured as a project manager for the ERRF projects.

To some extent, the publishing of the results of Western Research's modified-Claus research had already been started by Dr. Richard Kerr. He had already published several papers on his research. What the book would do was to pull all the research together so that the work of Harold Paskall and Robin Rankine was also detailed. The ac-

Dr. Bob Ritter (rear) project managed several of Western Research's studies.

tual tasks of authorship and editing were primarily taken over by Harold Paskall.

Harold Paskall was a company legend for his thoroughness and meticulousness, and the book project extended that mythic status even farther than before. Piece by piece, the work of several years was reviewed, analyzed and presented, in diagrams, algorithms, graphs, and prose, such that all you could ever want to know about modified-Claus sulphur recovery, vintage 1977, existed between the covers of a single book entitled: *The Capability of the Modified-Claus Process.* The decision of whose name, or names, should appear on the book belonged to Joe Lukacs and he chose Harold Paskall for that honour. Though the work described belonged to several people, Harold had, without doubt, done the lion's share of work that brought it together in book form.

When the book was nearing completion, Joe Lukacs attended one final meeting with Dr. Ritter and the ERRF committee. The purpose was to present the work to date toward the release of the final project payment. During the discussion, one member of the committee issued a challenge. Now that there was a book, what did Joe and his company intend to do with it? Put it on a library shelf and forget it? Or did they have a plan for disseminating the book and its contents that would justify the Alberta taxpayers' investment in it?

In fact, no such plan existed, but, out of the blue, and much to the surprise of the Western Researchers on hand, Joe Lukacs said,

"We'll give seminars. We'll give seminars on sulphur recovery, and we'll give out the book as a handout to those who attend."

Though Joe Lukacs says he surprised even himself with this assertion about seminars before the ERRF committee, the idea of seminars had a lengthy history at Western Research. The company had already put on two of them.

In 1974, Western Research undertook a project on the fuel efficiency of tail gas incinerators, led by Richard Kerr. The idea was spurred to life by the unprecedented high energy prices of 1973. Nobody knew at the time where the price of oil and gas might end up; a hundred dollar barrel of oil didn't seem out of the question.

Brand your company. Create for it a unique and memorable look and personality.

Within Western Research, this had led to a theory that tail-gas incinerator stacks on sulphur plants could be run at a lower temperature, thus saving fuel and money. If Western Research could figure out a way to do it and then convince government to let processors change from their current practice (as defined by their permit), incinerator stack fuel savings might turn into a money-making venture for Western Research and a money-saving one for their clients.

The usual squad of Paskall, Rankine, Dimmer and Stevens were all involved in the study, along with Richard Kerr. They found that satisfactory reduction of sulphur species to SO_2 could be achieved in sulphur plant incineration stacks, along with adequate plume rise, at a temperature of 850 degrees Fahrenheit. This was well below what the government regulation called for. Operators also tended to increase the fuel to tail-gas ratio in times of cold weather. What Western Research suggested was reducing the amount of cold air in the stack instead, while leaving the fuel ratio about the same.

To move toward implementation, Western Research started with their contacts in government. Western Research already had a good track record for innovation, and the Alberta government regulators not only approved the change but offered to help Western Research convince industry to adopt it.

With the government on side, Western Research looked for a way to get the word out to the plant engineers and operators who would actually be using the new plan—or not.

The idea of giving seminars for this purpose was born in one of those epic and stormy boardroom meetings that Western Research was becoming famous for. The pro side, the side in favour of seminars, felt that you could best convince the plant personnel to go for the scheme by educating them thoroughly in the science and engineering behind the plan. Richard Kerr remembers being on this side.

The con side thought it was risky to go around telling people the trade secrets that the company had spent endless days of research acquiring. The people who went to the seminar could turn around and simply steal the offered expertise. There simply wasn't a guarantee that they would come back to Western Research for the product and service just because that's where they heard about it.

This was the first but certainly not the last time that this debate about giving away hard-won knowledge would be fought in the Western Research boardroom. Possibly because Joe Lukacs, as president, was in favour of seminars, that's the way the decision went, this time and every time. Joe could clearly see the sales value of the seminars, the way they showcased the company, its scientists, its engineers, its technicians, and its products. In this case, they were trying to sell a fuel savings plan and an oxygen analyzer that could deliver the results, but in reality they were selling the whole company, with all its services and products. Even if the people present don't buy your incinerator product, they will remember you at stack surveying time or when they want their plant process optimized.

The first two Western R & D seminars, the fuel-savings seminars, were held in Calgary and Whitecourt in 1977. Harold Paskall was the key presenter and Don Stevens did much of the organizing and coordinating. Elmer Berlie, a moderator of great ability, took on that chore. Bill Schnitzler came along for the ERCB to vouch for the fact that processors would be allowed to run their stacks below the regulation required minimum temperature, if they used the Western Research method and oxygen analyzer.

Everyone recalls the seminars as a success, and everyone remembers as well that the fuel incinerator fuel-savings plan was a bust (at least for the time being). There was nothing wrong with the science, or with the application; it really did deliver the fuel savings it promised with no compromise of incinerator efficiency. But there was a problem with history. The price of oil did not go up to a hundred dollars a barrel, nor did it even stay at the heights reached during the OPEC-induced supply crisis of 1973. OPEC's resolve faded, supplies rose, and the price fell. This, combined with inter-governmental feuding in Canada, gave the petroleum processors of Alberta fits of various kinds, but a problem that concerned them not at all in 1975 and 1976 was the amount of fuel they were burning in their tail-gas incinerators. (The fuel-savings project was not thrown away; it was only held in reserve for a time when it would have more marketability.)

What had not failed, however, were the seminars themselves. They had done what they set out to do in terms of educating the potential consumer while showing off Western Research leadership and expertise. This fact stayed with Joe Lukacs right up to that auspicious day when he blurted to the ERRF committee that he would use the seminars again, this time to disseminate the company's sulphur recovery knowledge and to circulate the company's new book.

Back at Western Research after the Edmonton trip, Joe had to sell his own company on doing the sulphur recovery seminars he had promised ERRF, and it was not an easy sell. Harold Paskall and Robin Rankine all but told him where he could put his seminars. Others were again concerned about giving away the company secrets and the company's technological edge. It was even a graver danger this time because of the man-years of research that had gone into the gathering of the information on modified-Claus that Joe was now threatening to deliver to seminar guests. But Joe was just as certain that the seminars were the way to go, the way to crack the U.S. market, where they were still an unknown quantity—the way as well to sell the new ADA and the CSEM on both sides of the border. Once again, Joe and his allies prevailed.

Perhaps the zaniest thing about the first sulphur recovery seminar delivered by Western Research was its location. Whereas anyone else would have chosen to pilot such a frontier venture close to home, where company friends could be prevailed upon to attend, and where the reception had the best chance of being positive, Joe Lukacs announced that Western Research would deliver its first sulphur recovery seminar in Houston.

Don Stevens, who was by now in charge of instrument sales for all of North America, and Ron Dimmer, who was marketing on behalf of his Lab and Field department across the same broad territory, found themselves in charge of many local arrangements by dint of being the employees spending the most time in the States. Stevens and Dimmer may also have had the best grasp of just how hard it was going to be to win American acceptance of Western Research's alleged superior knowledge of sulphur recovery. For one thing, the majority of potential customers in the United States were not sour gas processors but oil refiners. What they had were sour gas streams coming off their refineries, containing ammonia and complex hydrocarbons. Flaring the gas had once been their solution, but now the Environmental Protection Agency said they had to process it. For them, the sour gas and sulphur recovery plants were just nuisance garbage-disposal facilities stuck on the back end of their refineries. They had a limited desire to understand them.

Then there was the fact of Western Research's being Canadian. The minority of seminar candidates who really were sour gas processors, or sour gas plant designers and builders, perceived themselves as having taught Canada how to build and run sulphur plants. That they were now coming down to Texas to tell the Texans how to get the sulphur out of sour gas was downright laughable. Joe Lukacs's response was to say, "That was longer ago than you think. We've learned a lot since then." Nonetheless, Elmer Berlie was fairly certain that at least some of the people who were signing up for the seminar were coming "just to tear us apart."

To boost Western Research's credibility with the American audience, Joe Lukacs asked for the assistance of a well-respected American. That person was sour gas plant design engineer Gene Goar. A chemical engineer of great repute, Goar had come up through Pan American and Amoco to become a design engineer with Stearns-Rogers. A lot of the work he did with Stearns-Rogers took him to Canada, building the

When taking a new technology into a new market, prepare the ground carefully.

1960s generation of mostly Albertan sour gas plants. While there, he had met Fina's famous scientist Dr. Alec Petrunic and Petrunic's talented apprentice, engineer Joe Lukacs.

In fact, Gene Goar knew many others in Western Research's employ. At Stearns-Rogers-designed plants, he would often run into the Western Research's testing and optimizing crews: folks like Ron Dimmer, Don Stevens, Harold Paskall, and Robin Rankine. The work of the designer and the contract plant tester was comple-

mentary; both were both interested in finding out whether the plant was delivering its target efficiency and how high it could go. Over the years, a close association had developed.

By 1977, Gene Goar was operating his own design engineering company out of Tyler, Texas, under the name Goar-Arrington.

That was the name he donated to Western Research's Houston sulphur seminar. Goar-Arrington acted as seminar host and the invitations were mailed out of Gene's office in Tyler.

Ron Dimmer recalls a day when he drove to Tyler to pick up a stack of cheques from those enrolled in the seminar, money badly needed to cover expenses back at Dunphy's Royal Coach Inn in Houston. Gene Goar's accountant took one look at this tall Canadian kid and said, no way. She wasn't handing $60,000 worth of signed cheques over to the likes of him. Eventually Gene Goar arrived and vouched for Ron and the hand-off was completed.

A strategy meeting during the first Western Research sulphur seminar in Houston in 1978: (l. to r.) Joe Lukacs (back to camera), Elmer Berlie, Robin Rankine, Don Thurston, Ron Dimmer (back), Harold Paskall.

The team for the first sulphur recovery seminar consisted of Paskall, Rankine, Beamish, Dimmer, Stevens, Berlie, and Lukacs. Harold Paskall would give the lead presentation on modified-Claus; Robin Rankine would speak to aspects of the sulphur process as well; Michael Beamish would explain the workings of the Air Demand Analyzer in relation to plant feedback control;

and Ron Dimmer would speak on sulphur plant testing techniques. Elmer Berlie would moderate. Ron Dimmer and Don Stevens did much of the work of coordination. To visually stress that they were a team, Joe Lukacs inaugurated the practice of dressing them in matching blazers–bright red.

A feature of the seminar that Harold Paskall insisted upon, now and forever, was that there would be no selling in the conference room: no sales literature or brochures, and absolutely no pitch talk. They were there to educate and even Mike Beamish had to find a way of talking about the ADA and CSEM without seeming to sell them. A further proof that this was not a Western Research sales seminar was that even a Dupont representative was invited. He attended too, although Dupont declined to send representatives to future Western Research sulphur seminars.

Finally, it was showtime. Arriving at Houston, the Western Research team discovered that the advertising campaign had over-delivered. Eighty people were signed up, which was exactly double the highest number Harold Paskall felt capable of handling. A furious meeting ensued. Against solid objections from most of his team, Joe Lukacs argued for somehow accommodating everyone. It was the old Joe/Western Research system of never saying no to a challenge. What he proposed, and finally talked everyone into, was that they deliver two 2 1/2 day seminars during the week to forty participants each.

The first forty participants started Monday morning, and the second forty on Wednesday afternoon. The teaching during the day was only part of the heavy schedule. In the evening, the "Quiet Room" was open for cocktails and conversation, and the Western Research team had to be on hand to entertain. Here, as well, Harold's rule applied: no brochures or other sales material; no selling. By the end of the two compressed seminars, Mike Beamish recalls being so tired he could barely rise from a chair.

But the consensus was that the seminars had succeeded. The sceptics had been met head on and indeed Western Research seemed to know a thing or two beyond the usual understanding of the sulphur recovery business. Buoyed by the success in Houston, they brought the show back to Canada and staged it for the second time in Jasper. This was another success, and, as Joe had predicted and tirelessly promoted, the sessions did their work of "selling" the company without anything apparently being sold. After hearing for several days how the air demand system could enable a sulphur plant to achieve efficiencies in the high 90s, seminar attendees would go home to their high efficiency targets, from the U.S. EPA or Alberta's ERCB, and frequently the next step was to call their newfound Western Research friends to look into buying an Air Demand Analyzer or to have them come and run a few tests on the sulphur plant.

An early sign of how well it could work came from Continental Oil Company in the United States. Continental had purchased an old sulphur plant in New Mexico and now the state authorities were telling them it would need to be upgraded to meet their new emission standards. An engineer from the company had attended the first Houston seminar and informally discussed the New Mexico plant problem with Western Research. His company had estimated the upgrade was going to cost them around $2.5 million, and, off the cuff, Western Research was pretty sure the emission target could be met a lot less expensively.

The Western Research team wasn't back in Calgary long before Continental called. They wanted Western Research to come south and test their plant as soon as possible. Harold Paskall and Peter Dale were there within a week. As Elmer Berlie recalls, the main problem was that the mixture of air and acid gas was being heated in a pre-heater to too high a temperature. It was burning in the pre-heater and on its way to the reaction furnace, which had severely damaged both the pre-heater and the piping. Harold's and Peter's inspection and test results confirmed that the problem could be solved by modifying the current design, rather than replacing the entire plant.

Continental asked Western Research to present these findings to the State Pollution Control Branch. In June, 1979, Elmer Berlie, along with a team of Continental engineers and lawyers, met with representatives of the state at Santa Fe. After the introductions, Elmer did most of the talking. It was a short meeting. The authorities accepted the modification proposal.

Western Research got to work, testing, modifying, and re-testing the plant, so that it met the state emission standards. A final report was issued, and Continental was out of the regulatory woods at a cost of about $275,000. Western Research had saved the company $2 million.

From the first Houston seminar onward, sulphur recovery seminars became an effective marketing tool for Western Research, bolstering the work of the company's strong sales force. The company gave at least one seminar States-side and one in Canada per year. When asked how the ADA was sold, Joe Lukacs gives the one-word answer, "seminars." As Elmer Berlie describes it, "The people who had problems started to come. They became believers that we knew what we were talking about."

Recognize the power of branding.

The seminars were also a means by which Western Research could set itself apart from competitors. The fact was that mammoth Dupont had an analyzer that could do what the ADA did. Joe Lukacs describes the Western Research ADA as "a more elegant solution" than the Dupont analyzer, but, in terms of ability to automate a sulphur plant, the two were similar. But, for Dupont, the plant optimization analyzer was a small corner of its enterprise, a product they sold off the shelf without any engineering analysis thrown in. Western Research with its non-selling approach to seminars was different even within the seminar business where most companies sold hard to anyone they could capture in a room. Also very different from Dupont, the ADA was a huge part of Western Research's total business. When Western sold an ADA, it went with the system to ensure it worked and the customer was happy. Customers were urged to come to Calgary for education. "We lived in our clients' plants," as Joe says.

From then on, at conventions like the Laurence Reid Gas Conditioning Conference, the Instrument Society of America, and the Air Pollution Control Association, Western Research became the "red coats from Canada," a phrase coined by Gene Goar. John Jackson describes the red blazers they wore as "a hunting shade of red," which was pretty embarrassing to wear between the hotel and the convention area. When they gave a seminar one year at the Jasper Park Lodge, they discovered their jackets were the same colour as those worn by the bell boys. They spent the week giving directions to other guests, except for the days when they wore their blue blazers, and the bell captain could relax. These uniforms were not optional, and Elmer Berlie was the sergeant-major in charge of making sure everyone turned up in the right blazer and trousers for the day.

Another Joe Lukacs image innovation was that the plant testing crews should be dressed in white and that crews and sales people should arrive driving sulphur-yellow automobiles. It is generally held that the white coveralls were a good thing, which would eventually result in their being called the "sulphur doctors," but almost no one in the world is a fan of sulphur-yellow as a colour for an automobile. The salesmen who put on the most miles and so went through the greatest number of company cars had various tricks for not buying yellow. They would buy a tan car, for example, saying it was the closest thing the dealer had. Al Niven bought a bluish-green car claiming that it was the colour of liquid sulphur at one stage of processing.

But, all jokes aside, the blazers, the white coveralls, and the yellow cars were all part of branding the company, of giving it an image, an image that people would identify with the quality of their instrumentation, the knowledge backing it up, and the service they were willing to provide. As for the blazers, John Jackson comments that the first time he went to a convention in his red jacket, complete strangers crossed the floor to ask him if Joe was around, or if Elmer were present. In other words, it worked.

When you worked for Joe, the principle was not, "The customer is always right," or "Treat the customer fairly." The principle was: "The customer is your best friend." It sounds far-fetched by the colder standards of today, but Western Research delivered on that wish. They did become their customers' friends and, by dealing in the personal, and by delivering good value, they began to take the sulphur plant closed-loop analyzer business away from Dupont. They began to take it to the world.

❖ *Were the Western Research seminars a sales or a marketing effort?*

❖ *How can customer education impact sales revenue?*

❖ *What did Western Research do to successfully create brand image?*

❖ *How was Western Research's marketing strategy consistent with the company's overall business strategy?*

19

A Family of Products

Use your field production people to do your product development. That's the most cost-effective way.
—Joe Lukacs

Selling the Air Demand Analyzer proved to be one thing; making it work, another. Or rather, given how the mystery unfolds, the first thing Western Research needed to do was keep believing that the instrument was working.

Although the first ADA sales were through Chevron/ Bechtel for new sulphur plants at the Irving Oil refineries in New Brunswick, these were not the first ADAs to go into service. After the New Brunswick sale, Don Stevens struck again, selling an ADA to Hudson Bay Oil and Gas for their Lone Pine Creek plant. Because Lone Pine Creek was an already existing facility and the New Brunswick plants were under construction, the Lone Pine ADA was up and operating sooner.

And it didn't seem to work.

During the field trials of the ADA system at Coleman, a heated box with a filter had removed sulphur vapour from the gas prior to its entering the analyzer. By the time the system was installed at Lone Pine, the heated box had been removed. What would eventually be discovered was that without some form of sulphur vapour removal in the sample conditioning system, the sulphur vapour would get into the analyzer and distort the readings.

The clue to figuring this out involved understanding what the ADA was saying. For one thing, the instrument was telling them that Lone Pine Creek was achieving a sulphur recovery well beyond what anyone thought possible. The ADA was also calling for air to be added or subtracted when the operator's instinct was that the plant was running as it should.

The ADA seemed to be entirely out of whack and, as Mike Beamish puts it, it would have been very easy for the operating company to declare the instrument a piece of crap, throw it out, and replace it with the more proven Dupont equivalent. The truth was that Western Research was very lucky to be dealing with HBOG on its first time out with the ADA. HBOG had also been their client for the first CSEMs (at Edson and Kaybob) and so had some experience of test piloting Western Research instrumentation. The fact that things had turned out positively then gave the company confidence that the same thing might occur again. The particular plant engineer involved, Brian Cuff, was also a lucky pick for Western Research. He was calm and patient, and allowed the Western Research installers and testers to trust their instrument farther than many would have done.

Robin Rankine and Mike Beamish kept vouching for their instrument, and trusting what it was telling them. By that means, the team was able to figure out the sulphur vapour interference problem. The other half of the puzzling Lone Pine readings was that the plant had recently changed out its catalyst. The fresh catalyst was causing the sulphur to adsorb at unusual rates: hence, the barely believable efficiency of the plant.

In the end, after a truly nerve-wracking interval, the Lone Pine ADA was working and, what's more, Western Research could explain how it was working.

Once Western Research had its new instrument in the field in Alberta, several factors encouraged a rapid dissemination to other plants. First of all, the compliance dates for the new and tough Alberta standards had come and gone for most plants. Any of the plants that were failing to meet the regulation through more catalyst beds and tail gas clean-up systems were desperate for a solution. Western Research's near-promise to increase a plant's efficiency through automated control of the modified-Claus plant sounded awfully good to those in need, and good as well to those who wanted to put a little distance between themselves and the standard they were already managing to meet. There was never any harm in over-achieving in the eyes of the government regulators.

Secondly, Canadian gas processors were a communicative and cooperative lot, used for the most part to sharing what they knew with other processors, even across company lines. The Canadian Gas Processors Association, with which Joe Lukacs and Elmer Berlie had been affiliated since day one, was built on this concept of free informational exchange and mutual improvement. In fact, the CGPA's mutual problem-solving approach probably groomed both Elmer and Joe to prefer the openness principle on which the Western Research seminars were built.

People in the business who came from American roots, or had American experience, often noted that engineers and operators down south were not as generous with their knowledge. Some of their companies wouldn't stand for giving away information and commercial advantage.

What this meant in terms of selling the ADA in Alberta was that word circulated almost instantly after the system was well launched at HBOG Lone Pine. The other Canadian engineers and operators knew about it quickly and a lot of them wanted the same advantage for their sulphur plants.

Also important was the fact that Western Research had by now built a considerable credibility and loyalty among Canadian gas processors. There were very few processors in Alberta who were not signed up with the company for either air monitoring or stack testing or plant testing or CSEM main-tenance. Often they were signed up for all four. If Western Research said they had a product that boosted efficiency another several percent, then probably they did.

The process of building credibility was at a younger stage in the United States but was moving in the right direction.

After the ADA was in the field, Western Research added other instruments to the company's product line. The truth about these other instruments was that they were basically offshoots of the ADA. The ultraviolet photometer, or UV analyzer, that Robin Rankine invented because he knew he could come up with a more elegant device than those Western Research was currently using, was at the heart of pretty well every product the company made. Mike Beamish, head of instrument manufacturing, underscores this fact. "The UV analyzer carried the instrumentation group for years," he says. The family relationship between the instruments based on Robin's UV analyzer was formalized by calling them the 700 Series. The ADA itself was called the 700.

The way product development worked at Western Research was as follows. Sales leaders like Don Stevens and Ron Dimmer might come back from a client or a conference having heard engineers say: wouldn't it be great if we had a device that could do this? The concept would get kicked around in the management meetings. Could Western Research come up with a device that would answer the need? Was it a natural outgrowth of their technology? Was the need widespread enough, and likely to last long enough, that the company could justify starting down the long road to a new product? Did the industry want it in a philosophical way or would they really pay the price? And so on.

A technological edge in a growing market is a winning scenario.

If it made it past the management meetings, the product would then go into development, which was Robin Rankine's area. The process by which Robin found his solutions is the subject of much legend at Western Research. He would often disappear for a length of time, or else would work nights instead of days. One of his techniques was to go home to the one-hole golf course he had built on his property and to play the hole over and over again while he thought. He also had a cabin to which he could retreat. Then suddenly he would be back, with an idea that he wanted to test. Ron Dimmer recalls that it wouldn't matter one whit if it happened to be the weekend when he arrived. He wanted the tests done, and Ron or someone would work with him to get them done. After 1979, Barry Glenn worked with Robin as the technician supporting his product development plans.

Robin's work would proceed from idea to method. Methods would be tested, discarded, replaced, and tested again, until he had what he believed was the right approach. Then would come the building of a prototype, which would undergo more tests and then field trials. As many at Western Research point out, these research and development endeavours were never closed to the larger group of Western Research employees. Robin got along particularly well with the technicians and many would be drawn into the process. By the time a product made the grade, everybody felt they had a stake in it. The technicians were huge in this aspect of things, and it may be one of the reasons that so many company technicians went to university in the midst of their Western Research experience to pick up engineering degrees.

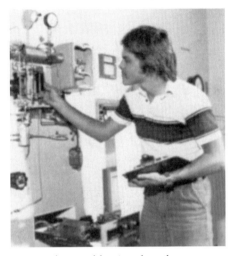

Once the product development was on a promising road, Mike Beamish would become involved and eventually there would be a hand-off to his manufacturing group, who would proceed to do all the things they had to do to bring out a fully dependable, standardized, consumer-ready product.

Barry Glenn, calibrating the sales gas analyzer prototype

The one-man assembly team in 1976 consisted of newly arrived Calgarian Barry Glenn. He spent a lot of time *tin bashing*: cutting holes, insulating, and so on. Then there was the electrical squad, who from Barry's perspective worked in a nice, clean electronics lab: Gord Tallin, Dennis Hniden, Frank Imbrogno, Don Fisher, and Don McCharles. Charles Imer was the machinist. Kevin Anderson joined the group around 1977.

Another addition to the instrumentation group at this time (December, 1976) was Andrew Kusmirek, who was hired on as a draftsman. Andrew was in fact a master's degree holder in precision mechanics from Poland but had been finding it difficult to get work as an engineer in Canada, partly because he was

Don Fisher

still learning English. In order to be hired as a draftsman, he concealed the fact that he was an engineer.

The actual skill of drafting was not a problem because it was highly emphasized in the tough Polish university engineering program. Andrew remembers that among his first assignments was the drawing of an incinerator for Dr. Bob Ritter. When he said he would do it as a three-dimensional cross-section, Dr. Ritter was somewhat flabbergasted, but pleased.

In his three years as Western Research's top draftsman, Andrew Kusmirek enlarged the company's portfolio of technical drawings from forty to around 8,000. In the process, he became a human catalogue, the resident expert on every part and piece of every product in the Western Research inventory.

Gradually, Andrew Kusmirek revealed his engineering prowess and was given applied engineering responsibilities in addition to the supervision of a pair of draftsmen. One of his tasks was

Andrew Kusmirek

the design of more professional-looking shelters, free-standing enclosures, and cabinets for the instruments. He designed air-conditioning and heating systems for them as well that served to eliminate temperature-related errors. Later, Kusmirek would redesign the sample conditioning unit, producing a more effective (instantaneous) drier in advance of the CSEM.

Another way that Andrew Kusmirek contributed to his division's profitability was by designing new parts for manufacture in Calgary that would relieve Western Research of costly reliance on American or other outside suppliers. One was a pump or ejector that drew the gas into the sampler. They were paying US$750 for this part until Andrew figured out how to manufacture one for $120 Canadian. By redesigning the sample conditioning unit's stainless steel filters, he again set up a situation whereby Western Research was able to manufacture at a fraction of the cost that they had formerly paid their American supplier.

Each 700 Series instrument came about as the answer to a demonstrated industry need. The key to the product business is understanding what drives your market, and Western Research was long on that kind of understanding in the sulphur business and, to a fair extent, in the power generation business as well.

The original product, the CSEM, went into the product line under the number 710. It was a complicated device able to continuously measure and analyze SO_2 concentration, while also measuring total effluent, velocity, and temperature. With that information, it computed the mass emissions.

Barry Glenn recalls that, when he arrived at Western Research on the first of June, 1976, the next product, the first SO_2 analyzer, was already on the manufacturing floor. It was called the 720. The niche it would fill was stack monitoring where only SO_2 was a concern, and where a quantity measurement was wanted as opposed to quantity and velocity (from which you could compute mass). In a sense, it was a simpler or stripped-down version of the CSEM.

Doug Heinen

One of Western Research's claims to fame was its hot sampling methods, but in the late 1970s, especially as they entered the U.S. market, it became obvious that some people didn't want the "hot and wet" method, but preferred dry sampling (i.e., water removed). For one thing, dry sampling was cheaper, and it was also the standard for source testing under U.S. regulations. For the U.S. market, and for the bargain hunter, the product development and manufacturing groups came up with the 721 analyzer, which was a dry sample-based instrument.

There was also a call for instruments that would measure only hydrogen sulphide. The first of these was a high-concentration H_2S analyzer, the Model 730. Later came a low-concentration H_2S analyzer called the 733.

The idea for the low-concentration H_2S analyzer came from Canadian Western Natural Gas, and interest in the product was confirmed in discussions with Alberta Gas Trunk Line (which became the pipeline giant NOVA). The problem these customers were seeking to solve was how to detect a slip of H_2S from the amine plant into the sales gas pipeline. What was needed wasn't so much detection as speed of detection. Unless they could detect the off-spec gas within seconds, quick enough to suck the tainted gas back into the plant, there was no way of preventing a serious disruption of gas delivery to the pipeline.

The Western Research team went to work on it. As Ron Dimmer recalls it, Barry Glenn and Don Stevens worked on the plumbing and electronics while Dimmer himself and Robin Rankine studied lamps and columns. It was by no means a straightforward extension of the high-concentration H_2S analyzer. While the detection block was the same, and the lamp, they had to deal with trace quantities of other sulphur compounds, like mercaptans, that were absorbing in the same part of the spectrum as the H_2S. These "interferences" seemed to make the task of low-concentration H_2S detection inaccurate and perhaps impossible.

Then Robin Rankine struck on one of his brilliant schemes. He decided to add a gas chromatograph to the UV analysis. The idea depended entirely on the chromatograph column and the affinity the different species had for the material of the column. Differing affinities would cause them to delay for different lengths of time and that, along with Robin's knowledge of what was in the gas stream and how the different species tended to behave, was the clue to detecting the species as they filed out of the column. Another critical invention was a column-switching system in which one column would be loading while the other column was flushing out.

Much of this was worked out by Robin Rankine and Barry Glenn. Under Robin's guidance, Barry did all the field testing at a NOVA metering station, plus the mechanical design. A further challenge in all of this, as Barry recalls, was the fact that the instrument had to be built to work in hazardous environments, which meant, among other things, designing explosion-proof cabinets.

That is how the Sales Gas Analyzer got to market. It became the industry standard for pipeline monitoring of hydrogen sulphide.

The growth of the product line and the instrumentation group flowed naturally from the success Don Stevens, Michael Beamish, and Joe Lukacs were enjoying in finding buyers for the products. Selling, in fact, took place all through the organization. The stack and plant testers under Ron Dimmer were also, in a sense, advocates and hands-on demonstrators of Western Research products. Once started in 1978, the seminars were filled to capacity every time they were given, and this, as Joe Lukacs says, was the greatest source of sales the company had. Softened up by the non-selling seminars, the clients would tend to come back to them for products.

This, then, was the golden age of Western Research, the product company.

❖ *What benefits are achieved by closely linking sales, service, and R & D?*

❖ *How did Western Research achieve this linkage?*

❖ *Would it work today?*

❖ *What are the challenges of linking sales, service, and R & D?*

20

Stack and Plant Testing

A strong company culture inspires employees to grow professionally and personally.

In Lab and Field (the department in charge of stack and plant testing), operations ticked along through the late 1970s much as they had done earlier in the decade, but with certain basic improvements in technology.

John Jackson

In 1976, the Alberta government brought in a new stack sampling code, which included a variation of the EPA's "Method Five." Method Five was for measuring particulates in power plants, cement plants and in the pulp and paper industry. It was an iso-kinetic sampling system, meaning roughly that the sample was drawn through the orifice at the same rate as the gas was coming up the stack. The probe itself had evolved quite considerably. Now the pitot tube, sampling nozzle, and temperature meter were all on one head.

When Elmer Berlie and Ron Dimmer interviewed Mount Royal College technical graduate John Jackson in 1977, he noticed that they were paying special attention to his Method

Five training. When he arrived on the job, he found out their intent was to have him build a Method Five sampling train, and that's how his first month with the company was spent.

The CSEM maintenance techs were still flying to the northern plants in the late 1970s. So, at times, were the stack testers. John Jackson got in on almost too many memorable voyages this way. Dick Cooper was making the transition from his Cessna 195 to his vintage Aztec when Jackson came aboard, and then Dick hired Paul Fuller to fly his second plane. In these days, equipment was piled in any old way, even in the nose cone. It was all fine as long as Dick or Paul could figure out the weight and balance. No one cared if anything got spilled on a seat.

But after Dick Cooper left and Paul Fuller eventually convinced BVI to go for the ultra-fancy new Cheyenne, stack testers were hardly welcome aboard. John Jackson had to make a sock for his old pitot tube because Paul didn't want it dirtying up the aisle of the Cheyenne and, another time, when they were heading into a grass strip at Poplar River, Paul complained bitterly about the potential damage to the plane.

The fact that the plane was now too good for its work was one of the factors that brought the flying technician era to an end. Simple cost was the other. The cost of the plane had risen greatly over the years, even with the older planes that Dick Cooper owned. When Chemex started getting serious about competing with Western Research for the stack testing contracts up north, those costs became critical. The fact was that, driving a truck up north instead of flying, you could tie a lot more plants together into one run, and there was no more worrying about how to get from the local airport to the plant, or how to start the plane after it had soaked in the cold at thirty below all day. With great sadness for many, the flying technician era came slowly to an end. Or rather it was coming slowly to an end when the National Energy Policy (NEP) hit the industry in 1982. Then it slammed the rest of the way shut in a hurry.

What didn't change of course was stack climbing: the hard work of it, the unpleasantness on a rotten day, the sheer distance from the ground. In 1978, John Jackson's cousin Ross

Jackson, a chemical engineering technology graduate from Centennial College in Toronto, came west to join Western Research. John had the honour of taking his cousin to the Chevron Kaybob plant for his first experience of stack climbing. The engineer at Kaybob at the time was future Western Research stalwart John Sames, and he wanted a stack test pronto before he put his plant into turn-around (annual maintenance).

Things did not go well from the start. First off, John and Ross found out they couldn't fly to Fox Creek. The ceiling was low, and the pilot didn't want to risk it. They had to drive the next day.

When they got to the Kaybob plant, the stack platform was in the clouds. Ross had just arrived and had no equipment beyond a hard hat and boots. John had a rain suit and a parka so he gave Ross his choice. He could have the rain coat or he could have the rain pants. It was basically a choice of which end of yourself you preferred to get soaked.

The stack at Kaybob was 465 feet with a platform at 305 feet. This made

Ross Jackson

it the highest stack for climbing purposes in the circuit. When at great length they finished the tests and got back to the truck, both soaked to the skin, John felt it had been the worst day of stack testing he had ever put in. He said to his cousin Ross, "You know, I've been at this awhile and I have various reasons to continue. But if I were you, I think I'd jump right on the bus and go back east." Ross didn't take the advice and remained a Western Research employee into the 1990s.

Another interesting stack testing debut belonged to Al Niven. Al's wife Debbie Niven was already a Western Research office employee and, when he started to get sick and tired of his job as a respiratory technologist, he came to Western Research and was offered a look-in as a stack tester. He did a couple of stacks, and there was only one problem: he was deathly afraid of heights. So he went to see Ron Dimmer and said something to the effect that, if this was the nature of the job, he'd better quit. But Ron Dimmer wasn't about to lose him that easily. He suggested that Al try a few of the smaller stacks and ease himself into it. Then Ron thought to put a real carrot in front of Niven. He said, if you can get yourself to the point of climbing to the 305-foot level of the Kaybob stack, there's a raise in it for you.

The raise idea appealed to Al, and about one month later he came to John Jackson and said, "I hear you're going to test at Kaybob soon. How about taking me with you?"

When they arrived at the base of the Kaybob stack, Al was looking more than nervous. The plan was that John would go

up first and Al would winch the equipment up to him. Then Al would climb up and join him. It wasn't just an exercise in bravery; Jackson needed Niven's help to do the test.

Andrew Kusmirek (left), Al Niven (centre), and John Kuldanek

After 45 minutes, Al Niven made it to the 150-foot platform. He stopped there for some time. He walked around and around, and appeared to be talking to himself. Finally he started up the next ladder. Another long period of time passed until Niven seemed to freeze just twenty feet below the 305-foot platform. He was hugging the ladder hard and had his face buried in one arm. John leaned down and called to him.

Al Niven looked up very slowly and perhaps only then realized how close he was to the goal. He made it the rest of the way and was surprisingly helpful in completing the stack test.

Develop relationships with your customers.

Now they had to go down. Again John Jackson went first. Al Niven's job was to hook the equipment on so it could be winched back down to John at the bottom. Then he had to come down himself. Jackson's gambit for getting him to do so was to threaten to leave in an hour, whether Niven was down or not. The descent took another full 45 minutes, but Al Niven had his raise.

His future at Western Research was in another area, however. Al Niven went into instrument sales and did very well at it.

After a reorganization in 1975, compliance stack testing was in the management area run by Elmer Berlie. The stack emission test results that the government regarded as official in terms of a plant's licence to operate came from the manual stack testing crew managed by Elmer and run by Ron Dimmer. Continuous Stack Emission Monitor calibration, maintenance, and results were in a different management area. They were the responsibility of Instrumentation, Michael Beamish's management area.

What this meant was that you had two sets of results measuring the same thing in a different way, and that they were supposed to match. When they didn't match, there tended to be spirited rivalry, and occasional downright acrimony, over whose figures were right and whose were wrong.

Ron Dimmer and Don Stevens pioneered a few methods for getting the two sets of readings to match. For example, they ran extra tests and calibrations on the CSEM shortly before the official annual compliance test was done on that stack. Thus, peace was restored.

Compliance stack testing, plant performance testing and plant acceptance testing were basically allied arts. To a large degree, they drew on the same pool of able-bodied technicians. Mainly, it was the group that operated under the Lab and Field title. Each one would tend to have a specialty. John Jackson's was Method Five stack sampling. Peter Dale and Doug Deleff tended toward plant testing and GC work. But really, when the call went out, everybody pitched in at whatever tasks were handed out.

Electrostatic pre-cipitator testing at power generation plants officially fell under Consulting (Don Colley's group) but Lab and Field people often made up the crew. The group could have just as easily been named: "Those who get the call when the job is to drive or fly a long distance, and live in motels, and babysit some kind of plant, undergoing some kind of test."

In about 1977, the group consisted of John Jackson, Doug Deleff, Garry Gawryletz, Al Niven, Ron Dimmer, Peter Dale, John Carr, Ken Shaw, Randy Hauer, Ron York, Al Mayhew, and Mike Chmilar. Bill Wong, a chemical technologist from SAIT, joined the group in June of 1980. Many others probably could be named, in that membership was determined often by how many were needed and who happened to be around when the crew left.

John Jackson in his first year of stack climbing: 1977

Peter Dale joined up in October of 1974. A technologist from SAIT, he had already worked four years at the University of Calgary, running chemical instrumentation for profs and grad students. He remembers that he was hired to work

Bill Wong: Lab (left) and Field (right) with Hans Gjerdrum in the lab, under the management of Paul Vetro at that time. It was lab work, and he was assured that he wouldn't be doing much field work. On day two, he was called out to the field. A couple of weeks later, he was sent to Grand Cache for a big ESP study on a coal-fired power generation plant. He didn't get back for another two weeks.

Peter Dale was with Lab and Field until 1981, and the conditions of his employment stayed about the same throughout. Sometimes he was doing stack compliance tests. Sometimes he was doing plant tests for Harold Paskall. Sometimes it was ESP testing for Don Colley. Once in a while he was even in the lab. People always claim to remember where they were on the day that Elvis died (August 16, 1977). Peter Dale was doing acceptance testing of the Fort Nelson sulphur plant's brand new sulfreen tail-gas clean-up unit.

It went on that way year after year. In 1980, Randy Hauer stopped marketing for Lab and Field to take on a similar sales role with Instrumentation. Doug Deleff and John Jackson were chosen to divide Randy's work while continuing to do testing. They were told to spend a quarter of their time on sampling and technical work, and three-quarters on sales (booking stack and plant performance tests). In fact, the percentages were exactly reversed.

People who were part of the Lab and Field crew will often speak of what a close-knit bunch it was. They were a little wild, they worked hard, they liked to party. It had a great deal to do with just how much time they spent together. They drove long distances. When they were on the road, or testing a plant, they ate dinner together every night and stayed at the same motels. They drank beer together at night, often with the crew from the plant. They shared funny memories that would take too much time to explain to anyone else.

You would think that, with all that sharing of life, they would try to escape on days off, but it wasn't so. On weekends they often partied together, skied together, played sports together, visited one another at home.

An aspect of the plant testing business that John Jackson recalls is the part played in it by *Harold Paskall's Brain*. In this era when PCs were not yet common nor all that portable, Harold was essentially acting as the Western Research computer memory. He had the uncanny ability to remember the data from past tests, and when they were doing a fresh round of testing and trying to figure out what today's plant was up to, it was Harold who could look back through the files (in his head) and find similarities. This mental cross-referencing was an important part of making sense of each sea of data.

As computing advanced, Joe Lukacs initiated the project that would become PERFORM, and later Sulsim®: sulphur plant performance software. Dr. Bob Ritter and his daughter Judy Ritter (a computer whiz who did most of the programming) basically programmed the contents of Harold Paskall's book *The Capability of the Modified-Claus Process* (including Robin Rankine's ground-breaking algorithms) into the computer to come up with Sulsim®. When it was finished, the data results could be entered and become memory, finding the overlaps and parallels much as Harold's brain had been doing all along.

There were times, however, that Harold's ideas weren't absolutely the most practical. At one point, he was very concerned about a problem with the testing equipment. Test equipment was often calibrated in the controlled temperature conditions of the lab. Once out in the field, the copper orifice would expand or contract, depending on ambient temperature, creating an error. Harold's idea was to put an ice box on the unit and connect it to the orifice. Then, whether you were inside or outside, whether it was cold outside or warm, the orifice would be, within a degree or so, always the same.

But you had to fill the ice box.

John Jackson had noted that people would fill the ice box when under supervision at the lab. Out in the field, they would never bother. Far from solving the temperature problem with the orifice, the ice box system was exaggerating the temperature (expansion/contraction) error.

John took matters into his own hands. He would cut off the ice boxes and that was that. Somebody present asked, what if Harold catches you doing it? And John laughingly replied, what are the chances of that? In the middle of John's sawing off the first box, Harold walked in. "Severe chastisement" followed. But then, Harold listened to why John was doing it and agreed it should be done. They sawed off the remainder together.

The other major change in plant testing during this period was the amount of it done in the United States after the first Houston seminar. As the main marketer of this service, Ron Dimmer found himself in the United States more and more of the time. As this relates to the total topic of expanding into the U.S. market, it will be dealt with at greater length in Part IV: "Going International."

❖ *What advantages are gained when a company that is attempting to expand into new markets already has dominance in one market niche?*

❖ *What are the ways to capitalize on market dominance?*

21

Air Quality Monitoring and Meteorology

> We maintained our company intact during the down times. When the boom came, we were flying. —Joe Lukacs

Air Quality Monitoring (AQM) was perhaps the steadiest of all the departments. Paul Vetro claims that it lost money in only one year, 1975. There wasn't too much shame in that. Everything lost money that year. And if AQM was the steadiest, then Douglas Leahey's meteorology group was the most quietly successful. He and his troops were authoritative to an intimidating degree, and practically every major project they undertook resulted in publications. The two groups, AQM and Meteorology, are handled together in this chapter, due to the number of projects the company took on in this period that involved both of them.

Dan Violini, who worked for air monitoring from 1972 until 1980, describes working in this era as a proud experience. They were by far the best in their business. All the competition put together had fewer air monitoring trailers in the field than Western Research did. Generally the work and the income rose each year and the air monitoring group grew accordingly.

When Joe Brigan left Western Research on a leave of absence in 1976, Dan Violini took over his job as coordinator of air monitoring instrumentation. Though Violini started with the company in 1970, he was just returning from a six-month stint as a Syncrude employee. Ironically, one of his first

Find and encourage the synergies between departments and disciplines within your company.

assignments was to return to Fort McMurray and to Syncrude to install five air quality stations. These were remote location trailers and two of the five ran off diesel generators. The farthest one from the plant was twenty miles away. With no phone lines to tap into, all five transmitted their data by radio telemetry to the plant. It was state-of-the-art equipment, Dan recalls, with low-temperature sensors and engine-warning signals also telemetered to the plant control room.

Another major project that was outside of the usual realm of gas plant air monitoring was BC Hydro's proposed expansion of a coal-fired power generation plant at Hat Creek (near Cache Creek, B.C.). This project involved various arms of Western Research. The coal testing, ESP work, was also conducted by the company and will be described more in the next chapter. Air quality came in early on the project to do the background study (collecting air quality data in advance). Douglas Leahey and his team erected 100-metre towers festooned with telemetered equipment to collect meteorological information, all part of determining where the emissions and fly ash would go and stop if the project were to continue.

Dan Volini had a special relationship to this project because he had written a thirty-page preamble to the proposal document, describing Western Research's strengths. He wrote it, and re-wrote it, to Joe Lukacs's specifications until: *a*) it was a work of art, and *b*) he couldn't stand to look at it anymore. But the half million dollar contract came their way.

Another important contribution that Dan Violini made to Western Research at this time was the hiring of the first female field technician. The company had hired women as engineers before (Gillian Clark and Linda Biswanger, for example) and these women certainly went to the field. As well, other women in the company's history had performed as technicians, though mainly in the lab.

But Jackie Hudson, hired by Dan Violini in 1978, was a full-fledged, air quality monitoring field technician, and she was the first woman hired in that capacity.

Jackie Hudson had an Environmental Technology Diploma from Mount Royal College and had worked for Alberta

Environment as an ambient air technologist three years after graduation. When Dan went to Joe Lukacs and said he wanted to hire her, Joe wasn't too certain. He could imagine problems developing out at the plants. Dan urged him, and Joe consented, albeit with the proviso that he would fire Jackie *and* Dan if problems developed.

Dan Violini and Jackie Hudson

Looking back, Jackie says that the Western Research group was quite good about accepting her, and so generally were the people in the gas patch. It did amaze her, though, that men could leave their homes and families, come to work, and proceed to act as though they'd never seen a female before when she showed up to do a job. The fact that a woman's washroom was an unheard of thing in an Alberta sulphur plant in the late 1970s was another obstacle.

Jackie Hudson gives a lot of credit to Dan Violini for his love of training. He would teach you not only what you had to do but always why. He insisted that his technicians know the theory behind the air quality procedures they were carrying out. When Dan left to pursue his love of teaching at SAIT in 1980, Jackie Hudson, who had risen to field supervisor, left too.

Douglas Leahey's meteorology group and the air quality group often worked in tandem, or at least in sequence. One such project was a study of NO_2:NO_x emissions at a turbine-driven gas compressor station at Hussar, east of Calgary. The public had become concerned about compressor stations along major pipelines. Was the NO_x in compressor exhaust causing harm? Again, Air Quality Monitoring went out to test concentrations at ground level. Technical information was gathered on the compressor plant. Stack velocity and emissions were tested. On behalf of the Meteorology department, Mervyn Davies and Martin Hansen studied the wind currents with theodolites and weather balloons, and measured many other aspects of weather. Instrumented helicopter flights on each study day were also used to record the composition and behaviour of the exhaust plume rising from the turbine-driven compressor.

Martin Hansen (left) and Dan Violini at Hussar compressor station.

Put all together, the study provided what Environment Canada and Alberta Environment were looking for: the ratio of nitrogen dioxide to total oxides in several time periods. Dr. Leahey and Mervyn Davies of Western Research, and H. A. Bambrough of Environment Canada, published an article on the study in the British publication, *Atmospheric Environment*.

Also in 1979, Western Research was back to Fort McMurray for the Alberta Oil Sands Environmental Research Project. The government had already been running this project through Alberta Environment and Western Research took it over. Primarily, this was a meteorological data-collecting mission and Douglas Leahey took the lead. Air Quality Monitoring supplied the data. Douglas's group crunched the numbers and came up with the reports.

When the second OPEC crisis of 1979 sent the price of oil and gas spiralling upward to new heights, and the petroleum industry moved into the Arctic with a vengeance, air quality and meteorology teamed up to do work that was as truly on the frontier as you could get on Planet Earth. On Melville Island, they worked for Petro-Canada on an ice fog study, designed to discover the average visibility in the area where aircraft would have to operate and land. Whereas the old problem had been whether or not you were close enough to a phone line to tap in, the Western Research group now had to come up with ways to collect and save data with no people present or nearby for months at a time.

This was largely a pre-satellite era, commercially at least. The types of strategies used had to work in extremes of wind and cold, and had to be able to function for up to months without maintenance. The method chosen for seeing and recording the fog patterns was time-lapse film photography. The cameras were set to shoot a frame every half hour. It is hard to keep lenses from freezing at minus twenty and colder so the cameras had to be seriously insulated but still able to see. After Meteorology set the project up, Brock Greenwell, Frank Cullen, and Jim Westlake were some of the Western Research types involved in the equipment's occasional maintenance.

Deliver value to your clients at all costs.

Paul Vetro remembers a major kafuffle with the client when a mysterious $10,000 invoice for a helicopter charter arrived on Petro-Canada's desk. Douglas Leahey and Paul Vetro went together to placate the man in charge, and hopefully to explain—but they could not. The bill was real enough, and a Western Research employee had run it up. It seemed that on a maintenance trip to the Arctic, the maintenance man had found himself without a plane to fly on to his next destination. So he called in a commercial chopper.

The Petro-Canada Melville Island study wasn't the first time the meteorological group used time-lapse photography to acquire visual weather data. Between January and April of 1977, the technology had also been used at Calgary Power Ltd.'s Sundance Thermal Power Station. The purpose then was to record the frequency, extent, and density of the fog rising off the Sundance cooling ponds. To relate the images to time of day, Mervyn Davies had included a large clock in each time-lapse frame. It was a large attractive clock and someone decided to steal it. Such was the luck of the thieves that the time-lapse camera caught them in the act, and prosecution followed.

An aspect of Air Quality Monitoring that saw a considerable increase in action in this period was the chart reading and reporting sides back at home office. This was the province of John McKee. John had started out with Western Research as a summer student in 1974. When he finished his BSc in Geography at the University of Calgary, he joined the company full time and started working for Douglas Leahey on plume dispersion modelling.

In 1975, he was told that he was needed by Paul Vetro in Air Quality Monitoring, to deal with chart reading and monthly reporting. What he found when he got to his new assignment was that the department was six months behind, and this in an area where the government regulation demanded reports be filed monthly. Getting rid of the backlog amounted to masses of overtime, which the company was generally reluctant to pay. Time off in lieu was the preferred way to go, but what time? Once, John took a week off, and it lasted a day. In any case, the backlog was cleared up in a year.

The problem was that chart reading was a hard job and most people didn't stay at it long. New faces all the time. Clearly this was a place for automation. No computer program existed for what they were doing, so they wrote their own. It was a partial success. This was all pre-PC and the computing involved the filling out of input sheets, which were sent to BVI for entry on their mainframe. Punch cards and all the rest. More OT.

Overall, John McKee remembers this period of 1975 to 1981 as hectic but not stressful. You'd finish one month's charting and reporting at exactly the moment when you had to start on the next month's charting and reporting.

Not all air quality monitoring jobs came with a requirement to do reports. Sometimes, what companies wanted of Western Research were their trailers, and perhaps maintenance of the trailers. They would do the data collection, chart reading, and reporting themselves. HBOG (six trailers) and Syncrude (five trailers) were examples of sales where the clients did their own reporting. Petrogas Balzac, with its seven stations, had always wanted Western Research to do its reporting, as an extra demonstration of the credibility of the

results. Most of the permanent installations were of the first kind: sale and set-up with the customers running the show themselves. Western Research would drop by monthly to do calibration and maintenance.

The air monitoring and meteorology group in 1981: (left to right) Craig Snider, Zoltan Gulyas, Martin Hansen, Gary Vollo, Ann Jamieson, Douglas Leahey, Cheryl Murphy, Frank Cullen, Gerry Walsh, John McKee, Natalie (Kramberger) Vale, Nelson Boychuk, Kevin Warren, and Mike Schroeder

❖ **What part does publication play in branding and building the credibility of your company?**

❖ **How can publication and the scientific reputation of your staff affect the pricing of your company's services?**

The Whitecourt / Edmonton Office

Joe Brigan was a senior technologist who rose to the top of his area (Air Quality Monitoring) and had nowhere further to go. He had started with Western Research way back in 1969 and, when Ron Dinsley left to pursue life as West Coast fisherman in 1974, Joe replaced him as supervisor of Ambient Air Monitoring. By 1976, Joe was feeling an itch to do something different and he left Western Research to start a sporting goods store in Drumheller.

About this time, Paul Vetro was studying up ways to replace the ever-more-expensive flying technician service to the northern sulphur plants. The idea that seemed to make the most sense was to replace the flying, and the driving too, by installing someone permanently at the geographical centre of much of the northern work. Whitecourt was settled upon as the location of the northern office, and now it was just a matter of picking someone to be in charge.

Joe Brigan

Having administered air quality for a long time, Paul Vetro was familiar with Joe Brigan and, because Joe had already demonstrated a desire for a new challenge (by leaving the company), Paul thought he might be interested in Whitecourt. He called Joe up, described the idea, and Joe Brigan bit.

The air quality monitoring side of this appointment was duck soup for Joe Brigan, but Mike Beamish had also agreed to have the CSEM maintenance for the area run out of Whitecourt. Mike trained Joe for this part of the duty, but also lent him the support of CSEM maintenance man Rocky

Oshiro. Once a month, Rocky came up to Whitecourt to do a calibration and maintenance tour.

After a year and a half in Whitecourt (ca. late 1978), the centre of Western Research's northern activities had shifted somewhat and a further decision was made to move the northern office to Edmonton. This was acceptable to Joe Brigan, and the company moved to the east side of Edmonton, sharing office space with a company Western Research was hoping to acquire. When the marriage plan fell through, it became necessary to move again, first to southeast Edmonton and finally into central Edmonton (99 avenue and 99 street). In July, 1980, the CSEM maintenance crew for northern Alberta was brought back to Calgary.

A goodly number of Western R&D employees worked at the northern office over the years. Toni McKee was a long-time employee in the office. Dennis Gerber, Rod Nussbaumer, Glenn Sabo, Kerry Campbell, Kevin Warren, and Craig Snider are a few of the others who had the Edmonton experience.

Rocky Oshiro

22

Environmental Impact Assessments (EIAs)

> *We created our market pull by making new EIA-related services available in Canada through our company. We encouraged industry to use them and the government to regulate them.*
> —Joe Lukacs

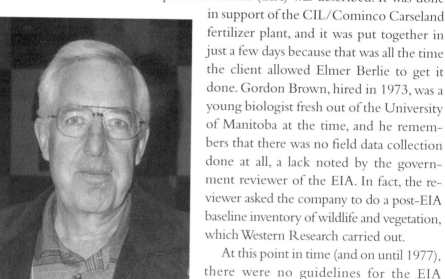

Don Colley

In an earlier chapter about the evolution of the consulting side of the company, the first Western Research Environmental Impact Assessment (EIA) was described. It was done in support of the CIL/Cominco Carseland fertilizer plant, and it was put together in just a few days because that was all the time the client allowed Elmer Berlie to get it done. Gordon Brown, hired in 1973, was a young biologist fresh out of the University of Manitoba at the time, and he remembers that there was no field data collection done at all, a lack noted by the government reviewer of the EIA. In fact, the reviewer asked the company to do a post-EIA baseline inventory of wildlife and vegetation, which Western Research carried out.

At this point in time (and on until 1977), there were no guidelines for the EIA process. When doing an impact study for a project, Western Research had to figure out its own, based on the big EIAs that were already a fact of life in the United States.

In 1975, Don Colley joined Western Research. He was a chemical engineer with bachelor's and master's degrees, plus several years of pollution control experience in the United States. Don had started his first degree in Calgary when the university there was a branch of the University of Alberta. After two years, he had to shift to Edmonton's U of A campus to complete his bachelor's degree. He started his master's in Edmonton but, when his advisor, Dr. Bob Ritter, moved to Calgary to head up the new University of Calgary Chemical Engineering Department, Don followed and completed his master's there.

Don Colley's consulting group in 1981 (left to right): John Sames, Cathy Seright, Sheena Bates, and Gord Brown

At that point, 1968, Don Colley talked to Joe Lukacs about a job at Western Research but then decided to head for the States. He worked for Wheelabrator on dust pollution problems for several years, becoming quite familiar with fabric filters, wet scrubber and electrostatic precipitator technology in the process. Later, he worked in Pittsburgh for DRAVO on such pollution problems as desulphurization of flue gases in power plants.

In 1975, Don Colley returned to Canada and joined Western Research under manager Elmer Berlie. Essentially, he was filling the gap left by Paul Beauchemin in 1974. In Don's words, he was a "one-man consulting engineering group."

Don Colley walked in on the very last stages of the first EIA (CIL/Cominco Carseland) and so, like Gordon Brown and Elmer Berlie, he saw the EIA process in Alberta from its nascent stage to the full scope and complexity it would achieve in not very many years. He also saw how EIA budgets grew. The early ones were budgeted around $50,000, a figure that rose to over a quarter of a million by the next decade. That was for a focussed development like a plant. The EIAs that accompanied entire industrial developments (like the tar sands) were much broader and more expensive still (and usually involved many environmental companies rather than just one).

But, in 1975, there was simply not a lot cooking in the EIA area. EIAs are about new developments, or expansions of older developments, and they happen in times of growth. The mid-70s price slump (between the price spikes of 1973 and 1979) and the federal-provincial feuding over energy, had more or less devastated the western Canadian petroleum industry– and the market for EIAs.

It was this situation, Elmer Berlie's encouragement, and a cold day in December that inspired Gord Brown to head back to the University of Manitoba for his master's. The cold day in December was the twenty-third day of that month in 1974. Gord had spent it 250 feet in the air on the platform of a power plant stack at 25 below. It was black dark when the test was complete and they finally descended. Thoughts of higher education had come to mind during that day.

What the consulting department could and did do in the 1970s, under Elmer's and Don's leadership, was continue the work Paul Beauchemin had pioneered in the power industry. That is, they continued to do ESP testing for the coal-fired power generation plants, and general emissions testing for the entire power industry. They were also looking into testing needs of the pulp and paper industry.

A major power project that involved several company departments was the BC Hydro proposed power plant expansion at Hat Creek. Because of the remote wilderness location and the quality of the lignite feedstock coal, the expansion was an environmental hot potato. In an endeavour to fairly test the environmental impact before the project started, BC Hydro commenced the extensive campaign of air quality testing and meteorological modelling mentioned in the air quality portion of the last chapter. There was also extensive ESP testing done to see if the fly ash from this type of coal could be effectively collected.

Western Research was in on the project at many levels and, in the end, it amounted to proof that not all environmental studies come out favouring industry. The result of the BC Hydro study for Hat Creek was that the project did not proceed.

Then, in the 1977-78 period, several things happened that entirely changed the face of Environmental Impact Assessments in Alberta. First, the Province passed EIA legislation in 1977, specifying when and how EIAs were to be done. Second, Peter Lougheed's determination to see the provincial economy diversify spawned a new generation of ethane-based petrochemical plants.

Third, another provincial government initiative, decentralization of industry, placed those petrochemical plants away from the major cities and traditional industrial sites. Fourth, the Iranian Revolution of 1979 caused another round of massive increases in the global price of petroleum. All four things had the effect of stimulating industrial growth in Alberta, only this time around, EIAs were the standard way to prepare for it.

Alberta's EIA legislation was not particularly hard and fast. It was made to be flexible in order that the particular circumstances surrounding each development could influence the kind of assessment that was done. Some projects automatically required EIAs, but the majority were at the discretion of the minister of the environment.

Looking back, Don Colley says that one of Western Research's greatest strengths in this area was that the company had "a very good understanding of the mood of industry, the public, and government with respect to a particular project." They were able to take the temperature of those who held a stake and tailor their effort to meet the needs.

The second strength was the team they had begun building even before EIAs were a fact of industrial life. Gord Brown came back with his master's degree as well versed in EI Assessment as anyone in the province. He handled the biological side of EIAs. Douglas Leahey and his group (which included aeronautical engineer Abid Umar, master's degree meteor-

ologist Mervyn Davies, and physicist Martin Hansen) would do the meteorological modelling and climatological analysis. The Air Quality Monitoring group would be called upon for data collection, where necessary. Graham Latonas, who Gordon Brown had met during his master's at the University of Manitoba, came aboard as a bio-physical systems specialist. Doug Boyd, with a degree in natural resource management, did the socio-economic impact analysis. Bruce Burns was the original engineer in the group, assisting with the process side of the EIA work. Later, Mike Zelensky took over in this capacity. Cathy Seright was the group's social scientist and public consultation specialist.

John Sames   In 1980, New Zealander John Sames came to Western Research from Chevron Kaybob, where he had been plant engineer (and a Western Research customer). He joined the consulting group under Elmer Berlie and Don Colley and set about building a process analytical engineering group with the help of Harold Paskall.

Whether or not the consulting group should also have a noise pollution component was a debate that had been around for a very long time. Way back in the early 1970s, ham radio specialist Hugh Hicklin had experimented with sound surveying for the consulting group, and a (then) impressive piece of sound measurement equipment was purchased. One of his early sound pollution projects was measuring traffic sound in the Weazlehead wilderness area of southwest Calgary.

In 1976, an opportunity presented itself in the person of New Yorker Les Frank for the consulting group to not only have a presence in noise control but to take a leadership role in that part of the pollution business. Les Frank had a master's in acoustics and had already worked in noise pollution for a national U.S. company. Elmer Berlie liked the way Les would complete the consulting package Western Research had to offer and hired him.

Les Frank warmly remembers the way Elmer took him under wing. If Elmer was going downtown for a meeting, he would often grab Les Frank and take him along. Les marvelled at the way Elmer couldn't go a block in downtown Calgary without shaking hands and visiting with at least one person. It wasn't like that in New York.

In the field, however, Les was given the traditional "sink or swim" treatment. He remembers going out to the ANG Cochrane plant: a 26-year-old urban American with no petroleum industry experience, and on his own. An operator led him around, leaping from pipe to pipe over concrete chasms. At

Les Frank

one point, Les took a suggestion to turn his safety harness belt around so he could be put on the hook of a crane. "There I was flying around like Peter Pan," taking sound measurements.

Noise equipment is expensive, and Les felt he badly needed several state-of-the-art pieces. Elmer's response was that he could get those pieces if they got the projects the equipment was needed for. He was always as good as his word.

*Richard Patching
measuring sound
in Calgary*

Western Research had soon surpassed its nearest competitor in the Alberta sound pollution business. Les with his high
tech approach was doing things that had never been done in
Alberta before. It turned out that so were some of his suppliers.
Early on, Les needed acoustical pipe lagging (a kind of sound
control jacket for pipe), and the supplier was from Ohio. He
gave the company a call and found out that its Calgary office
was just a block away. And they gave great service. The company's top noise control man came up from Ohio to help out
with the contract. Les recommended the Ohio supplier and
the client, ANG Cochrane, went for it.

Ten years later, Les Frank met the Ohio noise control man at a conference. They got talking and only then did Les find out that the pipe lagging job was the first one of its kind the Ohio company had ever done anywhere in the world.

At times, Les felt like the black sheep of Western Research because of how different his work was from the rest. But in fact there were great similarities. Whereas they were in the plants sampling gas streams and off gases, he was in the plants sampling sound. Like the plant optimizers, he tested, he analyzed, he recommended. The big difference was that his recommendations required mechanical changes to the plant. As sound control became more accepted, he found himself working more with the plant designers and spending less time retrofitting existing plants.

Dan Hall joined Western Research in 1977 after finishing a mechanical engineering degree. Because Dan had already worked in plants and didn't like them, but did like acoustics and noise control, he was assigned to Les Frank. If the sound work was slow, he would be nabbed to do stack surveys, which he didn't mind in summer. But sound surveys were definitely preferable in the wintertime.

Because about 20 percent of Les Frank's sound work was for EIAs, Dan Hall got a look at the legal and regulatory side of the petroleum industry. It fascinated him. He liked it so much that he left Western Research to study law in 1979, with the long-term wish of doing legal work associated with EIAs and Energy Resources Conservation Board hearings.

The relationship between several top law firms in Western Canada and Western Research was that the law firms often recommended Western Research to their clients when they were involved in an EIA. The law firms recognized the quality of Western Research's work and, very important in the EIA business, they knew that the government regulators also respected the company. This was an important source of work for the Western Research consulting department.

Les Frank left Western Research in 1979 to start his own sound pollution control company, the first time a Western Research employee had left for the purpose of starting a competing company. Joe Lukacs called him in to talk, and Les was relieved to find that, basically, Joe wished him well. That they should respect each other out in the marketplace was the only caution Joe had for him. As Les recalls, he wasn't in business on his own very long before Joe was calling him to be on various committees.

Les Frank was replaced in noise control by a very experienced man, Dr. Balu Balachandran (now with Stearns-Rogers in New York). Later, Richard Patching joined the fold to work with Dr. Balachandran.

Balu Balachandran

For the consulting group as a whole, the new wave of petrochemical projects that hit Alberta in the late 1970s provided a major lift. Peter Lougheed had wanted Alberta to develop a diversified industrial base by adding more value at home. In petroleum, that primarily meant removing the ethane from the natural gas before it left in the export pipelines, and using that feedstock to create intermediate, ethane-based petrochemicals like ethylene, ethylene glycol, and polyethylene. The process of putting together this petrochemical industry had been going on for about a decade, led by Dow Chemicals, Dome Petroleum, and, more recently, Alberta Gas Trunk

Line (NOVA). Finally, the three were urged to work together to build a broader petrochemical industry for Alberta. Thus, Alberta Gas Ethylene was founded.

To provide feedstock for these petrochemical plants, the gas processors were urged to add turbo-expanders (centrifugal compressors) to their plants. The turbo-expanders super-chilled the gas until it liquified a high percentage of the propane and ethane. Dome was into this field a little ahead of the bunch, having exported an ethane-propane-butane mix to its Sarnia plant through the IPL pipeline in the late 1960s. Later, Dome built an export pipeline to the United States, called Cochin, which also carried ethane. The Cochin Pipeline went into business in 1979. ANG Cochrane, Dome Edmonton, and the Dome Empress straddle plant were gas plant pioneers in this ethane-harvesting wave.

The Alberta Gas Ethylene joint petrochemical project was proposed for a site near Joffre, northeast of Red Deer, and the most thorough and complex Environmental Impact Assessment ever called for in Alberta began. First came site selection. Then there was the baseline flora and fauna survey, climatological modelling, and background air quality surveying. The consulting engineers did extensive study on the designs of the plants to forecast the kind and quantity of emissions and effluents, cooling water needs, and so on.

The emerging science of the EIA was to examine the impact of the proposed project on the natural flora and fauna, and on human health, economy, and community. How many people would it add? How much traffic? How much farmland would be lost? What would be the effect of ethylene on human health and agricultural crops? Would the existence of the plants change the local culture?

In 1971, Environment Minister Bill Yurko had promised that the Alberta public would be invited to be involved in proposed industrial developments. Thus, the assessment of impact involved extensive interviewing in the affected community, and extensive public meetings and hearings at which people asked their questions or made their fears known.

It was a huge process and Western Research was far from the only company employed to carry it out. But the company had a variety of contracts in the total EIA process and was among the best-equipped companies around to take on the work.

In the early years, Elmer Berlie was a primary spokesman at hearings. Later, specialists like Gordon Brown, Michael Schroeder, and Douglas Leahey became Western Research's

star witnesses at public meetings and hearings, and at ERCB hearings. Michael Schroeder, who had a master's degree in plasma physics from the University of Calgary, joined Doug Leahey's group in 1981, eventually specializing in risk assessment related to sour gas releases.

Don Colley remembers how the Alberta policy of decentralization figured into the EIA process during the late 1970s boom. Besides spreading the economic opportunities and benefits, which was the goal of government, it also placed industrial facilities where there had never before been any. These were communities in the old sense of the word, with shared values and pride of community and culture, and a lot of determi-

Mike Schroeder   nation to keep their place from being invaded and changed.

The Joffre area had been a farming and ranching community since the homestead era. Now there were to be ethylene plants. They worried about the lost farmland, about pollutants, and about lost culture. Who could blame them? There were a great many questions to answer, and it fell to Western Research to answer a lot of them.

In doing this work, Don Colley would often make known that he had experience on both sides of this type of procedure. For one thing, he had grown up on a farm near Cereal, Alberta. For another, he had been a town councillor in Cochrane for several years. Knowing this made quite a difference. The various parties present at public meetings and hearings tended to have confidence in his understanding of their position and concerns.

The petrochemical plants themselves did not come into production until the 1980s. Alberta Gas Ethylene (the name given the joint-venture at Joffre) built two plants: Stage I in 1981 and Stage II completed in 1984. Various other existing plants expanded. The parade of plants built or expanding, all of whom needed EIAs to go ahead, included Shell Chemicals Scotford, Union Carbide Prentiss, Novacor at Joffre, and Dow Chemical at Fort Saskatchewan.

Rely on your market pull to lead you.

Elmer Berlie singles out the Union Carbide Prentiss EIA as being one of the most important and successful the company did. He credits Don Colley with having done an excellent job, a fact emphasized by a letter of commendation the company received from the President of Union Carbide after the work was done.

After the Iranian Revolution of 1979, and the consequent leap in petroleum prices, another building and expansion boom hit all sectors of the oil and gas industry. Offshore and Arctic plays that might have otherwise remained pipe dreams despite promising underground structures were proceeded with, many not to fruition, but all requiring EIA work before any exploitation could occur.

Conventional land drilling and development also picked up and this meant new fields and new plants in far flung corners of Alberta, British Columbia, and Saskatchewan. Chieftain Hythe/Brainard was one that Don Colley remembered particularly well. For starters, the choice of plant site was bad, too wet, and they convinced the company to move to higher ground. Then there was the fact that the community was so remote. Many who lived there had come to get away from such things as noise and industry, and here was industry coming out to find them. Don remembers the genuine sensitivity of his clients to the public's concerns. "They were willing to go out of their way to do things," says Don. "There's pride in working for companies that take that approach."

Another interesting late 1970s consulting job was representing PanCanadian in a bid to build a gas plant on the Morley

Indian Reserve. An architect who lived in the nearby community of Ghost Lake was fighting against having the sour
gas plant located there, and one of the devices he was using to
build support was a photograph of Shell Waterton superimposed over the Rocky Mountains. It was a dramatic picture
but not particularly representative of what the Morley stack
would look like in its landscape context. Knowing this man's
picture would be part of an upcoming hearing, Gord Brown
and Jerry Smolarski went out and took fourteen photos of
the plant site and superimposed a drawing on each showing
where the actual stack would be and to what height it would
reach. At the hearing, after the architect had presented his
photo, Western Research put on their slide show and it
dramatically turned the tide of opinion.

On the same job, Western Research was able to get Transport Canada permission for a green plant stack that would
blend into the forest, rather than the usual candy-striped stack.
The purpose of the candy stripes is to alert flyers to the stack's
presence, and this safety feature was duplicated by the strobe
on the stack's top.

In the midst of all these EIAs, the consulting engineering
group also managed to do a little inventing, lest the product
development group get all the glory. The invention of a line
of waste gas incinerators began with an odour problem in the
old Redwater oil field. The client was the Redwater Water
Disposal Company, which asked Western Research's consulting group to look into it in 1978. Elmer Berlie, Denver Smart,
and John Carr tested several of the field's flares. A final report
was presented in 1979.

As Elmer Berlie had long suspected, based on incinerator
studies conducted by Harold Paskall and Robin Rankine, the
flares were not hot enough to burn the H_2S, which was therefore getting into the atmosphere and creating the odour problem.

When asked if they could come up with a solution, the
consulting group put their heads together and invented the
flame-tip incinerator. Mike Zelensky, Elmer Berlie, and Don
Colley worked on the design of the incinerator, and what
made it unique was that it was designed to operate with a

natural draft. This meant it didn't need any pressure in the pipe ahead of it but was designed to create any draft it needed to operate through combustion. The other specifications they had been asked to meet were that the incinerator should require neither power nor a human operator.

In the end, three prototypes were tested for the incinerator contract. One of them came from an Edmonton supplier, and this prototype lasted a week. The second one came from Portland, and it lasted a month. The Western Research model is still running today.

Finally, there were three incinerators in this product family: the flame-tip incinerator, the waste gas incinerator, and the in-stack incinerator. They were effective anywhere the industry had low pressure vents (mere ounces of pressure) and bothersome odours. They would work on tank vents, on stack gases after sulphur recovery, on annulus gases at well sites, and on producing well sites. A particularly good market was on glycol dehydrators.

The original patent on the incinerator is held by Elmer Berlie, Denver Smart, and Mike Zelensky. The more odour sensitive the world became, the more marketable and exportable the waste gas incinerators were. Jerry Smolarski, who started work with Western Research in the consulting area in 1977, became the company's waste gas incinerator sales manager in the 1980s. He followed the product when the incinerator division was sold by BOVAR to Bradon Industries in 1997 and again when it went to Delta Combustion. He is currently the designer of waste gas incinerators for Toronado Tech.

As the 1970s closed and the 1980s began, the flurry of activity created by the second OPEC-inspired oil crisis of the decade was in full swing. Western Research was a hive of activity that could scarcely be comprehended. Some veteran alumni remember it as a time when the different groups within the company acquired a more tribal sense of themselves within the context of the total company. Lab and Field was a tight-knit bunch. So were the air monitoring types. Douglas Leahey liked to keep his meteorology group a bit separate and very much under his exclusive direction. Consulting was carving out its considerable identity through the greater prominence of EIAs. The company had, in a sense, grown too large to continue in the family way it had lived in its first decade. It was still a family but an extended one: the people from different departments were more like cousins than siblings.

With the right vision and strategy, you can create your market pull.

On the product side, the growing success of Western Research instruments was a financial and credibility boon for the company. It was as simple as this: all over the industrialized world, industry was being compelled to raise its efficiencies and reduce its emissions. Among the most seriously regarded emissions were the sulphur compounds that Western Research specialized in. In Canada, in the United States, and in Europe, processors and refiners were being asked to capture almost 100 percent of the sulphur they produced, and Western Research had the instrumentation, and the expertise, that would enable them to do so.

More and more, the company was pushing its products and services into the giant U.S. market. Europe, with its combination of stringent regulations in the north and a need to catch up in the south, was a beckoning siren. The developing countries were becoming aware of the need for environmental controls as well. All in all, Western Research was poised to burst out of its original Alberta and Western Canadian marketplace, and that would be one of the major stories of the company throughout the 1980s decade.

Before leaving the 1970s for the 1980s, one last change in Western Research's life history should be noted. In 1977, the company had ceased to be owned directly by Bow Valley Industries. That year, BVI created a new, wholly owned subsidiary called Bow Valley Resource Services (BVRS), and Western Research was one of the BVI companies that was placed under the new BVRS umbrella.

As B.J. Seaman recalls it, the company had always had a certain difficulty defining itself. Was it an oil exploration and development company, or was it a service company? By split-ting the company in two along the fault line between exploration and resource services (drilling, oil field services, environmental work, and manufacturing), it was hoped that both companies might become better defined and more ap-pealing to investors. BVRS started out as a wholly owned subsidiary, but BVI took their service company public in 1980. Joe Lukacs remembers being in Europe when the initial share offering was made. Don Thurston contacted him to ask if he wanted to exercise his option as a BVI executive to purchase some of the offering at the outset. To his eventual detriment, he did.

But even the share offering only reduced BVI's interest in BVRS from 100 percent to 78 percent, and the "feel" of Seaman brothers ownership remained strong at Western Research. The sense was that nothing much had changed, and so it would remain until the mid-1980s when BVRS began to stumble, the first step toward a dispersal of assets that would affect Western Research greatly. But, as of 1980, all of that lay far ahead, obscured in the mists of the future.

❖ *What synergy did Western Research achieve through building its consulting business?*

❖ *What are the pros and cons of creating a broad-spectrum environmental company versus a specialized consulting business?*

The Breaks

Joe Lukacs describes himself as a person who got a lot of breaks in life. Others might say he made a lot of them himself but he doesn't see it that way. Various people took the time to help him, especially in his younger years, and, when he got a chance, as a company leader, to help other young people, he was more than willing to do so.

Also important to the break-giving nature of Western R & D was division manager Elmer Berlie. Elmer and Joe seem very different on the surface, but many of their values are the same, including a shared belief in helping people get what they need and deserve out of life.

Because education had played such a big part in Joe's life, he didn't like to see people in his company held back from what they wanted by a deficit in education. Technicians and technologists were the bedrock on which Western R & D was built and Joe had no desire to convert them all into engineers and scientists. Many were excellent technicians

Dave Earl

who wanted to remain excellent technicians. Others, like Ron Dimmer and Don Stevens, found their new lease on life in sales. But for the ones who did have the desire for more education, Joe tried to assist in making it happen.

Two early examples were Gillian Clark and Dave Earl, a couple who met and married while working at Western R&D. Gillian started out with the company as a computer technician in 1967. She had already completed one year of engineering at U of C. Joe was determined that both she and Dave would make good engineers, and, never afraid to resort to the theatrical, he threatened to fire them both if they didn't go back to university.

Gillian did finish her engineering degree at the University of Calgary in 1971. Later, Dave Earl enrolled in engineering at Carleton. Gillian went to Ottawa with Dave, and Joe took the opportunity to open an Ottawa office with Gillian in charge.

Al Brotherston was another technician who took leave to become an engineer. Part of the early stack brigade, Al noticed that, while engineers might start out with the company doing stack tests, they were soon nabbed for warmer and drier tasks. Returning to the company with his degree, Al led several interesting projects. He improved on the company's calibration techniques, and he calculated the error factor in S-shaped pitot tubes. Later, he would move to Vancouver and become an engineer for BC Hydro.

Gordon Brown is an exceptional example of the University of Western Research at work in that he parlayed two leaves of absence into an eventual PhD. His goal was to become a more complete Envronmental Impact Assessment scientist

Al Brotherston

and, during the down days of 1975, he returned to the University of Manitoba, which had the only multi-disciplinary environmental master's in the west at that time. He was allowed to do an EIA for a proposed sour gas plant as his thesis, and Western Research's Don Colley, Elmer Berlie and Douglas Leahey were all part of his review committee. Gordon also remembers how enthusiastic Elmer was to see him make this career move.

During the deep and long economic crisis of the early 1980s, Gordon Brown went to UBC and completed a PhD in Resource Ecology. His wife took a master's in nursing at UBC at the same time. Though Western Research did not help pay for these degrees, the company assisted in other ways. Gordon worked for them in the summers, for example.

Barry Glenn was another technician who went for a degree on leave from Western Research. After ten years of building instruments, he enrolled in electrical engineering at the University of Calgary. He too worked the summers during his degree for Western Research and, though he had no absolute guarantee of work afterwards, there was a strong understanding that he would have a job if there was a job to give. He did return after graduation and continued with the company deep into the BOVAR era. In 1995, he left to join Brimstone Engineering.

Lou (Howe) Conron

Lou (Howe) Conron started with Western Research in 1973 as a chart reader. Her baptism by stack survey took place at Amoco Crossfield. She soon moved to the position of accounts payable clerk under accountant Noel Llanos, and began taking SAIT accounting courses with company assistance. Later she would take most of the courses required of a CGA. Lou Conron finally rose to be Western Research's head accountant, the position she held until leaving the company in 1990. "Western Research gave people a chance," she says, "and there was a lot of loyalty to the company because of it."

Other people needed other kinds of breaks besides educational ones, and Joe and Elmer Berlie often managed to deliver or at least point the way. When engineer Ludo Zanzotto escaped Czechoslovakia and wound up in Calgary in 1981, he found a job at Western Research. Very soon after he was hired, the bottom fell out of the oil and gas industry. People were being laid off all over the industry except at Western Research, which rolled back the salaries of its managers instead. Ludo, like Joe, was able to capitalize on that beginning. After managing an asphalt research project for Husky/NOVA, he secured a chair at the University of Calgary's faculty of engineering.

Another kind of example is Les Frank. When Les came to Elmer Berlie looking for a raise, Elmer gave him a smaller one than seemed fair. "It's like you were my dad and I asked you for a car and you gave me bicycle," Les said. Elmer replied, "By giving you a bicycle, your father shows that he cares."

Then Elmer produced an even better pearl of wisdom. He said that often when someone wants a raise, they really want something else. Raise or no raise, they often leave soon after. Les would be remembering this when, not longer afterwards, he realized he wanted to go out on his own, to start his own acoustical company, which he very successfully did.

Others who took a similar path into entrepreneurial ventures were surprised with what equanimity the news was greeted at Western Research. Even if they were headed into competition with Western Research, Joe would as a rule congratulate them and wish them well.

IV

Going
International

*When you have good employees,
you have to keep them challenged.
Push them to the limits
and give them an opportunity to grow.*

23

Environmental Alberta

Alberta was a perfect place for Western Research to grow up.
—Joe Lukacs

O ne of the many interesting facts about Alberta is how it manages to have a bad reputation for environmental practices, while maintaining some of the toughest environmental standards in Canada (and the world). Likewise, the Alberta business community is often depicted as hard-nosed and callous in its environmental attitudes, while at the same time pioneering new ideas such as (currently) the voluntary initiatives approach to improved environmental operation. At every step in the evolution of environmental awareness and improvement of environmental practices, both Alberta and Western Research were present and active, often working together.

The first stage in the development of an environmental strategy for Alberta was government regulation. Part of Western Research's success story is undoubtably how it was able to exploit the local markets created by Alberta government regulations (first, the 1960s emission monitoring standards, and then the tougher pollution standards enforced by the Conservatives after 1971). The concept was that industry's job was to serve shareholders and make money within the law. You didn't do anything about pollution until the government passed regulations, and then you met them as cheaply as possible.

But that was never the total picture, as was proven again and again by the kinds of jobs industry asked Western Research to do. Over and over, the company was hired by the oil and gas industry, or by power companies, to help them understand a pollution problem, or to improve their environmental performance, for reasons other than regulation. Sometimes, Western Research itself was the instigator. For example, when the company learned about fish testing (bio-assays) and recommended it to sulphur plants as a way of testing their water effluent, there was no regulation in place regarding the practice and, hence, no obligation for the companies to say yes. Yet many asked for the service. This was in the 1960s.

The power companies were another set of clients who tended to move ahead of regulation. When Western Research took on the Rossdale yellow plume problem for Edmonton Power (1966), it was helping to solve a public relations problem, not a regulation compliance problem. Alberta had no standards for NO_x emissions at that time, or later when Edmonton Power and Calgary Power (now TransAlta) hired Western Research to study and reduce those emissions. The study of electrostatic precipitators in the early 1970s, and the attempt to limit fly ash in low sulphur Alberta coal, was likewise a voluntary initiative of the Alberta power companies. When Edmonton Power endeavoured to find out if its process water was hurting the fish stocks in the North Saskatchewan, also in the early 1970s, it was the same thing: a response to public concern, not government regulation.

The pioneering of sulphur plant optimization at Shell Waterton in the 1968, and at a great many other plants in the early 1970s, was not required by either Alberta Environment or by the Energy Resources Conservation Board. Shell was independently looking for ways to improve its efficiency, to reduce its emissions, and to resolve its public relations problems in the community. Other plants and companies were accepting that required efficiencies were headed toward 100 percent sulphur recovery, and they wanted to get the jump on it, staging that recovery into their expansions and other alterations, before they were compelled to do so in a less efficient, retrofitting manner.

Here, Western Research was the catalyst. There was no commercially available plant optimization service available anywhere before Western Research created one in the late 1960s. The company essentially invented a way for the companies to improve their sulphur plant efficiency, while at the same time proving to government that the target efficiencies for sulphur plants could be set much higher than engineering design firms had been leading them to believe.

Ken McCready, former president and chief executive officer of TransAlta Utilities, and co-author of the book *Internalizing Environmental Costs to Promote Eco-Efficiency*, is an internationally known expert and advocate of the voluntary, non-regulation approach to the environmental practices of industry. He names several reasons why companies generally prefer to act before government regulation compels them to. A regulation, especially if it comes with a compulsion to use a certain technology to achieve a regulated standard, can be very expensive for a company to which that technology is foreign or misfitted. That expense is passed on to the consumer. It has nowhere else to go. It is far better for government to say, "This is what we want to achieve," and let the companies apply their own resources of science and management toward that end.

Seed your new business in good soil. Look for a marketplace that is receptive and densely populated with potential clients.

Internalizing environmental costs is a theory that simply extends that reasoning to all environmental costs of doing business. If environmental costs are accepted, or internalized, by companies as real costs of doing business, then their skilled managers can get to work applying their optimizing genius to the minimization of those costs. "Just stand back and watch the innovation," says Ken McCready. If we persist in taking less creative approaches, "command and control" approaches, then we will miss out on that innovation.

At the time Ken McCready's book was written, the new environmental frontier was taking environmental costs and transforming them into economic opportunities. As the world becomes more conscious of who's green and who's not, the environmental practices of companies and countries can count for or against them. Voluntarily becoming an environmental leader in your industry will help you trade into the most environmentally conscious marketplaces. Voluntary environmental initiatives can become your marketing edge.

Over the years, Western Research played a lot of roles in this process, usually pioneering ones. The company's dedication to technological advance and improvement often had the effect of raising the bar of performance for companies with or without the involvement of government. When Western Research invented the CSEM analyzer, they made it possible to continuously monitor stack emissions. A few companies voluntarily acquired the analyzer, and then the Government of Alberta regulated the use of–if not the CSEM–then some device capable of the same continuous monitoring. When Western Research pioneered the optimization of sulphur plants, the company was offering a cost-effective way of increasing efficiency and reducing sulphur emissions. The vast majority of sulphur producers were happy to have the service. When it invented and manufactured the Air Demand Analyzer, it made available to sulphur plants a relatively low-cost way of pushing sulphur recovery close to 100 percent.

These services and products were also an important part of convincing government to raise its sulphur recovery expectations. In other words, Western Research instigated and catalyzed developments that dramatically reduced sulphur emissions to Alberta's atmosphere. As the company moved out of Alberta and into the rest of the world, it continued to play a positive role in the efficient harvesting of sulphur. Simply put, Western Research helped many companies and countries to keep millions of tons of sulphur out of the sky.

If you look at the Western Research product line, each analyzer and incinerator represents a way to either better monitor or better control polluting emissions. Once the equipment was there, it tended to be purchased, either in pursuit of a regulated efficiency or emissions target, or to improve on existing standards.

Western Research's leadership wasn't always a matter of inventing and building equipment. As Western Research's meteorological group improved understanding of the way emissions move and are dispersed in the atmosphere, the impact of those emissions could be much better predicted and understood. Science replaced hunch in the determination of what was affecting what. The air monitoring group raised standards in their part of the operation by acquiring the best instrumentation available and becoming expert (and innovative) in its use and combination. Computerization dramatically improved data acquisition and air sampling accuracy and reliability, which in turn allowed improvement in weather and dispersion modelling. Again, Western Research was right there at the head of the parade, employing the new personal computer technology to best effect.

Pioneering the Environmental Impact Assessment approach to industrial development in Alberta was another way that Western Research helped Alberta to higher environmental standards. As the company carrying out as much as 80 percent of the environmental impact work in Alberta in the period 1975-89, Western Research was regularly orchestrating the three-way dance of government, industry, and the affected general public. All the parties had to be satisfied before any industrial development could proceed harmoniously, and Western Research became expert at finding the common ground whereon these parties could agree and coexist.

Which brings us back to Alberta and what a perfect place it was for a company like Western Research to grow up. Asked to compare the province of Alberta to other jurisdictions in Canada and elsewhere, company leaders will often describe Alberta as "more sensible" than other places. Since Alberta first created its regulatory authority for the conservation of natural gas back in the 1930s, the province has become expert in achieving levels of conservation and efficiency that protect the resource and prevent pollution, without at the same time preventing business. Because the province was also very early into official investigation of the effects of air pollution on health, it was moving into the regulation of airborne emissions like SO_2 before most jurisdictions in the world even considered them a threat.

What this meant to Western Research was that, from its first move into the pollution business in 1966, it was encouraged by government. The province of Alberta recognized the company as an ally in the improvement of air quality. It allowed the company to monitor air quality. It regulated continuous stack monitoring in response to the invention of the CSEM. It raised plant efficiency standards in response to Western Research's proving that the plants could do better than 95 percent sulphur recovery. The regulatory authority of the Alberta government often referred those looking for environmental work to Western Research.

When Western Research moved into the United States, the company found that the strict environmental standards back in Alberta helped it again. Especially when working with the American branch or head office of a Canadian client, their Albertan experience conferred on the Western Research employees a certain credibility. If the company could satisfy the Alberta standards, it could certainly handle what most of its foreign customers had to deal with locally.

Credit must also be given to the petroleum and power companies operating in Alberta. Companies like TransAlta, Edmonton Power, Shell, Hudson's Bay Oil and Gas, Dome, Alberta Gas Ethylene, Union Carbide, Canadian Occidental Petroleum, and Chieftain were willing to go the extra mile. In addition to their own research, they welcomed a company like Western Research to come in and improve what they could do environmentally, whether by actual technological intervention (CSEM, ADA, plant optimization, weather modelling and air quality monitoring) or by policy (the many impacts dealt with in the improving EIAs). One theory is that it is easy to regulate a foreign-owned oil and gas company, which most of the operators in Alberta have always been. They are operating by the grace of a foreign country's government and public, and are, therefore, more anxious to please than a local company might be. But the story is bigger and more positive than that. Many of the corporate environmental leaders in Alberta have been domestic companies, and the overall corporate atmosphere has been in the direction of quality environmental work.

As it plunged into the 1980s, and pursued its master plan of going international, there is no doubt that Western Research's Alberta birth certificate was a bonus (particularly in the United States). With a thicker concentration of sour gas plants than anywhere else on earth, Alberta had become a fabulous resource of knowledge about how to deal with H_2S-laden natural gas. Companies operating in Alberta were taking on sour gas that was in excess of 70 percent hydrogen

Look at the regulators in your target market. Check if their values mesh with your own.

sulphide, at high pressure too, a prospect that would have terrified engineers in many parts of the world. Where Western Research's reputation did not precede it, in much of Europe, for example, it needed only to get the word around.

❖ **What advantages does a Canadian company have in going international?**

❖ **What disadvantages does a Canadian company have in going international?**

❖ **What special advantage did Western Research have in going international?**

❖ **How can a company reduce risk in going international?**

24

The United States Market: The Red Coats Are Coming

By 1975, I knew we had to expand our market beyond Alberta to survive. —Joe Lukacs

As illustrated in the previous chapter, Alberta was a great place for Western Research to grow up. But as the company's penetration into that market neared saturation, the advantage became a predicament. In the quote at the top of the page, Joe was not saying he wanted or preferred to get beyond Alberta. He was saying he knew that Western Research had to leave in order to survive.

Calling the 1980s the international segment of Western Research's history is slightly misleading. The first analyzer sales in the United States were made before 1980, and plant testing had commenced there in the 1970s as well. A few Western Research analyzers had also been commissioned in Europe. But, though the ice had technically been broken in those markets, it was barely so. The major breakthroughs were yet to come.

After the first U.S. Sulphur Seminar, in Houston in 1978, a southern appetite for Western Research plant optimization services started to grow. Most of the folk on the testing brigade have stories to tell about testing American plants in the late 1970s. Peter Dale remembers flying to Lubbock, Texas, with Harold Paskall in BVI's airplane (piloted by Paul Fuller) and then continuing on by car to a town with the descriptive name of Levelton on the border between Texas and New Mexico.

With a good product and energy, a small, nimble company can out-compete a giant.

211

That night, Peter, who is not fond of bugs, spent many hours in his motel room dispatching cockroaches and setting duct-tape traps at every possible point of entry. He recalls other Texan testing forays, as well as ones to Wyoming and North Dakota.

Ron Dimmer was put in charge of the Denver office in 1981.

Because of the difficulties occasioned by American customs and immigration law, Western Research began to seriously consider opening a U.S. sales office for American plant service work. The decision was made in late 1980. It was Elmer Berlie's baby, and he chose Denver as the site, with Ron Dimmer in charge, if Ron was willing. Joe Lukacs chose the 1980 Christmas party as the moment to pop the question, and Ron Dimmer liked the idea straight away. Joe wanted him to talk to his wife before they went any farther, so they repaired to an office and Ron phoned home. "How mobile are we?" he asked his wife. "When are we going?" was her reply. The move to Denver was completed in August of 1981.

Western Research's American operation eventually employed eleven people. A few were engineers situated in various parts of the country who acted as agents, while the six-man test crew worked out of Denver with Ron. Only one of the U.S. team, besides Ron Dimmer, was a Canadian, and that was GC driver Doug Deleff, who came down about a year and a half after start-up.

What small companies have that giant companies often lack is flexibility and quickness: the ability to adjust rapidly to outside changes.

Looking back, Ron Dimmer recalls that it was not easy living up to the Western Research "sulphur expert" tag that was being built each year through the U.S. sulphur seminars. As he puts it, "We knew a lot about sulphur plants but we weren't as smart as we thought we were." Understanding the market you're selling into is one of the cardinal rules for success, and, at first, Ron had to do a lot of that learning on the job. The majority of the U.S. sulphur plants he worked on were small facilities hooked onto the back end of refineries. They were struggling to hit a relatively new and high EPA regulation on sulphur emissions.

One of the things Western Research did not know a lot about at the time was refinery operation. Some of the

American sulphur plants were running tail-gas clean-up units that were new to Western Research as well. The acid gas entering the refinery sulphur plants commonly contained ammonia, for which Western Research had no system of analysis. Harold Paskall got to work on the problem, doing a survey of the literature, and came up with a couple of possible methods for Ron Dimmer to try.

A Western Research plant testing trailer at a refinery and sulphur plant in Texas

The first test of this type was for Conoco's refinery in Denver. Bob Kammiller was Conoco's sulphur expert, and he helped Ron get through it. Ron remembers that they were sampling off the reaction furnace late one night when the water-cooled probe froze in the port. There was too much cooling water, and it had caused the sulphur to condense and freeze around the probe. The situation seemed simple enough. They would turn down the water, let the probe heat up enough to melt the sulphur, and then pull the probe out.

Understand the market you are selling into.

When the time came to extract the probe, they were masked up and ready. Ron told the others that he would put the probe on his shoulder and run with it. When the probe was out, one of the others should slam the port door closed. As Ron ran with the probe, gas began to escape behind him.

The blue flame was inches from Dimmer's behind, and for a time it looked to be gaining. When everything was safely sealed, Kammiller said, "Thank goodness we did that at night when the safety guys couldn't see us."

Air quality monitoring was added to the services available through the Denver office not long after the move into the United States. Paul Vetro, who managed air quality monitoring at the time, was against making the move. As he recalls it, the decision was made at the only Air Pollution Control Association convention he ever missed. Ron Dimmer remembers a meeting around a pool at a Four Seasons hotel, at which he was introduced to Jim Burns, a U.S. military vet who would be setting up the American air quality branch and running it out of Ron's Denver office. Paul Vetro's reason for resisting this move was that he foresaw too much competition, and he was more or less proven right. Some of that competition came from big instrument manufacturers who supplied the monitoring along with the machinery.

Don Stevens

Eventually, Jim Burns obtained some good contracts. An Exxon refinery near Houston was one of the biggest clients. Three air quality trailers were built in Denver and moved to that site. Another job was for a carbon black plant in Texas. What made this one memorable to Paul Vetro were the highest hydrogen sulphide readings he had ever seen. The profits were never great for air quality monitoring in the United States, and finally Western Research backed out of it. Jim Burns continued on his own and was successful.

In total, the opening up of the plant services office in Denver worked well, and Ron Dimmer was one of the main reasons. Ron assessed early on that the U.S. refinery business was a network of "good old boys," and he did his best to become part of it. If being from the gas patch and being Canadian counted against him initially, the obstacle wasn't insurmountable. By learning all the local plant processes, by showing capability, by becoming a little bit of a good old boy yourself, you could, in time, win out.

The Western Research move into the American marketplace began with the seminars. Beginning in Houston and branching out from there, the annual U.S. sulphur seminars tended to lead to plant optimization work and to analyzer sales. Either that or they led directly to analyzer sales. Harold Paskall's rule of keeping the seminars pure and educational, and never pitching Western Research products there, worked better than any high-pressure sales scheme could have. Joe Lukacs's law about the seminars was "never make money." Each seminar week was held in the best hotel available, and no effort or expense was spared to ensure that the participants enjoyed themselves. If a seminar threatened to be profitable, Joe's response was: "Buy more wine, or find some other way to spend it on the clients."

Establish a competitive edge in every market niche you enter.

Up until 1980, Don Stevens, as instrument sales manager, handled the United States market as an extension of the Canadian one. That changed in 1980 when fast-talking Lab and Field salesman Randy Hauer was selected to be Western Research's first U.S.-dedicated instrument salesman. Saskatchewan born and Calgary raised, Randy was a SAIT chemical engineering grad who began his career operating at the Amoco Crossfield sulphur plant. He joined Western Research's employ on January 1, 1974. In the next few years, Randy underwent the usual Western Research upbringing (stack surveys, plant testing, air quality monitoring). When he had the knowledge, Western Research decided to employ his personable character and gift of the gab as a salesman. For a year and a half, he sold Lab and Field services, and then came the analyzer sales opportunity in the United States.

When a client bought an analyzer from Western Research, the company came with the product.

By this time, Al Niven had also been added to Don Stevens' instrumentation sales team. After starting out on the stack testing brigade and "almost quitting on the third day," Al went to work for a time on an oil sands project, researching an alternative method of separating oil, sand, and water. Andrew Kusmirek joined Western Research about this time and was also on this project.

In May of 1979, when Al Niven went to work for Don Stevens in sales, he noted that the sales group didn't think much in terms of specializations or territories. Randy Hauer's coming on to do a lot of the U.S. work was mostly a matter that he was a single guy without kids who was happy to take on the lengthy road assignments that the U.S. selling entailed. Al and Don Stevens both had young families by then and liked to stay a little closer to home. John Jackson, selling for Lab and Field, would often team up with Al Niven on road trips up north, and he recalls that Al's determination not to be away from home for long resulted in absolutely demonic driving schedules. Al himself remembers a time when they were steaming up the Alaska Highway late at night, between Fort St. John and Fort Nelson, having left Calgary early that morning. When a herd of elk crossed the highway in front of them, and Jackson said, "Look at the size of them sheep," Al reckoned it was time to relieve him at the wheel.

Randy Hauer and Al Niven (seated), selling the Western Research advantage south of the 49th

Len Edwards was another addition to the sales team. He started with Lab and Field in 1979 and came across to instrumentation sales in the early 1980s. By then, Don Stevens had graduated to more of a marketing role, with Al Niven, Randy Hauer, and Len Edwards handling the actual sales.

There were not many Western Research analyzers at work in the United States when the sales team began seriously targeting this market. The Western Research product that suited the States best at this time was the tail-gas analyzer, the ADA, and the sales situation was very clear in that Dupont had the market entirely sewn up. The ADA had a technological edge over the Dupont product, however, and Randy Hauer and the others began leveraging that product superiority into sale after sale. "It helped," says Randy, "that Dupont didn't improve its product for ten years."

There was also potential for selling an SO_2 analyzer, but the existing Western Research one, the 720, would not do. It worked by wet analysis and the U.S. EPA regulation required a dry analysis. As described in more length in the previous section, this was the call into being for the 721. The approach to selling the 721 in the United States was to assign it to an American company, KVB, that had a complementary product line. Eventually, by this means, the 721 would take over twenty percent of the American market.

Len Edwards

In his travels States-side, Don Stevens met a man named Al Arnone, who was employed by the California Air Resources Board. In 1981, Arnone was seeking other opportunities, and Don hired him to be Western Research's special agent for dry emission analyzers (Model 721) in California. Al Arnone knew everybody in the business in that state, and the arrangement worked very well.

After the analyzers were sold, someone had to go south to commission them, to "turn them on." After having been a CSEM maintenance man out of Edmonton and then a builder of analyzers in Calgary, Glenn Sabo was "pushed out the door," to do a lot of this work. Before returning to Calgary to supervise the manufacturing shop and field service in 1984, Glenn spent two to three weeks out of every month in places like Louisiana, Mississippi, West Texas, and California.

The success in the United States was a good example of how a small company can grow quickly through niche marketing, even against a giant competitor like Dupont. There is some question, even today, why Dupont did not use its might to at least try and knock Western Research out of the market. Perhaps, if Western Research had been affecting Dupont's sales across a larger portion of its product spectrum, the larger company would have taken action. But, as long as Western Research was competing with Dupont only in the sulphur plant analyzer niche, the larger company let it go.

Glenn Sabo

Another theory is that the way Western Research did business made it difficult to unhorse as it galloped into the new market. For Western Research, the product itself had always been just a part of the total package. When a client bought an analyzer from Western Research, the company came with the product. Well-trained technicians came down and helped install it. You were invited up to Calgary for training in the analyzer's operation. If you had a problem, Western Research was johnny-on-the-spot to solve it. "Be your customer's best friend" was Joe's rule of customer service, and everybody in the company lived by it, in the United States just exactly as they had done in Canada. As Al Niven puts it, "relationship selling" is on everybody's lips today, but long before there was any such buzzword, that was how Western Research did business.

Through the 1980s, Western Research used a system of twenty-four-hour-a-day service, weekdays and weekends. Trouble calls were routed to the service groups home phones. Glenn Sabo recalls innumerable middle-of-the-night calls. He suspects someone kept moving his name to the top of the supposedly-rotating list. It was hard at times, but that was the way Western Research did business.

Western Research's performance in the U.S. market seems, at first glance, to have been a rapid accomplishment. In another sense, it had been brewing for fifteen years. From his earliest days in the environmental business, Joe Lukacs had been making contacts in the United States. Joe's American mentors had led him to the Air Pollution Control Association, and, once there, he had made himself and Western Research active parts of the organization. In this sense, the

American market had been softening up for a long time, long before the seminars, the plant optimizers, and the instrument salesmen made their debuts.

❖ *How did Western Research's company culture lead to success in the international marketplace?*

Air Pollution Control Association

The history of human concern over air pollution is ancient. It began in antiquity with someone's being annoyed over smoke from a neighbour's fire. In an article about the history of the Air Pollution Control Association (APCA), New York engineering consultant, William G. Christy cited the earliest instance he could find as A.D. 1257. That year, King Henry III of England moved castles, and his wife Queen Eleanor became bitterly angry at her new neighbours, who were forever producing "unendurable smoke" from "sea cole." The result was legislation, an act of English Parliament, dated 1273, prohibiting the burning of soft (bituminous) coal. By 1307, London had an anti-smoke law, and those who defied it were subject to "fines and ransoms." That was for the first offence. A second offence was punishable by demolition of one's furnace.

In the United States, an early flurry of concern over smoke was generated by Chicago's Columbian Exposition (World's Fair) of 1893. Rules were put in place to reduce smoke from the city so it wouldn't offend world visitors.

By 1906, most American and Canadian cities had smoke inspectors, and the first convention of smoke inspectors took place in Detroit that year. The result was an organization of municipal smoke inspectors, the official forerunner of the APCA.

The association was international from the start, with Canadians playing an active role. By 1912, membership had been broadened from smoke inspectors to anyone with a scientific interest in the reduction of smoke. This had the advantage of allowing inclusion of railroad officials, trains being one of the major contributors of smoke.

As the years went by, the association took on an educational role and became interested in problems beyond coal smoke: things like dust, sulphur dioxide, "atmospheric corrosion," and enlisting the aid of meteorologists to achieve standardized measurement of air pollution. In the 1940s, members began lobbying to have "air pollution" in the name. "Air Pollution Control Association" was the eventual choice.

Important to the relationship Western Research would develop with APCA was a 1960 decision to invite manufacturers to exhibit at the annual meeting. After 1960, the annual meeting became an enormous event, requiring several hotels.

APCA had several regional divisions and, in 1971, Western Research helped to host the Pacific Northwest Division regional meeting in Calgary, an event made memorable in part by Environment Minister Yurko's unveiling of the details of Alberta's new environmental agenda.

But the annual meeting remained the big show, and every year Joe Lukacs led a Western Research team to its centre. In Chicago, in 1973, the booth came complete with a working model of the Continuous Stack Emission Monitor. The head of the newly formed U.S. EPA came by to have a look.

Western Research booth at an Air Pollution Control Association convention.

Joe Lukacs was on the APCA board of directors for many years. He could have been the president except that he wouldn't back a plan to have himself acclaimed. He insisted that he must win in an open election against American candidates, which was not likely. Elmer Berlie also became involved with APCA, presiding over PNWIS in 1980.

Both Joe and Elmer understood the value of professional organizations. It was how you became known, how you built your network across national boundaries, and how you kept up to the minute on changes in your industry. Organizational involvement and publication were the two most economical and effective ways of building the reputation of a small company and its personnel.

In 1991, 43 Western Research employees attended the Air and Waste Management annual meeting in Vancouver.

Paul Beauchemin recalls how Joe instilled in him a genuine interest in APCA. Thirty years later, Paul is still a member of the Air and Waste Management Association (the organization's current name).

❖ *What are the business benefits of involvement in professional associations?*

25

The Road to Europe

If you're going to a place where the language and customs are unfamiliar, it's best to have an experienced guide.

Like the move into the United States, Western Research's entry into the European marketplace began before 1980. The first steps were made with relative ease and gave a false impression that the European fortress might be easily pregnable. In fact, Europe would prove a harder nut to crack than the United States for a variety of reasons.

The most obvious was that the cultural differences between Europe and Canada are greater than those between the United States and Canada. There were no language barriers when selling into the United States. The widespread notion that most Europeans can do business in English would soon be unveiled as a fiction. Maybe Europeans can do business in English in a pinch, but, like most of us, they prefer to do so in their own languages. The terms and syntax of engineering, technology, measurement, regulation, and specification also differed across the Atlantic, and Western Research found itself having to rethink almost everything it did for the European marketplace.

There were also many critical differences of style. Wilhelm Pier, who would become the key to unlocking Europe for Western Research, speaks of having to "put a European face" on the Western Research analyzers before they would appeal to the Continental customer. Wilhelm also notes a difference in the way Europeans take on a new technology or instrument. The

American tendency would be to slap a new analyzer on-line and see what happens, whereas the European inclination would be to take the same analyzer to the lab for extensive testing.

Then there was the colonial factor. If Texans felt suspicious of Albertan sulphur plant expertise, how much greater was that sense of scientific and engineering superiority in Europe? An example of this that concerned Western Research was the testing of the sulfreen process at the Aquitaine Ram River sulphur plant in the 1970s. When the Alberta government put its tough new sulphur recovery regulations in place, the biggest plants (1,000 to 4,000 long tons of sulphur per day) had the toughest standard to meet, and all but one were having major problems doing so. Aquitaine, a subsidiary of the French state oil company SNPA, was the exception. Ram River was a state-of-the-art plant, with a closed-loop process analyzer (chromatograph-based) and a brand new tail-gas clean-up technology called "sulfreen." Sulfeen was a sub-dewpoint system whereby the sulphur in the tail gas was adsorbed onto catalyst, then desorbed and recovered. The French claimed to be hitting 99 percent sulphur recovery but were having trouble convincing Alberta sulphur processors that it was true. What the Alberta group would believe was a Western Research plant test, and Aquitaine had to suffer the indignity of asking for one.

Western Research carried out its standard battery of tests and declared Ram River to be averaging 99.5 percent recovery. Instead of being pleased, the French said it was impossible. There had to be a mistake. They brought over their own expert, who reviewed the Western Research testing procedure, and then supervised a re-doing of the tests. It was no mistake—99.5 percent.

Although this was already vindication of the Western Research reputation, Harold Paskall counted a further coup. After the first test, he told Aquitaine that they had an air measurement error in one of their trains. Again, their reply was that it was impossible. They had calibrated and tested everything in advance. After the second test, Harold pinpointed the problem as being in a line heater. His conclusion was that something was stuck in the meter orifice plate. Again, Aquitaine was sceptical. But, come turn-around, they found a piece of welding rod stuck exactly where Harold said it would be.

Ironically, it was another French certainty that resulted in Western Research's European debut. A consortium of German, Canadian, and American companies, going by the acronym NAPC (North Aegean Petroleum Company), had discovered oil in the North Aegean Sea off the coast of the Greek island of Thasos. The reservoir was called Prinos, and it was sour. Its hydrogen sulphide content was very high (85%). The consultants advising the Greek government were French, and they had declared it impossible to safely produce the sour oil and gas. NAPC was blocked in its effort to bring the Prinos reservoir into production.

The general manager of NAPC in Athens, Lutz Speel of the German company Wintershall AG, was an old friend of Elmer Berlie, and he was fairly certain Elmer would disagree with the French assessment of the Prinos field. He gave him a call. He had Elmer paged on the golf course, and he asked him to come to Athens immediately. In a couple of days, Elmer was on his way, first to Athens and then by helicopter to Thasos. Thus began the four-year Greek odyssey that was Western Research's European debut.

Prinos was a Greek first in many ways and the infrastructure for producing a sour field had to be built almost from scratch. For example, there was no legislation for plant site selection, and Elmer urged the Greeks to adopt Alberta's rules. NAPC's goal was to put its sour gas processing plant on Thasos, an island that was popular with tourists, and Elmer, having run Texas Gulf Okotoks on the fringes of the town of Okotoks, saw no problem with that. To show that it could be done, Elmer invited a Greek government representative to Canada and gave him an aerial tour of the sulphur hot spots of southern Alberta, with particular emphasis on the proximity of plants to towns. Paul Fuller did the flying.

Finally, the Greek government decided that, if Elmer was representing NAPC, they should have an expert of their own. And who should it be but Dr. George Govier, former chairman of Alberta's Energy Resources Conservation Board and Elmer's former boss. The two Albertans agreed easily on some points such as the operating rules for the plant, but wrangled on others. Dr. Govier didn't like the company's selected plant site and insisted it be moved to a site near Kavalla, beside an existing fertilizer plant. He also adjusted the pipeline route so that less of it ran underwater.

Both before and after approval of the Kavalla sulphur plant project, Western Research was involved at almost every level, starting with site selection and environmental impact. One of the big steps was the outfitting and shipping of a sophisticated air quality monitoring shelter. While the air monitoring shelter was being built in Calgary in 1978, an NAPC instrument technician, Udo Tautaurot, was trained at Western Research for three months on the calibration, routine servicing, and maintenance of the equipment. He also received training on the ADA and CSEM instruments that would be delivered later. The air monitoring shelter was shipped in January, 1979, and was supposed to obtain one year of data prior to plant start-up. Paul Vetro, Dan Violini, Al Todd, Frank Cullen, and Joe Brigan were all in some way involved in putting it together, getting it overseas, and keeping it working.

It wasn't an entirely trouble-free venture either. There was something about important documents, ones required to clear the shelter through customs at the port of Piraeus, remaining on the back of a Western Research toilet in Calgary. A more serious blow came when a forklift drove through the side of the shelter where it sat on the dock at Piraeus. Paul Vetro and Frank Cullen got a run-down on what was needed to fix it, and, bearing tools, lumber and siding, they headed over to repair the injured shelter. Another problem surfaced when Frank pulled out his saw on the Piraeus dock. He and Paul were immediately descended upon by angry dock workers and union stewards. The Piraeus harbour was a union shop, and there would be no freelance carpentry allowed.

Eventually all this was remedied. Al Todd joined Paul and Frank in Greece. They put the system together, got it on site, and started it up. Joe Brigan made two trips to Kavalla to service the trailer. He remembers sending a memo to Elmer to the effect that the company should invest in a map of Kavalla given that the only one they currently had was on a placemat that Paul Vetro had seized out of a Greek restaurant.

All charts and data were shipped back to Calgary for interpretation, and a major user of this data was the meteorological group. Douglas Leahey, Mervyn Davies, and Linda Sa'ad did diffusion meteorological studies on Thasos, on the alternative plant site locations and pipeline routes, as well as interpreting the air monitoring data.

Because Elmer Berlie had succeeded in having the Alberta efficiency and emission monitoring standards adopted for the plant and field at Kavalla, Mike Beamish and Don Stevens were able to sell the project two ADAs and one CSEM for the Kavalla sulphur plant: the first Western Research instruments commissioned in Europe. The plant started operating in 1980, an excellent example of consulting, air monitoring, and instrumentation working together for the benefit of the company.

Frank Cullen (bottom) and Paul Vetro with an air quality monitoring trailer en route to Kavalla on the Greek Island of Thasos

An unrelated development put Western Research in touch with Holland. Mike Beamish's instrumentation division did a certain amount of marketing, and one of the ads they were running in 1978 for the sulphur dioxide analyzers brought a response from Dr. Van Rossen of Gasuni, the Dutch national gas company. He was wondering if Western Research also had a hydrogen sulphide analyzer. Mike hurried back a reply that, yes, they did. The result was that Dr. Van Rossen and Jan

Laurens of Gasuni paid a visit to Calgary, and Mike Beamish toured them around the Lone Pine Creek plant, where they would be able to talk to a Dutch engineer named Jan Doktor.

After the orientation, one of the Dutch visitors said, "You've showed us everything but those yellow buildings." When they were told that the "buildings" were in fact blocks of stored sulphur, they could not believe it. That much sulphur was astounding to them. Next, Mike Beamish called up Bow Helicopter and took them on an aerial tour of the Alberta sulphur sites. The final result was the sale of three analyzers.

The project in Holland for which the analyzers were needed was quite unusual. For their supply of natural gas, the Dutch at this time relied on one sweet gas field. Dutch appliances were built to the specification of this gas. Meanwhile, a new field had been discovered, which was slightly sour, and this upset the applecart. There would be a lot of problems using this gas in Holland. Across the border in Germany, however, was a gas-fired power plant at Meppen. A solution was found whereby Gasuni would blend sweet gas from their main field with sour gas from their new field and supply it by pipeline to Meppen. Western Research sold analyzers not only to Gasuni but also to the Germans so that they could test the gas they were receiving from the Dutch. Barry Glenn made his professional European debut when he commissioned these analyzers.

When entering international markets, bridge cultural differences with reliable strategic alliances.

Though these sales were certainly important steps in the European venture, they weren't the main thrust. Joe Lukacs's grander scheme for Europe was to launch sulphur seminars there and to operate through a European agent who had the right combination of good reputation, knowledge of analyzers, and ability to navigate Europe's major languages of commerce. Larry Maley, an American friend, recommended Wilhelm Pier, a German manufacturer of infrared analyzers, with whom he had done business for many years. Larry Maley put Joe in touch with Wilhelm Pier, and the two of them met in the Frankfurt airport to see if there was any possibility of a business relationship.

The meeting in the Frankfurt airport lasted no more than

three-quarters of an hour, but it cemented a business and personal relationship that was solid, successful, and long-lasting. Wilhelm liked Joe and everything Joe was telling him about Western Research, and Joe liked Wilhelm. Beginning that day, Wilhelm Pier became Western Research's main European representative, and it is a great point of pride for Wilhelm that there was never a written contract between them. Their handshake was enough. Wilhelm also admits that, after the meeting, he ran home to look up exactly what a modified-Claus plant was.

The arrangement with Western Research turned out to be exactly what Wilhelm Pier was looking for. For years he had been renowned in Europe as someone to whom you could come with a special analyzer request. He was making designer analyzers, one-ofs, never two the same, and he had built a strong reputation for his ability to meet any need. But there was not a lot of money to be made that way. As an alternative approach, Wilhelm had been looking for one industrial process in which he could specialize in and of which he could become the absolute master. Why not modified-Claus?

Compatible values may be the biggest secret to successful relationships in business.

The meeting between Wilhelm Pier and Joe Lukacs happened in 1978, before the first Houston sulphur seminar. Wilhelm made arrangements to be in Houston himself, but he also wrote letters to six European modified-Claus plant builders, to inform them of the Houston seminar and to encourage them to go. The only one he heard back from was the Dutch design engineering company, COMPRIMO. Jan Lagas, a respected COMPRIMO engineer, wanted to come to Houston.

The meeting between Jan Lagas and the Western Research group at the Houston seminar resulted in another European relationship that was central to Western Research's penetration of Europe. After having attended the 1979 Western Research sulphur seminar, Jan Lagas interested his own company, COMPRIMO, in co-producing such an event in Europe. Elmer Berlie went to Holland on behalf of Western, signed an agreement with COMPRIMO, and co-planned the first European seminar, which happened in Amsterdam in 1981.

It was a successful event drawing 100 participants. The next two European seminars were also Western Research/ COMPRIMO co-productions set in Amsterdam.

John Sames was one of the group who presented the first European sulphur seminar. He had joined Western Research

The first European seminar was held in Amsterdam in 1981. COMPRIMO and Western Research co-hosted the event. Seated left to right: Harold Paskall, Elmer Berlie, Mike Beamish and John Sames.

from Chevron Kaybob in 1980 and assisted at his first sulphur seminar in Jasper that year. His job at Western was to build a process analytical engineering group within Don Colley's consulting division, and, in so doing, he worked closely with Harold Paskall. This in turn brought him into the business of helping Harold put on seminars. Nothing could have pleased John Sames more. Part of the allure that the seminars had for him was that John came from a family of New Zealand teachers. Both his parents were of that profession, and he admits to being a bit of a frustrated teacher himself. The seminars were a natural outlet for his pent-up pedagogy, and John Sames and Harold Paskall became the mainstays of the seminars for many years thereafter. John has presented 127 seminars since that first one in Jasper.

The only person in the world who comes anywhere close to this attendance record would be Wilhelm Pier. Wilhelm, who had decided to specialize in the modified-Claus process, used the seminars both to support his marketing efforts in

Europe and to teach himself the ins and outs of the process that would increasingly become his livelihood. Evidence of just how highly the seminars were regarded was the fact that many companies left off trying to train their own people in the modified-Claus process. It was so much easier and more cost-effective to send them to a Western Research seminar and have them trained there.

After the Amsterdam seminar of 1981, all the tools and people were in place for Western Research's thrust into Europe, and, still, it would take years for any of it to come to fruition. As mentioned at the head of this chapter, the European market was tough to crack and could not be rushed. Given the challenges Western Research was about to deal with, it may even have been a blessing that the European sales held off for a while.

John Sames (right), with Jan Lagas of Comprimo (centre) and Gene Goar. Goar was Western's strategic partner for its first U.S. seminar (Houston, 1978). Lagas played the same role for the first European seminar (Amsterdam, 1981).

❖ **What should be included in the selection criteria for a strategic partner?**

❖ **Evaluate Wilhelm Pier as a strategic partner for Western Research.**

❖ **In what ways did Western Research underestimate the challenge of penetrating the European market?**

26

First Frying Pan, Then Fire

Early on, I learned not to fret too much if things didn't go according to my plans. In the long run, things often turned out better as a result. —Joe Lukacs

---

NEP stands for "National Energy Policy." They were the initials of a disaster that hit the western Canadian oil and gas industry in 1980. That year, the short-lived Conservative government under Joe Clark lost a non-confidence motion in the House of Commons, and Pierre Trudeau's Liberals came roaring back into office, determined to do something about what they felt were unfair profits being made by foreign-owned oil companies in Canada. They also intended to pry a bigger share of oil taxes and royalties away from the province of Alberta. Energy Mines and Resources Minister Marc Lalonde and the bureaucrats of his department put all their best efforts into the NEP, which was revealed as part of the federal budget in the fall of 1980.

The new policy was a document of frightening scope for the oil industry. One of its most hated provisions gave Petro-Canada, the national oil company, the right to "back-in" on 25 percent of any company's federal exploration lands. There were new taxes and a system of exploration grants (PIP) that were available proportional to a company's level of Canadian ownership. Even before the NEP, petroleum companies operating in Canada had been held below the world price for their products. Now, most of them were ruled ineligible for incentives while seeing their tax load increase. This double and triple taxation effectively destroyed the oil and gas boom in western Canada. It made Canada a poor place to do business, and that fact hurt Canadian companies and foreign companies alike.

The particular punishment dished out to foreign-owned oil companies in Canada did have one effect the federal government desired. In several cases, it made their foreign owners anxious to get rid of them. Two of the most prominent take-overs that resulted had personal resonance for Western Research. One was the take-over of Joe Lukacs's old company Canadian Fina by Petro-Canada. Trajan Nitescu was so outraged by what he perceived as Communist-style government intervention that he took out a full page in the *Calgary Herald* to write an open letter in reply.

The other major take-over target was long-time Western Research client Hudson's Bay Oil and Gas. Despite its Canadian chairman, Gerry Maier, and its Canadian president, Dick Haskayne, HBOG was too American for preferential PIP treatment. Dome Petroleum was technically not Canadian enough for PIP grants either but had so much clout with the Liberals and the banks that it was able to open its mouth wide enough to swallow HBOG. It swallowed, it choked, and it died: another example of how disastrous the NEP was, even for the companies it was designed to help.

The NEP's effect on Canadian exploration companies like Bow Valley Industries was to accelerate their speed as they approached a brick wall. Through PIP grants, companies like Petro-Canada, the quickly assembled Dome Canada, and Bow Valley Industries were directed to the new East Coast offshore play and urged to drill there as quickly as possible. It was a game of carrot and stick, mostly carrot, and the companies that went after the carrot most avidly were hit the hardest when, within six months of the introduction of the NEP, the world oil price began to drop.

The plain truth was that the world was in a severe recession, in part because of the extremely high price of energy. The recession had slowed demand for oil to the point where a glut now existed. Combine that with the fact that governments everywhere had resolved to combat inflation by raising interest rates, and you had all the reasons why the glory days

Camaraderie, loyalty, and company culture are built through surmounting adversity, as much as through the mutual enjoyment of the good times.

of the 1970s were well and truly over. You could practically hear a pin drop in the heart of Calgary where the construction frenzy had halted abruptly in the wake of the NEP. The world events that followed meant that the boom conditions were not likely to return any time soon.

Ludo Zanzotto

For Western Research, all of this was dismal news. A company that serviced and sold to the oil and gas industry necessarily faltered with the rest of the industry. It did not help Western Research all that much to be owned by one of the few companies favoured by the new NEP rules. They might be owned by Bow Valley Resource Services, but they worked for the oil and gas patch as a whole.

As in 1975, lay-offs were the general rule in Calgary and all over Alberta, and they were deep cuts too. Literally thousands of people were unemployed who had been looking forward to golden careers just months before. In 1981-82, Joe Lukacs was exactly as averse to the concept of layoffs as he had been in 1975, and this time he decided he wouldn't do it. He gathered his managers, and he made a proposal. He asked them to join him in taking a 15 percent salary roll-back that would enable the company to keep all its workers. The idea was accepted more readily by some than by others, but the rollback did happen; and it did have the desired effect. Western Research was one of the only companies in the whole of Alberta not to lay off workers in the dread days of the early 1981-82.

A company leader who will not ask his employees for extraordinary support will never receive it.

Ludo Zanzotto, an engineer from Czechoslovakia, got a job with Western Research on Christmas Eve, 1981. In his first month of work, he remembers that the temperature fell to −37 degrees Celsius, interest rates zoomed, and the company was in the doldrums. Everyone feared for their jobs, and a lot of engineers who had the misfortune to graduate in this slump weren't getting hired. As a refugee, and as the last man hired, Ludo couldn't have been more vulnerable, but the no-layoff rule at Western Research stretched to include him.

It was a difficult time. At meetings, Joe Lukacs would exhort his team to work harder, sell harder, and, when one of his people said, "Work harder at what? We have nothing to do," it made him furious. But it was the truth.

Then, as if the gods wanted to make a particular example of Western Research, another tragedy struck. In the spring of 1983, after a Friday night when many Western Research employees had gone to Red Deer for a Bow Valley hockey game (Edmonton versus Calgary), the Western Research lab caught fire. The lab and research area were destroyed, plus a good deal of the storage area. Several more bays were affected with smoke and water damage. Two high-pressure hydrogen tanks took off like rockets through the roof, fuelling their own flight. They landed in yards two blocks away.

Adversity is the ultimate test of management.

As the bus bringing the Western Researchers home from Red Deer approached the company's neighbourhood in northeast Calgary, they could see the smoke. Someone made a joke about hoping it was Western Research, and then the sad truth dawned that it wasn't a joke after all.

Everyone has a story about the fire and its aftermath. John Jackson wasn't on the bus, but he got a call to come down to the office. He remembers sitting over coffee with some of the others long into the night. Ludo Zanzotto remembers walking through the smoke and rubble to his office in search of personal treasures: two chemistry books sent to him by his father and his dictionaries. The books were smoke and water damaged, but they were there, and he still has them. Ross Jackson had left his department's TRS-80 computer turned on, and when he rubbed the soot off the read-out, he found it was still on, awaiting new lines of input.

Given the condition of the economy, some must have felt that the fire was the final straw, that Western Research could not rally and that they would soon be out of work. But Joe Lukacs thought otherwise. Perhaps in his finest hour as leader, Joe called everyone to a meeting Sunday morning and informed them that, come Monday, it was going to be business as usual. "We've been through worse things than this," was his theme and, after an enthusiastic performance and the creation of a task force, he had made believers out of his most downcast employees.

Come Monday, everyone was scrambling to make it work. John Jackson remembers that five of them were sharing one telephone as they called all over to scare up enough equipment to do the work they were contracted to do. That would be the crux of the matter. Could they honour their agreements? If not, their customers, who had reporting deadlines to make, would have to go elsewhere. It happened that John Jackson had been teaching a course in stack sampling at Mount Royal College at this time and hadn't brought his sampling train back after his last night of teaching there. That meant they had one stack-sampling kit at least. They phoned their suppliers, explained the situation, and found out who their true friends were. While some of their gas chromatograph suppliers didn't seem to think they could help, Hewlett Packard offered a loaner GC while they took the damaged ones away for evaluation. John Jackson and Peter Dale became lifetime HP customers right there and then.

On the insurance front, Robin Rankine took the lead. He had some background in accounting, and, because his research facility was completely down, he had time on his hands as well. Elmer Berlie credits Robin with saving the company a great deal of money by his ability to convince the insurance adjusters that partially assembled pieces of electronic gadgetry had to be valued much higher than their parts. He was also able to get replacement value for many of the old gas chromatographs that were destroyed in storage. It was another victory for the total absorption and dogged persistence of Robin Rankine.

In the end, though no one wanted to repeat the experience, the company came out of the fire as good or better than it had been before. Once again, Western Research had proven the power of its own resources, the sheer people power of its committed staff. They were a close bunch before, but the fire roped the employees of Western Research together in all new ways. For Joe Lukacs, the way his troops rallied around him in response to the fire is a positive and powerful memory, one of the proudest memories he retains of Western Research.

Reversals are a good test of your team and your relationship with customers and suppliers.

In the hard times, go back to the basics: your reputation at home and the strength of your people.

❖ *How can a company crisis strengthen a business?*

❖ *What economic and political lessons learned from the National Energy Policy in Canada remain relevant today?*

27

Phoenix Rising

The hardest sale to make is the first one.

Not many companies can say that they were reborn in their twentieth year, but this comes close to the truth for Western Research. The severe downturn of 1981-82, combined with the calamitous fire of 1983, meant that Western Research was literally rising from its own ashes as it approached 1985, its twentieth year of operation.

The company badly needed some good news in 1983, and Wilhelm Pier was able to offer it. His long campaign to break Dupont's stranglehold on Europe finally broke through with an initial sale to ÖMV, Austria's national oil company and the country's biggest corporation. The client was Josef Bohnenstingl and, when Wilhelm visited him in Vienna, he expressed the usual concerns about buying from a company on the far side of a far continent. Wilhelm countered with an offer to fly Bohnenstingl to Calgary so he could see the Western Research operation and meet the people standing behind the company's analyzers. The Austrian asked what the cost of such a trip would be, and Wilhelm told him 5,000 Deutschmarks.

Wilhelm Pier

"Instead of the trip, subtract the DM 5,000 from the price of the analyzer and you've got a deal," was the canny counter-offer.

It is easier to sell into a market once you've cracked it. For one thing, Wilhelm Pier could now illustrate his amazing customer service capacity. Giving out his home phone number to clients was standard practice for Wilhelm and, when he got a call for service, he was into his car and on his way immediately, making trans-European voyages at a speed that some found astounding. Though initially he needed a lot of support from Calgary, he would in time be able to do installation, start-up, and servicing all by himself. Calgary crews continued to be needed, but because of the volume of work rather than because Wilhelm needed personal assistance.

Listening to Wilhelm Pier describe his values as regards the customer is very like listening to Joe Lukacs on the same subject. They both believe in creating a friendship with the customer, in listening to the customer, and in helping the customer gain some advantage, or make some step forward in his own business or career. This matching of values was perhaps the most important glue that bonded Wilhelm Pier and Western Research. They were never disappointed in one another's approach or level of effort.

Once Wilhelm had cracked the Dupont edifice in Europe, he proceeded on to other successes. He sold to Marathon Petroleum for Burghausen, Germany; to BASF, and then to Lurgi, builder of turnkey plants of all kinds and the biggest engineering company in Germany. Lurgi would become Wilhelm's largest and most reliable customer. Not all of the sales Wilhelm made in Europe were for installation in Europe. He sold an analyzer to Shell's instrumentation centre in The Hague, that was destined for Singapore, for example.

Though Western Research had its fair share of employees from around the world, the great majority of the company's workers were from Canada, mostly from Alberta. Many, it is fair to say, were not widely travelled before the company's international surge. The first foreign opportunities did not involve much of a culture shock because they led into the American states most like western Canada: Wyoming, Texas, and North Dakota. But, later on, "international" started to mean anywhere on this planet. A plant testing job or instrument installation could take you anywhere from Denmark to Dubai, and the Alberta boys of Western Research rapidly became international sophisticates—although not always in one surefooted leap.

The jobs generated out of the European seminars took the

company to wherever the seminar attendee did business, which could mean Europe or a lot of other places too. As manager of the process analytical engineering group, John Sames was in charge of many of these forays. The only professional engineer anyone knows who also managed to get accepted as a certi-

Budapest Castle: the Western Research Sulphur Seminars moved to Hungary in the mid-1980s.

fied technologist (by ASET), John Sames liked to see the Western Research technicians get a shot at foreign duty. As a result, many have memories of epic car journeys across Europe in John's company. John Sames was very insistent that they see the famous sites wherever they were, and fairly regularly this would lead to adventure or even trouble.

One time on their way through France, a Western Research testing team happened to overnight in Paris. They had to be on their way early next morning and most everyone was content to hang around the hotel and hit the sack early—except for John. This was Paris, he exhorted them, the City of Light. They should jump on the Metro and go see the Eiffel Tower. So off they went to look at one of the prides of Paris, all lit up to best advantage. It was very late by the time they reboarded the Metro to return to the hotel, and, when they got off one train to board the next, they found the platform strangely silent. And it stayed that way. A thorough search of every possible exit revealed that all were closed and locked with big iron gates. Shouting for help only alarmed the people of Paris, who raised their collars and hurried on. When it seemed certain that they were in the Metro for the night, John Sames' greatest annoyance was the fact that he had already paid for the hotel.

Searching the underground further, mostly to pass the time, they did find a Dutch couple in the same predicament, who in turn were able to unearth a night watchman. He spoke neither English nor Dutch, nor anyone's schoolboy French– or so he pretended–and he let them stew for quite a while longer before allowing them to leave. Nor was that automatic salvation in that a cab had to be found in the now deserted streets of Paris. They did manage to hit the sheets of their hotel that night–for about an hour–before next morning's take off.

On another famous venture, Gerald Bohme and Brent Lloyd were on their way by car to do a job in Finland. En route through Sweden, they arrived at a ferry port just as the ferry was set to leave. It was a near thing, but they made it aboard, only to begin wondering if they were on the right ferry. Brent got off to check and, yes indeed, they were on the wrong boat–which abruptly left, with Gerald, for who knows where.

Another memorable job was in Saudi Arabia at the Jubail sulphur prilling towers in 1984. For this trip, John Sames' team consisted of John Jackson, Ross Jackson, Mike Zelensky, Tim Seedhouse, and Mark Towill. Their purpose was to test for sulphur-dust emissions and come up with a method to prevent dusting. Next door to the prilling facility was an iron foundry, whose concerned owner was afraid sulphur dust was going to mix with and ruin his iron. The concept of sulphur prilling is that the sulphur is sprayed as liquid from the top of the tower. As it falls down the tower, the sulphur cools and solidifies, forming the prill, a small ball of sulphur. In Canada, prilling towers were 55 metres high. In Jubail, with an ambient temperature of 52 degrees Celsius, the towers needed to be 90 metres high because of the greater length of time it would take for the liquid sulphur to cool and solidify.

To test the towers, it was necessary to be inside them, and the six-man team went at it day and night in two shifts of three. The temperature in the pod room at the top of the tower was more than fifty degrees, and the only relief available was in a partly finished tower nearby, where a slight desert breeze could be felt.

The Western Research team returned home, filed their report, and, four months later, the Jubail prilling facility blew up. As this was in the midst of the Iran-Iraq war, a bomb was one of the possible reasons considered, but most believed it was a sulphur dust explosion. Sulphur producers moved away from prilling to other methods of sulphur handling, thereafter.

A second and longer trip to Saudi Arabia came about because Aramco's Harry Van der Venne attended an Amsterdam sulphur seminar. Van der Venne decided he wanted all of Aramco's Saudi Arabian facilities tested the Western Research way, and John Jackson, Bill Wong, and John Sames were dispatched to Saudi Arabia in 1985 to take care of it. It was a thirty-one-day job.

Among those who worked for John Sames' world-roving process analytical engineering group over the years were: Laszlo Kiss, Bob Hensley, Mike Zelensky, Tom Ho, Bruce Klint, and Gerald Bohme.

In this way, Western Research spread itself around the globe. It took the final years of the 1970s, and all of the 1980s, but the company gradually mined its sulphur analyzer niche to the virtual ends of the earth. Wilhelm Pier would, in time, lock up the vast majority (over 90%) of the business in the countries he served (virtually all of Europe except the United Kingdom, France, and Spain). What Wilhelm accomplished in Europe, the North American sales team was doing in the United States. Don Stevens, Randy Hauer, Al Niven, Len Edwards, and Al Arnone upped the market penetration for Western Research sulphur analyzers in the United States to between 60 and 70 percent.

At its peak, Western Research was doing business in fifty countries.

As Western Research accomplished this internationalization, the company was careful not to neglect its core businesses and its home market. By 1985, it was again every bit as strong a market presence in these areas as it had been before the NEP slump and the fire.

As any successful company must do, Western Research had finally attracted competition, but Joe Lukacs felt in no way threatened by it. His competitors in the old core businesses of stack testing, air quality monitoring, and environmental impact assessments tended to be bottom feeders, competing mainly on price. Joe's policy was to ignore them, except for taking every opportunity to further the company's reputation and to enhance the value of the company's products for customers. He refused to compete on price.

Price cutting should be a last resort, not a first strategy.

As Paul Vetro puts it, people who just wanted numbers, for compliance with a regulation, might go to the competition for a bargain. But, if they genuinely needed data they could rely on, they came to Western Research, paying more, and happy to do so.

In the area of environmental impact assessment and data gathering for scientific studies, reputation was everything and Western Research enjoyed a good one. Clients came to Western Research because of its reputation, because they knew the government and the public trusted the company to do fair and accurate work. This was very difficult for the competition who could hardly go out and buy a legendary reputation with which to combat them.

All in all, the phoenix had risen.

❖ *What problems are created by price cutting?*

❖ *What alternatives are available when there is pressure to cut prices.*

❖ *In what ways is your customer your best friend?*

❖ *How can you get a sale when the customer is your competitor's best friend?*

Fun

From the time that it joined the Bow Valley family of companies, Western Research would have an odd reputation-for play. The rate of participation by Western Research employees in any Bow Valley social or recreational activity so outstripped that of Bow Valley Industries and Bow Valley Resource Services as a whole that there was just no accounting for it. At one point, Western Research organized a slow-pitch league for all of BVI and BVRS. Western Research had three teams; the rest of the companies had six. B.J. Seaman remembers this well and gives a lot of credit to Joe Lukacs. Joe went to a lot of trouble to make sure that Western Research employees felt that they were part of the BVI/BVRS family. "We had a family aspect to our company," says B.J. Seaman, "and that fit Joe Lukacs to a tee."

B. J. Seaman

On one occasion, a bus trip to the mountains to ski, Doug Deleff made a punch and put it in a collapsible water tank on the bus. It was rigged up with a tube that ran the length of the bus, with downspouts every couple of feet. The idea was that everybody would get into it on the way home. Punch was a polite word for this mixture of hard liquors. It should have been called "goof." When people started drinking the stuff on the way to the mountain instead of on the way home, the results were disastrous. One of the more tellable incidents was when a Western

Research type lost consciousness in a line-up for the chair. He keeled over backward, creating a domino effect that wiped out his entire line.

The Western Research company barbeques were legendary, as was the company's annual Stampede Breakfast on parade day. The Stampede Breakfast featured chuckwagon races around the building and so much thought was put into the particular wagons and how they were driven and pulled that management had to put a stop to it: not to the races but to the preparation of the wagons on company time. Another amazing event, at which the principals of the political correctness movement will only be able to shake their heads in alarm, was one year's Stampede Breakfast "Gluteus Maximus" contest.

Another aspect of the Western Research concept of fun was that practical jokes were rampant. An example that contains the flavour of many such jokes begins with John Jackson on a business flight back from somewhere. John noticed an ad for cheap watches with the inscription of your choice on the face. He ordered a couple inscribed with the BVRS logo and the words Western Research. When the watches arrived, John and his accomplice put them on and went down to see one of the machinists, making sure, in the course of the conversation, that he noticed the watches. When the fellow asked about them, they said, "Didn't you get one? Everybody who's been here over five years gets one." The machinist said that, no, he hadn't been included and then he marched down to Kevin Anderson, his boss, and demanded his watch. Anderson said he didn't know what the machinist was talking about and sent him back to work. Meanwhile, John Jackson and his accomplice had given the watches to two other fellows who also found their way down to the machinist's bench that day. Before the practical joke finally stopped, the machinist had made three trips to see Kevin Anderson, each time more furious than the time before.

Road trips were great occasions for jokes, the crueller the better. In one story of a long drive in a company van, the person behind the wheel refuses to stop so another can pee. No amount of begging will change the driver's mind. Finally the desperate one has no choice but to open the van door, hold on at the top, and let fly. But, here's the clincher, the driver chooses that moment to pass. It sounds like a joke, but it happened.

Wiring a little electricity into a new employee's console, putting sandwiches in the stack testing port and watching them blast out the top of the incinerator stack, jamming on the brakes when someone is about to take a mouthful of banana split–all in a day's work.

The "pit party" was another Western Research institution, and what it meant was an after-hours drink at the office. It was never as wild as it sounds, just a chance to unwind with the help of some alcohol at the end of a long day. The outcome when a new manager insisted that this drinking at work must stop was predictable. A pit party was organized immediately and the manager invited to share in a libation. In the manager's defence, the pit parties must have looked like laxity, but they had also become traditional: one of the liberties earned and enjoyed by the people of the Western Research culture.

Level of participation in the social aspects of a company's life is almost certainly a reliable measure of company health and morale. Western Research was by this measure robust all its days. If employees will play hard for the company, it is probably true that they will work hard too. From Joe Lukacs on down, Western Research management understood this. Fun, at Western Research, was practically compulsory.

*Starting with the United States,
then proceeding to Europe,
Joe Lukacs led Western Research
around the world in the 1980s.*

Wilhelm Pier (r.) in action. Wilhelm sold Josef Bohnenstingl of ÖMV (seen here at a seminar in Vienna) a Western Research analyzer in 1983.

Joe Lukacs and Wilhelm Pier riding at Joe's ranch: trans-Atlantic partners from 1978-1992.

Western Research moved its European seminars to Budapest in the mid-'80s.

Bill Wong, John Sames, and John Jackson, play it safe in the Middle East, in 1985.

A Chinese delegation visits Western Research. Fourth from left (holding flags): Randy Hauer. Fifth from left: John Sames. Sixth from right: Joe Lukacs. Fifth from right: Bob Ritter.

The annual Western Research Stampede Breakfast chuckwagon races.

*Children loved the Western
Research family events.*

*The Stampede Breakfast Gluteus Maximus
competition. Contestants and judges.*

One of the many company barbeques at Joe's ranch: (left to right) Dennis Hniden, Andrew Kusmirek, Craig Snider, Nancy Weigel, Joe Lukacs, and Gord Tallin.

Mike and Rhonda Schroeder (left) and Maureen and Douglas Leahey.

Gord Tallin (l.) and Don Colley: full-contact lawn darts.

Dan Hall (l.),
Bruce Burns (c)
and Les Frank.

Joe Lukacs at the barbeque.

Randy Hauer
and Helen Lukacs

Evelyn and B.J. Seaman
with Ed and Tilly Hardy

Doug Boyd with the
Rick Lukacs (et al)
painting created for
the 20ᵗʰ anniversary.

Joe Lukacs as fireman: no more fires for Western Research.

A group celebrating the 20th anniversary: (left to right) John Carr, Kevin Anderson, Randy Hauer, Martin Hansen, Laurel Rankine, and Bill Wong.

28

Western Research Turns Twenty

Raising your own management group builds loyalty and rewards longevity.

When Western Research turned twenty, the company did it up proud. The celebration was held on September 19, 1985, a barbecue at the Western Research's northeast Calgary headquarters. Some 150 people attended: employees, customers, and old friends. The Seaman brothers, Doc, B.J., and Don, were present, as was Bow Valley vice-president of drilling, the former Chicago Black Hawks hockey star, Bill Hay. Paintings of sulphur recovery plants and stacks by Joe Lukacs's son Rick and a group of his artist friends were unveiled, one of which is the cover image of this book. Joe Lukacs gave

his employees rodeo-style belt buckles with an antique gold look. From his employees, Joe received a plaque. It was a howling good party and, like Western Research parties generally did, it carried on into the night.

Another commemoration of the twentieth anniversary was an article called "Two Dynamic Decades for Western Research"

Plaque presented to Joe Lukacs on the occasion of the Western Research twentieth anniversary.

that appeared in *Horizon*, the BVI company publication. What is noticeable in reading it is how very many of the early employees still remained with the company, and to what positions of authority they had risen (also with what pride they spoke when they were interviewed for the article). Those whose photographs appeared included Robin Rankine (Vice-President of Research), Ed Hardy (Supervisor of Machining), Ron Dimmer (Manager, U.S. Operations), Mike Beamish (General Manager, Process Instrumentation), Paul Vetro (General Manager, Air Quality Management), Douglas Leahey (Manager, Meteorology), Don Colley (General Manager, Consulting and Technical Services), Lou Conron (Chief Controller), Harold Paskall (Vice-President, Contract Research), Gord Tallin (Manager, Process Instrumentation Manufacturing), and Don Stevens (Manager, Process Instrumentation Sales).

Robin Rankine, Vice-President of Research, 1985

An interesting fact about that group of leaders is that every single one of them had a decade of service with the company, or more. "We raised them," was Joe Lukacs's comment on this amazing continuity.

Although Elmer Berlie had left Western Research in 1983 to become a Project Manager in BVRS's Engineering and Special Projects division, he came back long enough to be photographed and interviewed for the article. Of the company he had helped to build, Elmer said, "We were problem solvers. We were giving industry accurate environmental assessment, and we were telling them how to control these effects on the environment. Really, we led the world in this approach to sampling and analyzing."

Joe Lukacs also stressed the problem-solving ability of the company in his comments: "Western Research is, in essence, a group of specialists, expert engineers, scientists and technologists, with the ability to provide practical solutions to industrial problems. And this could be almost any problem. We can take this type of expertise anywhere in the world."

As the Western Research employees celebrated their company's twentieth anniversary, it is very doubtful if anyone, including Joe Lukacs, knew what a watershed year 1985 was going to be. They did not know because much of what was about to affect them would come from beyond their offices and beyond their marketplace. While Western Research had successfully dug itself out of the twin pits of NEP blight and fire, the mother ship, BVRS, was just as steadily digging itself down. From a profit of $19.8 million in 1984, BVRS dropped to a loss of $5.6 million in 1985. The company's total debt rose to $300 million in 1986.

Gord Tallin

The reasons were numerous, but many traced back to the enormously expensive offshore work into which the company had been led by the federal government's NEP incentives (the famous PIP grants). Believing that energy prices would remain high and that Canada's offshore plays were the future, BVRS had invested heavily in offshore drilling rigs, supply vessels, and mobile drilling islands for the Arctic. When the oil price plunged to ten dollars a barrel from forty, most of that investment amounted to debt with no short-term hope of revenue. There were simply too many rigs, offshore and on land, for the amount of work, a situation greatly aggravated by the financial collapse of Dome Petroleum and the relatively cheap availability of its offshore fleet. It was a bad situation, and it did not look apt to change for some time.

Douglas Leahey,
Manager,
Meteorology, 1985

When Bow Valley divided itself into BVI and BVRS, the drilling had gone to BVRS, and now so did the debt. Though the two companies were still owned somewhat in common, BVI was doing reasonably well while BVRS slid into ever deeper trouble.

In the early part of this decline, BVRS was handed an opportunity that fit well with the environmental side of its expertise, and particularly well with the know-how of Western Research. The province of Alberta had long been concerned about the problem of hazardous waste management. The problem had been handled to date by sending the waste to the United States for treatment, or by handling it at the source. Some handled it by burying, storing, or hiding it. Alberta, showing its national environmental leadership once again, was looking for a more reliable and responsible solution, and so had begun to move toward building its own hazardous waste treatment facility.

*Harold Paskall,
Vice-President,
Contract Research,
1985*

One of the steps was finding a site, and many communities competed for this economic plum, even though the government went to considerable effort to make sure that they were aware of the hazards. In the end, the community of Swan Hills was chosen, after its citizens voted 79 percent in favour.

Next, a company was selected to build and operate the facility. Chem-Security Ltd., a Canadian subsidiary of an American company, led by John Richardson and headquartered in Vancouver, was chosen. Among its recent projects, the company had played a role in the reclamation/remediation of the Gulf Pincher Creek sour gas plant site, one of the first 1950s sulphur plants decommissioned in Alberta.

Not long after Chem-Security was chosen for the Swan Hills job, a big problem arose. Chem-Security was purchased by a Chicago company with a less-than-sterling record. Alberta was not happy and informed the company that it would have to change parents if it was going to continue to be involved at Swan Hills.

This was the stage at which BVRS was brought into the picture. Various parties approached BVRS about taking over Chem-Security and the Swan Hills project. On December 10, 1984, it happened. Chem-Security became the newest member of the Bow Valley family.

The structure the government had in mind for the waste treatment facility was a government and private co-venture. Alberta had formed the Alberta Special Waste Management Corporation (ASWMC), a crown corporation, to be the government player. It now sought an agreement with Chem-Security (BVRS) by which the two would share the costs, risks, and profits.

The Swan Hills Waste Management System was a difficult prospect for a private investor for various reasons. First, it was established to meet the government's and Alberta's needs: the requirement being to build a facility with the capability and capacity to treat *all* types of hazardous waste. Because economics didn't enter into it, it represented a considerable investment risk. Given that BVRS already had considerable debt problems, the deal had to be such that the company's debt was not increased and the considerable risk was eliminated. If the government could give BVRS that kind of deal, the company was willing to give the government the kind of system for which it was asking.

Eventually, the Alberta government would agree to these demands. The deal the two sides fashioned was that BVRS would get a guaranteed rate of return: prime plus three percent.

Lou Conron,
Controller, 1985

Basically, it was a utility model. The government also promised BVRS that the Swan Hills facility would be the exclusive provider of this level of hazardous waste treatment for the province of Alberta.

Once the Swan Hills plant was up and running, it proved to have insufficient capacity in some areas and excess capacity in others. The under-utilization stemmed in part from loopholes in the regulations that allowed Albertans quite a lot of leeway if they wanted to deal with their hazardous wastes in some other manner than sending them to Swan Hills. At the same time, Swan Hills could not keep up with the demand for organic waste treatment by incineration, and so, applied to the government for permission to expand its incineration capacity. This permission was eventually granted.

Scan the horizon for the next big wave. Get on it.

Where Western Research entered the Swan Hills Waste Treatment Centre scenario was as a source of expertise for getting it done. The interest BVRS had in Chem-Security and the Swan Hills facility project was partly due to Western Research's capability in many related areas. First and foremost, Chem-Security wanted to borrow Joe Lukacs to oversee the management, design, and construction of the facility. As a person who had always kept his eye out for the next big challenge, Joe was interested. He had devoted his career to the environmental business, and this was the next horizon: to move beyond sulphur and nitrogen compounds into a new generation of poorly understood complex pollutants: PCBs and other dangerous trace organics; dioxins and furans. With the expertise it would develop at Swan Hills, Western Research would be able to move beyond the increasingly saturated sulphur analyzer marketplace.

As for whether Joe Lukacs would be able to take this partial leave of absence from Western Research without creating problems, he was quite sure he could. Nancy Weigel, Joe's assistant at the time, remembers how confident he was in his Western Research managers. Given his management style over the years, which allowed considerable autonomy to all managers and department heads, it should, for the most part, be business as usual–especially if Joe could still attend and referee the management meetings.

A significant change wrought by the Swan Hills project was the loss of Paul Vetro. Joe Lukacs decided to take his faithful lieutenant, his friend from university days in Hungary and long-time ally, with him to Swan Hills, to design and manage the all-important laboratory there. Just as he had fifteen years earlier, Paul refused, was cajoled, and finally accepted on terms that turned out not to be quite the terms he worked under. What was clear was that Paul had left Western Research behind. He would spend much of the remainder of his career with the consortium that ran the hazardous waste treatment facility at Swan Hills.

In Joe Lukacs's partial absence, the Western Research management team consisted of Mike Beamish (Instrumentation), Robin Rankine and Harold Paskall (R&D), Ron Dimmer (U.S. Opertions), Don Stevens (Marketing), Lou Conron (Accounting), and Don Colley (Consulting, Meteorology, Lab and Field). Upon Paul Vetro's departure, Don Colley's area further expanded to include air quality monitoring. The overall result was that, by 1987, Don Colley was managing over half of the company.

❖ *What are the business risks associated with chasing government incentives?*

❖ *What are the best ways and what is the best time to use government incentive programs?*

❖ *What was the benefit and the liability of the Swan Hills plant to the rest of Western Research?*

29

The Computer Revolution

Twenty years after starting out as a computer solutions company, Western Research finally reaped the benefits of the comptuer age.
—Joe Lukacs

Western R & D came into existence as a computer solutions company. It quickly evolved into a pollution control or environmental company. Ironically, many years later, when computing became a widespread method of dealing with data, and as the personal computer went from being a tantalizing idea to an affordable consumer product, Western Research would become a company whose innovations and expertise relied on computers at almost every level. The electronic brain of the computer could provide logical pathways through the sulphur plant. It could improve and expand the scope of data collection, which in turn improved the accuracy and refinement of findings. Overall, one can say that science itself was improved, and Western Research was a private industry company able to move with that progress. Western Research became able to follow and assist scientific researchers in their pursuit of targets not even visible before refined computer data brought them into view.

By 1980, Western Research had developed several programs that ran on mainframe computers. The first was Joe Lukacs' early flash calculation program developed in the era when computer innovation was still supposed to be the company's business and future. Ten years later, after Robin Rankine and Harold Paskall had created a mathematical model of the sulphur plant, Linda Biswanger took on the task of creating a computer program that would replicate that model. The resulting program was called PERFORM, another mainframe program for use in-house as support for the sulphur plant optimization service. PERFORM remained Linda Biswanger's responsibility until her departure in 1980.

When personal computers came on the scene (for practical purposes in the 1980s), the programming of Western

Research know-how had the potential to become a new product family for the company. Judy Ritter, daughter of Dr. Bob Ritter, was hired to update the PERFORM program and transform it into a commercially viable piece of PC software. Two programs resulted: a commercial sulphur plant program called Sulsim and a second, fuller-featured program used internally by Western Research, called ISUL8. As well as containing the sulphur plant model and the air demand optimization equations, ISUL8 included Western Research's catalyst evaluation program.

Another program with a lineage tracing back to Richard Kerr and Linda Biswanger was Cauldron. This PC software,

Sulsim®, a Western Research contribution to the computer age.

also programmed by Judy Ritter, contained the free energy minimization method of calculating equilibria.

What to do with Sulsim now that it existed became the greatest of all Western Research intellectual property debates. Sulsim was nothing less than a software operating manual for most everything Western Research knew and could do that others did not know and could not do. The question was: what would happen to the company if that knowledge was put on the open market as commercial software? Would it boost Western Research's reputation as an industry innovator and bring in fresh business on all fronts? Or would it bring in some short-term cash while erasing a great deal of the company's market for optimization services?

Judy Ritter (Arrizza), Dr. Bob Ritter's daughter, programmed the original and subsequent versions of the sulphur plant simulation software Sulsim®.

This type of debate had always been resolved in the past in favour of the open approach, making the knowledge available to all comers, and so it was again. Sulsim went on the market in the early 1980s, priced at US$7500. It sold many copies then and it is still selling copies today. John Sames markets Sulsim through Sulphur Experts. The program is up to Version 5 (for Windows) and it is still programmed by Judy Ritter (now Judy Arrizza).

Sharing what your company knows earns respect and builds customer loyalty.

Sulsim was not the only Western Research software development. Besides ISUL8 and Cauldron, Harold Paskall developed several other computer applications of Western Research knowledge. GComp, developed by Harold with assistance from Ron Dimmer, was a program that could turn gas chromatographic data into readable results. INCWRD was a computer version of the incinerator optimization program developed by Harold's team in the 1970s, in response to the first OPEC oil supply squeeze. The program allowed gas processing companies to realize enormous fuel savings by reducing their incinerator stack temperatures. Looking back, John Sames feels it was a mistake not to tie the price of the service (and then the program) to the fuel savings realized from it. At the giant Ram River sulphur plant alone, fuel savings were 50 percent. The total fuel savings realized in Alberta due to the optimization program would have fuelled the city of Red Deer.

Another early venture into computing that started on a mainframe and graduated to PC was Air Quality Monitoring's automation of its chart reading and reporting department. Several efforts were made to find a computer solution to the painstaking job of chart reading. The poor Western Research chart readers poured over air quality strip charts all day long, hand-entering data that would find its way into the government-required monthly reports. It was drudgery and, except for fifteen-year veteran Nancy Mura, chart readers came and went with dependable frequency. Finally, when the computer solution was found, the chart reading team was reduced from twelve to three.

Ironically, Western Research was programming software and selling computer services before it ever owned a computer. When the company finally did own its first computer, it didn't know it. Around 1980, the first privately owned personal computers started showing up around the office. Denver Smart had a Commodore Pet. Ross Jackson brought in his Tandy TRS-80. Ron Dimmer badly wanted a computer for Lab and Field, but it seemed unlikely that the company would spend that kind of money on this latest fad. So Ron used some creative accounting to raise a computer purchase fund out of various budgets. In through the back door came another TRS-80, called by its competitors the "Trash-80," which eventually moved up from a 4-bit to a 16-bit memory. With this computer, Ron was able to run VisiCalc (short for Visible Calculator), the first electronic spreadsheet, released in the United States in 1979.

Nancy Mura worked fourteen years as a company chart reader.

Meanwhile, no one outside of Lab and Field knew about the secret TRS-80. It was kept under lock and key and operated only behind a locked door. Soon, Ron Dimmer's intricate and precise department budgets were becoming office legend.

It all worked like a charm—until the fire of 1983. Suddenly, having lost a computer that didn't officially exist, Lab and Field had no means of getting it replaced. When Lou (Howe) Conron figured out what had happened, she made them swear never to do it again.

It would not be long, however, before computers at Western Research would be seen as a savings, not a cost: costly time on a mainframe replaced with work done in-house at a desk. The company leaders in this regard proved to be Meteorology and Air Quality Monitoring.

One of the great steps forward in the remote monitoring of airborne emissions, perhaps the greatest since telemetry, was having a computer that could read and store data in the field. The story goes that Frank Cullen was working in southern Saskatchewan when he looked across the U.S. border and saw a strange device on an air quality station. A long-time Western Research hand, Cullen was working that day at a Saskatchewan power plant, which the U.S. air quality trailer was monitoring. The mysterious device he saw was in a blue box set amongst its other standard equipment, and closer scrutiny suggested it might be a computerized data acquisition system. Further research traced the system to its source: a Bozeman, Montana, company called Western Telecomputing (WTC).

Frank Cullen

The device in the blue box was a data-acquisition system and WTC called it ICIS (pronounced IKE-US, as in Ike and Tina). The man behind WTC was Dick Weaver, whose father had started the company out of his basement. Western

Research got Dick to come up to Calgary and show them the system. As Paul Vetro recalls, the ICIS was a level of automation well beyond what Western Research Air Quality Monitoring was used to. Besides the basic miraculous fact of field acquisition of data, the ICIS could re-start itself after power failures and calibrate automatically. The price was also right.

Within a very short period of time, Western Research became WTC's biggest customer. They took so much of the total production of WTC that Western Research was able to ask that systems be built to their specifications. Over the years, WTC and Western Research invested together in various products that the Calgary company needed and the Bozeman company could then try to market Statesside for its own profit.

In 1984, WTC came up for sale and several of the Western Research managers, including Paul Vetro shortly before his departure to Swan Hills, wanted badly to buy it. Perhaps remembering too well the last time he'd bought a one-man company (Dominion Instruments), Joe Lukacs wasn't interested and WTC remained an outside supplier.

Doug Simpson, Mike Schroeder, Ben Kucewicz.

Small-scale computers with memory capacity created the potential for a new standard of data collection. The point at which Western Research had to step up to the plate and realize that potential was when it became involved in large-scale scientific research initiatives. A big difference exists between data collection for meeting government air quality standards and that required to realize significant scientific results. For example, to meet Alberta's air quality standard for SO_2, it is necessary to be beneath a certain maximum level–anywhere beneath. Precision beyond determining whether you are above or below the standard would be wasted. In a scientific study, where tiny exposures need to be measured exactly, as in the case of studying vegetation effects, the level of precision has to be much greater.

Western Research confronted the difference in early 1984 in an Alberta Research Council study of pollution deposition in the forest canopy. Called the Sandalta Forest Canopy project, it involved Western Research as a data gatherer. Kevin Warren, who had come to Western Research from a job as an environmental technician with HBOG Edson, was a senior air quality technician on the Sandalta project, and he remembers that it was critical to the success of the project that the canopy not be disturbed. The sampling system consisted of two parts: a twenty-metre tower upon which four sampling points were situated, and a thimble-shaped wellhead cover, air-conditioned and full of the monitoring instrumentation, that was situated at ground level below. The 350-pound, loaded wellhead cover could not be flown in. To protect the canopy from disturbance, it was walked in by three people, at the cost of at least one major back problem.

Western Research had inherited this study and was supposed to be its saviour, but there were a lot of problems with it. The technicians found it very hard to keep the back pressures equal in all four sample lines, and the data-collection system wasn't precise enough to measure if the pressures were equal. In other words, as Kevin puts it, the study was "flawed even before we started." In the end, the data was not up to the precision that the Alberta Research Council needed. The client was unsatisfied.

Western Research's next involvement of this kind, overlapping Sandalta, was as a player in a major Alberta acid rain study. Called the Acid Deposition Research Study (ADRP), it was spearheaded by Dr. Allan Legge, of the University of Calgary's Kananaskis Centre for Environmental Research (principal investigator), with Kenneth R. Smith, Assistant Deputy Minister of Alberta Environment, and Ronald L. Findlay, Manager of Environmental Affairs and Safety for

Raise the bar for your whole industry, not just for your company.

Amoco (as co-chairmen). ADRP was a huge project and Western Research was again responsible for collecting background air quality data at three different sites.

The monitoring took place over three years, 1985 to 1987, with one sophisticated trailer high on Fortress Mountain and two more near Crossfield. At the start of the program, Air Quality Monitoring started having the same kinds of problems they'd had at Sandalta, for the same reasons. They still did not have the resources required to process this amount of data to the required precision.

The project started as an air quality monitoring job, but, after a couple of months, responsibility was shifted to Douglas Leahey's group, though Kevin Warren stayed with it. Douglas Leahey in turn assigned the project to Martin Hansen. A physicist who had been with Douglas's department since 1977, Martin Hansen was aware of the data problems and agreed to do it only on condition that he have the power to do what was needed to turn the problem around.

The task was to improve the equipment and the standard operating philosophy to the point where they could accurately and dependably measure actual values of SO_2, even when those values were extremely low. Kevin Warren and Martin Hansen worked together closely to effect this quantum leap, and it didn't happen immediately. As Kevin puts it, "The first six months were insane." He was putting in twenty-hour work days collecting and charting data, and it was still not up to the needed standard. Martin Hansen corroborates this. When he took the first data batch to Allan Legge's University of Calgary statistician, the man handed it back and said, "Now get me some real data."

They persevered, working toward a system that could reliably denote the difference between a concentration of 0.5 parts per million and 0.75 ppm. After the first year, Kevin Warren moved into management, and Lory Whiteley took his place on the ADRP project. What came of it finally is now known as QA/QC: Quality Assurance/Quality Control. It means looking at data periodically to assess its validity, correcting systematic errors in collection, and baselining the data in a computerized, consistent manner. Meteorology and Air

Quality Monitoring cooperated with this standard, such that problems were caught and solved, and bad numbers eliminated.

Another major difference between the ADRP study, compared to Western Research's normal air quality monitoring methods, was the physical quantity of the data. Normally, air quality data were collected hourly. A typical station measured SO_2, H_2S, wind speed, and wind direction. That translated into 720 readings times four parameters, or 2,880 numbers per month. In computer terms, it was a file of 0.025 megabytes. Compare that to the ADRP trailers, which were each measuring 100 parameters every two minutes. That makes 2,160,000 numbers per month, or 750 times the data of a standard air quality monitoring trailer. Per site, it amounted to a monthly file of 17.2 megabytes.

Martin Hansen

The collecting was done on megadisks, about the dimensions of a letter-size writing pad. They contained ten megabytes each and filled up every two and one half days.

All in all, the ADRP project was an eye-opener for Western Research and, once through it, Meteorology, Air Quality Monitoring, and the combination of the two departments, would never be the same again. QA/QC became the standard for their work. As for computers, their increasing sophistication meant ever-smarter machines: analyzers that ran themselves and collected amazing arrays of data about themselves and on each parameter they measured. Data storage was no longer an issue.

The speed with which the computer revolution made its changes at Western Research, and in the environmental industry as a whole, is often obscured by how quickly people adapted to the changes. The new way of doing things, being so obviously better in most cases, swiftly became second nature. The old ways came to look primitive almost over night.

Manual chart reading in the air quality monitoring area is a perfect example. It seems part of a hilariously antiquated past, yet the last of the chart readers didn't depart from Western Research until 1988. For that matter, as Kevin Warren points out, aluminum towers on air quality monitoring trailers attract enough lightening that some manual chart reading still has to be done today, as a back-up when the electronic systems fail.

❖ *Did Western make the right decision in selling its intellectual capital through software sales?*

❖ *What risks were assumed when the software sales decision was made?*

❖ *Is this debate still valid for similar companies in the new millennium?*

30 | New Product, New Market: The Danger Zone

> *When we responded to market need with a product, that's when we got our biggest winners. When we relied on our instincts and creative ideas, we failed.* —Joe Lukacs

There are four kinds of product and market moves that a manufacturing company can make. A company can take a product it already has, an existing product, and sell it in an existing market. Or, it can sell an existing product in a new market. Third, it can sell a new product in an existing market; and, fourth, it can sell a new product in a new market. Each of the four moves has a different level of risk.

When both the product and the marketplace are familiar terrain (existing product, existing market), you are on firm ground. For example, by the last half of the 1980s, Western Research knew as much about selling closed-loop processing analyzers (their ADA) into the sulphur recovery market as any company in the world. This was the company's most secure market niche, and it was very comfortable there. Likewise, when it sold its EIA service or its stack testing service, or its continuous stack emission monitor, within Western Canada, it could do so with total confidence and a great expectation of success.

As the company moved into the United States, and into Europe, the product line was the same and the market differed only geographically; that is, it was still a sulphur plant market. Was this then a new or an existing market? The American market because of the cultural similarity between

264

Canada and the United States, especially within the oil and gas industry, was more of an existing market. Some hurdles existed (the difficulty some Americans had believing Canadians could know anything worth buying), but they were surmounted within a fairly short period of time. In Europe, however, because each country would tend to have its own language, regulations and specifications, and a business culture quite different from Canada's, it was more difficult to penetrate and the process took longer.

The risk was higher when entering these new geographical markets, but at least the product was the same. The company knew what it was selling, could demonstrate success elsewhere, and could answer all their customers' questions.

When Wilhelm Pier redeveloped the ADA for application to coke oven sulphur recovery, that was more truly an existing product entering a new market, and Wilhelm deserves great credit for surmounting the greater risk and making it succeed.

In conclusion, Western Research had entered the riskier realm of taking its existing products into new markets and done so successfully.

Several of the products that the company developed in the late 1970s can be termed new products aimed at existing markets. These included the Model 733, the H_2S in sales gas analyzer, and the three variations on the waste gas incinerator technology. The commercial sulphur plant software Sulsim can also be considered in this category.

Here again, the company had a certain comfort level going in. Because the marketplace was the one they were most familiar with, and because the products had been developed in response to real problems that industry wanted solved, success would be more or less guaranteed if the products were good enough to do the job. The industry wanted a means to very quickly detect trace amounts of H_2S in the sales gas leaving a plant. Robin Rankine came up with the combination of a UV analyzer and a GC column and solved the problem. Success. The waste gas incinerators were developed because the industry had an odour problem in low-pressure flaring situations. The product worked, and worked so well that variations of it could be created for a variety of other applications. Success again. Sulsim was also a fairly safe bet in that it was the computer equivalent of a service the company had been providing within the sulphur recovery industry for some time. Success a third time.

When you take a new product into a new marketplace, it is by far the highest risk move you can make. The chance of failure is greatly elevated.

So why do it? Why take the chance?

One very powerful reason is that the market for a company's products is finite. The world may look enormous and unfathomable at the beginning of a company's career, but, given success, the farthest reaches of that market will be reached. For Western Research, the matter could be summed up in the statement: there are only so many sulphur plants in the world. Such was the company's success that, by the mid-1980s, it had sold its analyzer products to most of them.

In 1987, salesman Randy Hauer was moved off his U.S. beat into Europe to see if the European footprint could be broadened and to use Europe as a launching pad into the few remaining markets of the world. The sulphur seminar, always the company's most successful sales forerunner, was taken far afield as well, even to Singapore to embrace the southeast Asian petroleum industry. But, as Randy Hauer puts it, it's hard to sell into places where you physically are not. It was also hard to interest agents in these faraway places in Western Research's fairly narrow product line. Randy and the other salesmen lobbied head office for the development of more products to help them sell the ones they already had.

The saturated market for Western Research's manufactured products might have been less pressing if dramatic growth had existed in the other parts of the company, but the truth was they too were reaching the outside perimeters of their marketplace. Western Research's market for EIAs, air monitoring and stack sampling was basically western Canada. As soon as they crossed an international boundary, they either hit severe competition or very unfamiliar regulatory terrain. Simply, they had no market advantage outside Canada for these services. When they had mined out Canada, they were out of growth.

There were honourable exceptions to this such as the Malaysian air and water monitoring system, an enormous job that Don Colley's combined consulting and air quality department began working on in the late 1980s and completed as BOVAR in the 1990s.

John Sames' process engineering group was successful in going international with plant testing and optimization. They tended to travel the route beaten by the seminars and the analyzer sales. For them as well, the world was wide but not infinite.

Joe Lukacs had watched all this coming for a long time. Looking at the market potential for what his company did was an important part of his role and, as he moved into the 1980s, he was desperate for new products and diversification. If Western Research stayed in its comfortable niche, there was a fence in every direction. If it regarded the world outside that niche as a new frontier for Western Research to conquer, potential of all kinds existed, but the company's expertise, reputation, and other market advantages might not travel with it. Another factor pushing Joe was that he now had an actual research and development department, headed up by Robin Rankine. That department had to produce to justify what it was costing, and, at present, it was stuck on a plateau. It had driven its frontier UV technology out to the edges but did not have new technologies to vend. Joe and others in the company were trying to come up with ideas that the R & D department could work on.

In traditional management terms, the way to enter the new market, new product quadrant is with enormous preparation. You must learn so much about the new market that you can approach the confidence and certainties that you enjoy in your own niche. You should performance test and market test your new products so thoroughly that you are certain of their advantages. This is all well and good to say, but when Western Research tried to put it into action, certain unforeseen problems arose.

The first new product for a new market in which Western Research invested heavily was the TRS, a continuous emissions monitor for the pulp and paper industry. The emissions of concern to that industry, pollutants that the analyzer would need to be able to read, included SO_2, CS_2, COS and H_2S_x.

Paprican, the Pulp and Paper Research Institute of Canada, had created the TRS analyzer in its own research laboratories and brought it to Western Research as a working prototype in search of commercialization. For Joe Lukacs, there were a lot of things right about the project. Because British Columbia and Alberta had extensive pulp and paper industries, it was an opportunity to get into an industry with a large local base, which could then lead into an enormous world market. That is, it had exactly the same type of potential that the sulphur recovery market had for the company way back when— and more so, given the relative enormity of the world pulp and paper industry. Secondly, it was an analyzer project and many of the steps toward commercialization would be familiar ones. As well, there was the fact that Paprican was a respected authority, supported by member companies all over Canada and abroad, and affiliated with three major Canadian universities: University of British Columbia, McGill, and École Polytechnique. Not only had Paprican taken the TRS to the prototype stage, the organization also vouched for the market demand for the product.

So Western Research took the TRS on. The company had, in its past, jumped into so many waters that were unfamiliar (beginning with the leap into power generation work in the 1966) that a certain cockiness was involved. Let's go. Why not? We've never failed yet. Another factor in their taking the plunge was government funding. Paprican did not come empty-handed. The organization was able to swing some government funding Western Research's way, and this made the project look even better.

When something goes wrong, the stories of why are seldom in short supply. With the TRS, the first problem would be that the Research and Development department didn't much like the look of the new analyzer. They proceeded to redesign it into something that would be more elegant and more of a match for the other analyzers. In order to do so, they needed to know about the pulp and paper process, and perhaps this knowledge never did catch up to the development of the product. The effect on the project of R&D's desire to redevelop the analyzer, and the need to learn the new process, was time lost. A project that may have looked neat and compact at the outset started to drag on. A further complication was the difficulty of sampling in the pulp and paper plant. It was a wet corrosive environment, much different from the sulphur plant, and figuring out how to do it would further complicate and elongate the process of development.

A very serious problem with the TRS was that no one liked the project all that much. It had no champion. People worked on it but probably did not work on it the same way they would have done had it been a popular idea. Part of this may have been that it came from outside. The culture of Western Research was very much geared to ideas that grew organically out of the company's work. Over time, this generated a suspicion of ideas that came from elsewhere. This way of thinking tends to produce self-fulfilling prophecies. *We didn't like it from the start. And look, it failed.*

If the company thought of ditching the project, the commitments associated with the government funding were there to stop them. There is a saying in business that government funding can be very expensive money, and the TRS would prove a prime example. Government funding can make you take your eye off the ball, whereas if you're spending your own money you might make a lot more certain that it was well spent.

Finally, the TRS became a loser because Paprican's market forecasts proved to be wrong. It was the old problem that besets many who try to invent for the environmental marketplace. When you think up some device that will materially aid industry in reducing or controlling its noxious emissions, and you ask the industry would they be willing to buy one when it's built, they always say yes. To say no would be to proclaim yourself uninterested in the negative environmental effect of your work, and who's going to knowingly, publicly, say that? They greet your plan with enthusiasm; they tell you what a great company you are for going where no one has gone before. Then, when the product exists, and it is time to nickle up, they don't exactly refuse to buy, but they delay. Times are tough right now. We're not really in a position to take on something that new and expensive right now. Talk to us again early in the next budget year.

Most market windows are open only briefly, and the market for the TRS, to the extent that it was ever there, was no exception. While Western Research built its sophisticated (and consequently very expensive) TRS pulp and paper emission analyzer, a company in the United States came up with a much simpler and cheaper one. The U.S. company sewed up the market before Western Research got there.

In the end, Western Research had a serious and expensive failure on its hands, and its first lesson in the risks of entering a new market with a new product.

Technology alone does not guarantee success. You need to create a market pull.

Another new product, new market scenario that went awry began with a problem the sour gas processing industry was having with its amine units. The amine unit, upstream from the sulphur plant, is where natural gas is sweetened by absorbing its entrained hydrogen sulphide in amine. To try and improve their understanding of corrosion in the amine unit, the gas processors needed to be able to precisely measure the H_2S in the amine solution coming off the stripper, and at the moment they had no way of doing it.

Robin Rankine had been considering this problem and he believed he had a way of performing the measurement needed. What made it difficult was that the hydrogen sulphide existed in the vessel in both a vapour phase and a liquid phase. What Robin discovered was a way of correlating the vapour pressure of the H_2S in the vapour phase to the H_2S concentration in the liquid phase. With the correlation, he believed he could measure the total H_2S in the amine. By knowing this amount, operators could also operate the plant in a more fuel-efficient manner, using less steam, so fuel saving could also be listed as a selling point.

Joe Lukacs was very excited by this idea. He had long believed that the amine plant represented a logical market for Western Research to move into, being the next closest niche to their own. All they needed was the right idea, and maybe this was it.

The problem this time was that the product, the 736 H_2S in Amine analyzer, was not as marketable as Western Research had supposed. First of all, in corrosion control terms, it did only half the job the gas processors needed done. What they really needed was an instrument that could measure both the hydrogen sulphide and the carbon dioxide in the amine. The one without the other was of limited use. As for fuel savings, it was the usual situation: no one really cared. Western Research had just spent another $150,000 developing an analyzer they couldn't sell.

The post-mortem suggested that Western Research hadn't known enough about the amine plant process. Had they known, they would have realized early on that a successful instrument would need to measure both H_2S and CO_2 in order to help with corrosion control. From their earlier ventures (the incinerator fuel savings program), they should also have known better than to try and sell a product on fuel savings. Basically, they had allowed themselves to be led into product development not by market forces but by a neat theoretical idea. The lesson learned was: don't be lured into product development by research alone.

Once again, the high risk associated with the new market, new product scenario had proven true.

They say bad news comes in threes, and there would be one more product setback associated with the 1980s, which was a Dew Point Analyzer called the 241. The product also qualified as "a new product in a new market" because it was for dew point analysis in pipelines. What it had in common with the TRS was that it came from outside the company, from a credible source, with a promise of a strong, almost guaranteed market. This time, the bringer of the technology was NOVA Corporation, a major Alberta-born international corporation with a vast network of pipelines.

Several of the problems that had bedevilled the previous two products soon popped up with the 241. A prototype of the analyzer came from NOVA along with the idea, but to meet the electrical codes, it had to be redesigned. Another problem was that the market forecasts for the analyzer had

Because of the high risk, the new product/ new market situation is most dangerous to the small company.

been done by NOVA, and they had not been checked by Western Research. There was limited incentive to do so because the sale to NOVA alone was supposed to cover the project's cost.

That was the real crisis of the 241. When the analyzer was ready to go to market, even NOVA, the originator of the idea, didn't want it. The company's field people baulked at the expense. The only major sale of 241s was to Russia: an initial sale of fifty. But even this turned into a disaster. They were shipped to a remote part of Russia, and the Russians claimed they didn't work. The Western Research counter-claim was that the Russians couldn't make them work. In any case, it was hardly a success, and the life of the 241 was basically over before it started.

In one sense, Western Research was led into these product failures by its own hunger for new products to sell: its fear of saturating the sulphur recovery market and having nowhere to go. Another possible reason for the company's tendency to make these mistakes comes from its own history and its own culture. In twenty-five years, Western Research had often made its way in the world by leaping from one high wire to another, trying not to look down. It had a culture of not being afraid, of saying yes to everything, of saying yes and then counting on your own ingenuity to figure out how to do what you had promised to do. The culture was geared for plunging in, regardless of the dangers and consequences. It was a great way to be as long as it worked.

Now, Western Research may have developed the problem of not knowing how to say no when no was the correct an-swer. As Blaine Lee puts it, "Any strength carried to excess becomes a weakness."

When Western Research had been in the comfort zone of products and markets it understood well, the culture of not being afraid had helped them more than it had hurt them. At other times, plunging forward into darkness had panned out in fortunate, exciting victories. They had taken chances and won. But now, in the tough zone of new products and new markets, the company was on a losing streak. It needed to learn new ways of doing things, fast.

When entering a new market, lower the risk: learn all that you can about the market drivers.

When Joe Lukacs looks back to this time, certain lessons are evident, things that all entrepreneurial companies need to learn. The first is summed up by the quote at the head of this chapter: the fact that when Western Research had a separate, dedicated R&D department, it created losing products. When Western Research had resisted having an R&D department, when everyone had been involved in R&D and the product developments grew organically out of everyone's experience in the field, they built winners.

The difference was that in the early days they had always been responding to the market. They were creating what their customers hungrily needed. When they had an R&D department that was no longer doing its own field research, the ideas for products came from elsewhere and tended to prove less reliable.

The combination of an isolated R&D group creating new products for new markets was deadly. They were out of their niche, and they were not taking all the necessary steps to round up the knowledge that would make of the new market a new niche. Everyone thought they were doing it, but in hindsight it wasn't happening.

The question was, could Western Research turn the corner? Could it grow and diversify successfully? Or would it kill itself in the attempt?

> **When we made our biggest mistakes, we were strong enough to survive them.**
>
> —Joe Lukacs

❖ *Why is the risk so much higher when a company develops new products for new markets?*

❖ *Why is an isolated R & D department so dangerous for a small company?*

❖ *How might Western Research have reduced the cost associated with developing new products?*

The Russian Market

One of the last frontiers for Western Research's sales team proved to be Russia, with its enormous resources of sour petroleum. It was a big market but so were the problems associated with working there. The first penetration was by Wilhelm Pier when he sold analyzers to Lurgi for use in Tenguiz in modern-day Kazakhstan. To make further inroads, Western Research needed an agent, and they were able to get one who had represented another Calgary-based company.

Yuri Golubev seemed to know the right people and possessed a fax machine, the first of those anyone had seen in Moscow. This gentleman would soon hand them over to his employee and fellow Muscovite, Elena Zolatareva. Western Research was Elena's principal company and the arrangement worked out very well.

In time, the company sold analyzers into Mubarek (near Samarkand) in Uzbekistan and into Astrakhan in southern Russia. This led in turn to process analytical work in these areas. These areas of Russia were so far removed from tourism or even ordinary business travel that transportation, food, and lodging were major problems. Aeroflot reserved its best equipment for its international and tourism runs, and the aging Tupalov planes that conveyed the air traveller into Astrakhan and Uzbekistan were somewhat like third-class buses, chickens and all. Gerald Bohme and Bruce Klint were put up at the local asylum in Mubarek one time while working there—not quite up to Holiday Inn standards.

Elena Zolatareva

One of the strong things about selling into Russia was that, once an agreement was struck with Gazpromov, the U.S.S.R. government, or its national companies, the money was good. Letters of credit from the Russian banking system were as good as gold. This would not be as true after the velvet revolution of 1989.

John Sames, who moved to Europe to start a European office in 1991, made a sale of seven analyzers to Mubarek around the time of the revolution. Because of the company's comfort with the Russian banking system, they didn't bother to secure the letter of credit they had received for the sale. In the mayhem of the revolution, the letter of credit failed, and it took a year and a half of personal persistence by Elena, their Russian representative, to get the money. The people of Uzbekistan claimed they had paid twice and that the Russians were to blame.

The Russian experiment went even more radically wrong in the 1990s when fifty brand new Western Research dew point analyzers were sold to Russia for $2.5 million. They were shipped to a remote part of Russia, and they didn't work; or, more precisely, they didn't work the way the Russians wanted them to.

31

Reclamation, Remediation and Hazardous Waste Clean-Up

Hazardous waste was the new frontier. As a cutting-edge company, we had to go there. It was also important to give newer employees a taste of the excitement of our pioneer years.
—Joe Lukacs

When BVRS purchased Chem-Security in 1984, in order to partake of the Swan Hills hazardous waste treatment project, it was partly to do with what a good fit that business was with Western Research's established expertise. Basically, they had the whole support system in-house: risk assessment, test protocols, monitoring, EIAs. The two sister companies, Western Research and Chem-Security, would contract projects and sub-contract to one another as needed. A further connection was Joe Lukacs. While retaining his position with Western Research, Joe became president of Chem-Security Alberta, which had the contract to design and construct the Swan Hills plant. Chem-Security Limited, the company's international arm, would eventually bid on hazardous waste projects all over the world, marketing the expertise developed for Swan Hills.

Chem-Security was in the site reclamation/remediation business before becoming part of BVRS. It had participated in the clean-up of a CIL explosives site in Calgary and was part of the clean-up of the old Gulf Pincher Creek sulphur plant. The market for this kind of work was potentially huge. All the plants and gathering systems built in Western Canada since the Leduc strike of 1947 would eventually exhaust their fields and have to come out. Alberta regulation specified a regimen of reclamation/remediation responsibilities that each departing company must fulfill.

Western Research's ability to contribute to this work was well tested. EIAs, and the kinds of environmental monitoring required by government in Alberta for licence renewals, often required soil testing. Agrologists and soil experts had often been included on the Western Research teams. Soil sampling was a basic requirement on reclamation jobs so it was very handy to have a sister company capable of doing it.

Graham Latonas, Western Research's biophysical impact expert on its EIA team, further extended that soils expertise through work he did with Dr. Roy Krause, a University of Calgary physicist. By looking at the ratio of sulphur isotopes, they were able to tell the difference between naturally occurring and industrially deposited sulphur found in soil.

In the mid-1980s, Western Research got a very important contract to design the first reclamation/remediation of a Department of National Defence Cadin-Pinetree radar station. These radar stations, which crossed

Graham Latonas

southern Canada, were about to be shut down, and Western Research's job was to use the Penhold, Alberta, station as a pilot for developing a detailed decommissioning plan for all the stations. These radar stations typically had emergency-power facilities so transformer PCBs was one example of risk. Everything from how waste oil had been disposed of over the years to what their landfills contained, and of what material their doors were made, was considered. Dave Picard played a key role in this work for Western Research.

After Penhold, Western Research did a similar DND job at a Canadian Forces Base in Inuvik. This one involved the decommissioning of a radio station and intelligence gathering site.

Related to the reclamation work was hazardous waste treatment and clean-up, often dealing with PCBs. PCBs are polychlorinated biphenyls, synthetic compounds of chlorine, carbon, and hydrogen. Part of a family of synthetics known collectively as chlorinated organic compounds, PCBs are stable and relatively fire-resistant, characteristics that made them attractive as a cooling and insulating fluid for industrial transformers and capacitors, but which also make them extremely resistant to chemical and biological breakdown. Since the 1960s, PCBs have been recognized as an environmental and health hazard, and, since 1977, they have been banned in Canada for most non-electrical uses. Their manufacture in North America also stopped that year.

One of the earliest PCB jobs done by Chem-Security in Alberta, and assisted by Western Research personnel, was the clean-up of a PCB warehouse at Nisku, south of Edmonton in 1985. A company had been gathering PCB waste at Nisku with the intention of establishing a treatment facility in Alberta. When this bid failed, the company went out of business, leaving significant volumes of PCB waste stored at Nisku.

Chem-Security got the contract to clean up the site and borrowed Graham Latonas from Western Research to act as site manager. The job consisted of re-inventorying and re-packaging the PCB waste, and transferring it to another site to await treatment.

Another company called Kinetic Contaminants had been importing PCB waste into Nisku, much of it from eastern Canada. During one shipment, a serious PCB spill occurred in Kenora, Ontario.

In the wake of the Nisku situation and the spill at Kenora, the Alberta government declared a moratorium on the importation of hazardous waste into the province, a decision that would have major consequences for the Swan Hills waste treatment facility, the design and construction of which was then underway.

Several PCB-related projects followed for Chem-Security and Western Research. They investigated PCB contamination at the Fire Park site in northeast Calgary. At Windsor Farms in southeast Edmonton, they evaluated a site where

Air monitoring trailer on Fortress Mountain: one of Western Research's contributions to the Acid Deposition Research Project, 1985-87.

Air monitoring trailer in Malaysia: one of 50 called for in the joint venture between Western Research and its Malaysian partner.

Kevin Warren chasing weather balloons
for the Canadian Occidental Mazeppa project.

John Sames and Randy Hauer take turns being Red Guards in Red Square.

*Elena Zolatareva:
Western Research's
Moscow representative.
Norm Stein on left.*

Lou Conron (centre) and Don Colley (right) present Joe Lukacs with a western bronze to commemorate Western Research's 25th anniversary.

B. J. Seaman playing baseball at the 25th anniversary barbeque.

On left: Joe Lukacs and Helen Lukacs. On right: Zoli Lukacs and one of the twin granddaughters.

Joe Lukacs and Ed Hardy at the 25ᵗʰ anniversary celebration.

Joe Lukacs's ranch and refuge southwest of Priddis.

John Schurer
(1915-1999)

John Schurer was born in Calgary. His father died when he was fifteen and he entered the years of the Great Depression more or less on his own. He chased his living into Canada's north and there he ran a trading post for the Hudson's Bay Company. That was where he met his future wife, Emma, a trapper's daughter. They were married at Arctic Red River, North West Territories. During the 1940s, John worked on the CANOL pipeline project. He continued in Imperial's employ for the next thirty years, as a caterpiller operator and rig mechanic. By the time of John's early retirement from Imperial, in 1970, the five Schurer children were grown up. The youngest, Bob, started his career with Shell and moved to Western Research in 1973 as the company's first marketing manager. In 1976, Bob took a year off to travel, and, when he returned, he found his father somewhat dissatisfied with semi-retirement. Bob asked Western Research if there might be a job for his father, and John started with the company as its handyman that same year. Soon, John was also purchasing for the company. By the time he retired in 1981, he was Western Research's purchasing manager. John is remembered as a father figure at Western Research, with a particular gift for teaching the young. Zoli Lukacs, now an engineer like his father, Joe, worked summers for Western Research when he was a student, and he remembers being taken aside by John Schurer, sat down, and scolded. He also remembers how good he felt leaving those sessions. Joe Lukacs Jr. also worked summers for John and remembers him as being like a grandfather who fed him a steady stream of Dad's cookies. All in all, Western Research loved John Schurer, and the feeling was mutual. His son Bob recalls how often his father said that his five years at Western were the best of his working life. After retiring from Western in 1981, John Schurer and Emma returned to Edmonton where they had lived during John's Imperial years. He died in 1999.

*Canadian Gas Processors Suppliers Association award
received by Western Research.*

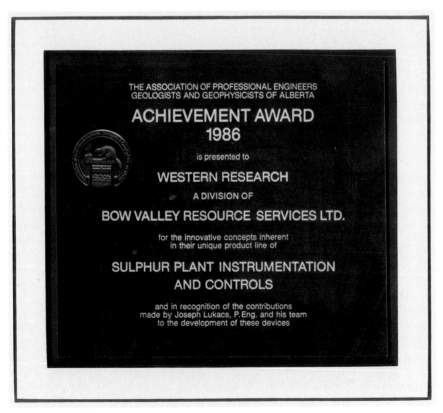

APEGGA award received by Western Research.

A consulting group at the Banff 2000 Western Research reunion workshop: (left to right) Dave Picard, Peter Gammell, Paul Beauchemin, Les Frank, Gord Brown, Mike Zelensky, Graham Latonas, Rick Connery, Elmer Berlie, Martin Hansen, Don Colley

Joe Lukacs and Elmer Berlie at the Banff 2000 workshop

Some of Western Research's 400-plus alumni at Banff, February, 2000.

the Edmonton tornado had strewn a scrap dealer's PCB transformers around an agricultural area.

Probably the most tricky PCB job the companies took on came in the wake of a fire at Suncor's oil sands extraction plant in the fall of 1987. A bank of transformers in a control room on the burned building's third floor had to be drained and re-packaged on site, all in a building left fragile by the fire. Afterwards, the PCBs went into storage, pending the completion of the Swan Hills plant.

Every PCB incident was further proof of the need for the Swan Hills hazardous waste treatment facility, which Joe Lukacs and his team were working hard to complete. Many consultants were used to perform the work at Swan Hills, but Joe Lukacs insisted that Western Research get the work in the areas where its expertise was superior.

Site selection and the environmental work prior to construction was done by Alberta Environment and the Alberta Special Waste Management Corporation (ASWMC). ASWMC contracted Western Research to set up the monitoring trailer with meteorological instruments and monitors for SO_2, NO_x, H_2S, O_3, and other standard pollutants. In addition, Western Research did some grab sampling for organic compounds, which were analyzed by Alan Legge's group at the University of Calgary. This was frontier work for the company, and the detection capability was not sufficient. The results were of limited value. Several other consultants were retained by ASWMC for study of wildlife, vegetation, soils, small mammals, and surface and ground water.

Another Western Research involvement at Swan Hills was a regional emission inventory of the Swan Hills area. Dave Picard worked on this project and developed a significant expertise in developing emission and fugitive emission inventories. This expertise would figure in his later business ventures.

Western Research's most in-depth involvement with the new Swan Hills facility was development of the Trial Burn program for the Von Roll rocking kiln, whose job it would be to destroy PCBs and other organic compounds at high temperature. This Trial Burn program was vital to the whole

Swan Hills venture, in that it would prove or disprove the kiln's ability to achieve 99.9999 percent destruction of PCBs, TCB, TCE, and PAHs.

Don Colley managed the Trial Burn program with Dave Picard as principal investigator. First of all, they had to develop the capability to sample and analyze the various chlorinated organics. Then they had to develop the strategic plan for the Trial Burn (and get Alberta Environment approval for it).

Bob Corbet

The team charged with developing a system for collecting the samples at Swan Hills was led by Ross Jackson. Ross's group put together a stack sampling system that could quantitatively collect the volatile and semi-volatile compounds.

Working at Western Research's Calgary lab, Bob Corbet was instrumental in developing the analysis of the organic compounds. Bob came to Western Research in 1987 and spent a large part of his first eighteen months with the company developing and implementing trace analytical techniques for point source testing of toxic organics and metals emissions. In the race to get Swan Hills up and running, this aspect had fallen behind. Bob Corbet together with Ralph Eng, Margaret Joo, and Paul Eleckna struggled to catch up. There wasn't a lot out there in terms of knowledge and equipment for sampling and analyzing these compounds at this level of sensitivity. For example, the high-acid, high-moisture nature of the stack emissions could not be reproduced in the lab without damaging the equipment. The team found ways to work through this and perform the tests fully two years before their instrument suppliers began attempting to deal with the same design limitations. The final proof of this capability was a series of blind quality assurance tests performed by an external auditor, the most heavily audited test series ever performed in Canada at that time. Western Research passed over 90 percent of the over one hundred tests thrown at them: an excellent result.

The Western Research lab parlayed their Swan Hills experience into a wide range of environmental projects. They did routine analysis and special trace clean-up projects for an ever-widening range of clients, based on their new and expanding ability to test for exotic trace organic pollutants in air, water, or soil.

Finding a way to prove that the Von Roll rocking kiln could achieve the 99.9999 percent destruction of PCBs was somewhat complicated by the fact that it had to be done without introducing PCBs to the kiln. What Don Colley's group did was find a surrogate, non-PCB compound that was as difficult, or more difficult, to destroy than PCBs. The compound chosen was sulphur hexafluoride (SF_6). By using it, Western Research was able to prove that the Von Roll kiln was up to the job. After that, tests with actual PCBs began: nine tests over six months. At the end of the process, the unit was approved for use by Alberta Environment.

Working in areas of public controversy exposes you to the risks of politically motivated change.

The development of this testing capability was a major advance for Western Research. The company went on to do test burns on a variety of other hazardous waste incineration devices. One of these was the VESTA portable incinerator, tested at Swan Hills by Western Research. The VESTA incinerator was designed to treat PCB-contaminated soil, and the test was sponsored by major government and utility clients in Ontario and Quebec, as well as the federal government. The incinerator in fact failed to meet the necessary standard of performance.

Western Research also conducted the performance evaluation (trial burns) on the two incinerators that were added to the Swan Hills facility to increase its organic incineration capacity: the CE Raymond Rotary Incinerator added in 1990, and the FB & D Incinerator added in 1994. Graham Latonas, who left Western Research in 1988 to work on setting up a hazardous waste facility in Manitoba, was lured back to Alberta by Joe Lukacs in 1990. Employed now by Chem-Security, Graham and Al Wakelin, an engineer and former plant manager, managed the EIA for the FB & D incinerator project.

Another exceptional test of Western Research's capabilities in the hazardous waste area was Project Swiftsure, undertaken for the Department of National Defence in 1989. The goal of the project was the destruction of mustard gas and mustard gas–contaminated materials at the Defence Research Establishment at Suffield in southern Alberta.

More than fifteen years earlier, Western Research had worked at Suffield on another mustard gas destruction project, led by combustion expert Dr. Roger Mellor, assisted by chemist Larry Peters. Mustard gas is in fact a liquid and the method chosen for destroying it in 1973 was to burn it in a type of kiln developed for the destruction of the hazardous pesticide DDT. Before combustion, the mustard gas was detoxified with lime.

The only way to keep high-tech innovators in your company is to challenge and excite them with work on the frontiers of their disciplines.

The 1973 trial burn was completed successfully. When the actual destruction of mustard gas got underway, the military did the detoxification and often used too much lime. The result was that the burners frequently plugged up with calcium. Larry Peters flew down to Suffield in his vintage Luscombe to supervise the project. The regular cleaning out of the furnace was part of his responsibility. Peters also had a serious accident with the liquid mustard gas. He burned his arm and, when the military doctors wouldn't treat him because he was a civilian, he had to go to a local doctor, who, not understanding the problem adequately, treated the arm with alcohol. The alcohol dissolved and spread the mustard gas, enlarging the burn area.

In part because of the operating problems, the project ran out of funds before all the chemical warfare agents could be destroyed.

Now, in 1989, Western Research was back, charged with the construction of a new incinerator, and the conducting of another trial burn. The regulatory environment had also greatly changed. Gord Brown, now Dr. Gordon Brown, having completed his PhD in Resource Ecology at UBC, returned to Western Research in 1988, and was given a major role in the project. His job with Swiftsure was to get the approvals that would permit the project to go ahead, and this was not easy. The secrecy of the military's work at Suffield had created a lot of suspicion in the community. In the first public meetings, Gord Brown says, "We got roasted." Recognizing that people were very concerned about their health, he felt they needed an expert who could speak to those health concerns. Having heard Dr. Bob Willes of CanTox give a paper on health effects related to the incineration of PCBs, Gord Brown felt this was the right person to carry the ball. Together, Dr. Brown and Dr. Willes took a risk assessment approach to the problem, which greatly helped it to succeed.

Western Research's involvement in Swiftsure included the design and installation of a Continuous Source Emission Monitor, design and implementation of the trial burn, and installation and operation of the air monitoring system. Key personnel involved included Bob Rutberg of Chem-Security, Kurt Hansen and Bill Wong. Tom Kinderwater, who joined the group as site superintendent, went on to become a vice-president of BOVAR and plant manager at the Swan Hills Waste Treatment Facility.

Gord Brown

In the end, Project Swiftsure was successful, and the chemical warfare agents at Suffield were destroyed without incident. During the project, BOVAR (which BVRS became during the Swiftsure project) developed and patented a chemical neutralization process for lewisite, one of the warfare agents it was charged with destroying. In the 1990s, BOVAR marketed the technology to the United States army for the destruction of a lewisite stockpile in Utah.

In 1990, the company's twenty-fifth year, Western Research was functioning at a peak of expertise higher than it ever had before. It was a world leader in sulphur plant process analysis and analyzer design. Its meteorological work, air quality monitoring, and EIA services were at a scientific research standard. The last five years had added a variety of hazardous waste treatment-associated services that had reinforced the company's claim of being broad spectrum, world class, and cutting edge in its field.

It was also, because of changes of ownership, on the verge of becoming a very different company than it had been.

❖ *What are the risks and problems related to having a dominant client?*

❖ *What were Western Research's growth constraints at this stage in its development?*

Epilogue

When asked what life was like for Western Research in 1989, Joe Lukacs responds that it was much the same as the year before, or the year before that. The company was doing great things at the time. In many ways, it had reached its peak. It was also profitable, so there was not much incentive or pressure to change. The corporate structure within which Western Research lived, however, wasn't making money and hadn't for some time. In 1989, that structure changed completely.

Bow Valley Resource Services Ltd.'s debt problems, incurred during the NEP years and the gathering world energy glut, continued to worsen through the mid-1980s until the company could no longer pay what it owed. In 1989, BVRS discontinued its offshore operations and put its semi-submersible drilling rigs up for sale. A massive write-down in the value of the company's assets translated into a huge loss that year. On March 8, 1989, trading in BVRS stock was halted. The Royal Bank of Canada stepped in and took control of the company.

After a complete financial reorganization, BVRS emerged with a new focus, revised ownership, and a new name. In May of 1989, BVRS became BOVAR Inc. Arnie Bygate was brought in as the new president, and he supervised the selling off of all BOVAR's assets that were not related to the environmental industry. The Hi-Tower, Sedco, and Apollo drilling companies were sold. Mainland Manufacturing and Oilfield Supply were also sold, as was BOVAR's fifty percent share in Western Star Trucks.

What remained in BOVAR were Chem-Security (Alta) Ltd., Chem-Security Ltd., and Western Research: the three units of the company that had always been directly overseen by Joe Lukacs.

In 1990, in the midst of these changes, Western Research celebrated its twenty-fifth anniversary. Nancy Weigel, Joe Lukacs's assistant, was largely responsible for organizing the anniversary events, and she remembers how Joe used all his patriarchal ability in this period to keep the group settled down. His attitude was that Western Research remained a solid company, financially healthy and successful in every way. It had never been anything but a plus for BVRS, and the only unfortunate fact was that Western Research hadn't been big enough to make a significant difference relative to the massive debts that brought the parent company down.

Ever the optimist, Joe Lukacs was determined to go with the changes: with the new ownership, the new board, and whatever new vision they had in mind. He would pull with them if he could, and he would encourage his troops to do likewise.

In this spirit, the Western Research twenty-fifth anniversary was celebrated with at least as much flare, fervour, and exuberance as the twentieth anniversary had been. The celebration was out at Joe Lukacs's ranch at Millarville. It was a family event with horses to ride, trails to hike, fish to catch in the pond, a horseshoe pit, and a baseball game. The employees gave Joe a western bronze, and there was a special cake. Joe's wife Helen made her special goulash and a top restaurant catered the rest of the food. Joe's parties were by now famous for their high culinary quality, and he didn't let anyone down. Some two hundred people came to share in the celebration.

If anyone attending suspected that this might be one of the last Western Research parties, with all the old familiar faces present, and that the company was about to change away from its old self and ways forever, it only added to the zest with which the people of Western Research celebrated their company's past.

❖

Western Research and Development, in the old sense of being a wide-spectrum environmental products and services company, did not survive the 1990s. It did not come to an end abruptly, but bits and pieces of the company were sold off, and services it had supplied were terminated, until it became a very different entity than it had been in the 1970s and 1980s. The part of the old company that stayed with BOVAR was the Swan Hills waste treatment facility, so that the only employees who had the option to remain were those most closely associated with that operation. Other personnel chose to move with their departments or groups as they were sold off to new owners. The remainder either retired or left to pursue other opportunities. They joined unrelated companies or started businesses of their own.

Whenever Western Research alumni gather, discussions of why Western Research broke apart are a conversational staple. That is inevitable. A company that was profitable and seemed tough as old whalebone had fractured into parts. A company that had been a major part of its employees' lives for decades was no more. As happens when a family member dies in an unexpected way, the tendency is to cast about for logical reasons, for a system of causation, or for someone to blame.

In management terms, it is also very important to know what went wrong at Western Research, so that other companies can spot similar problems in advance, and hopefully correct them before it's too late. What follows is a selection of the most often-cited reasons for the splitting apart of Western Research.

The most consistently stated reason is that the BOVAR ownership that came in after the Seaman brothers departed was too culturally different to retain the interest and loyalty of long-term Western Research employees. The new owners made sweeping changes and did not, from the point of view of Western's employees, seem to understand the value of the structures they were dismantling: how the service end of the company, low margins and all, supported the profitability of the products end; how service wasn't a complementary frill but an essential edge in a market where significant technological superiority wasn't possible anymore.

Unless your technology is widely superior, you will make it or fail on service and customer loyalty.

But that's not the only opinion. Others point back to the days before the change of ownership and see the beginnings of problems happening there, situations that magnified during the 1990s. This theory holds that, during the period when Joe Lukacs was drawn away from Western Research to supervise the Swan Hills waste treatment facility project, Western Research lost some of its focus and cohesiveness. The series of product failures might have been a symptom of this. Maybe if those failures could have been avoided or replaced with product successes, the company's internal glue would have been stronger during the time of crisis to come.

> *The stronger the sense of family within a company, the more difficult it becomes to tolerate new leaders from without.*

Another theory is that the cohesive culture of Western Research, its traditions and tremendous ability to retain employees for the long haul, had in some ways become a detriment to progress in that it had caused the company to become inflexible and brittle. When new leaders were brought in from outside, fault was always found with them. They didn't understand; they didn't fit in. The company rank and file rebelled against their authority. Not that rebellion was anything new at Western Research, but Joe Lukacs wasn't always present now to allow deviation and argument while retaining discipline and the ultimate authority.

Nor was it necessarily a better solution to find the new leaders within. The middle managers had always been one another's peers. If one seemed to get more attention or power than the others, the result was jealousy. The family metaphor applies. In a sense, Joe Lukacs had to be present as a paternal figure to prevent civil war. Or if that sounds too theatrical a description, certainly he was needed to decrease energy-wasting, creativity-deflecting internal strife. It is doubtful if the company would have ever accepted one of its own to be a new president, while Joe Lukacs moved more completely into the role of CEO.

The ability to pull one way in a crisis had always been a Western Research strength, perhaps the ultimate one. If that was lost, the company was in peril.

But the over-riding reason that Western Research did not last into the new millennium, except for the portions of it that still exist in other companies, was a combination of will and economics. The new ownership wanted different things out of Western Research: a different pattern of growth; a different emphasis in its mix of activities. Many in the company were uncomfortable with the new style and changes, and, willingly or unwillingly, they moved on rather than submit to them.

Not caring for the direction in which the company was moving, Joe Lukacs resigned in 1992, after twenty-seven years. For all the reasons cited above, he was a hard act to follow. Some of the alumni interviewed describe their career journey after Western Research as a search for the culture and values of leadership they had enjoyed under Joe Lukacs at Western Research. At least one used the word "spoiled," that they had been spoiled by the openness of his management and his willingness to let his key employees pursue their own directions and instincts. Some would have to start their own companies to replicate that experience.

When Joe Lukacs looks back on what could have been done to maintain his company at its peak, he looks back much farther than anyone else: past the difficulties of new ownership in 1990, past the financing crises at BVRS in the 1980s, all the way to 1970, the year that Western R & D took on its powerful new owners. There is little doubt in Joe's mind that Bow Valley Industries was the salvation of Western Research in 1970, because the Seaman brothers shared so many values with Western while having the financial clout to allow the young company to realize its potential. There is also no doubt, for Joe, that when BVRS went down, it took Western Research with it. The unique loyalty of the Western Research employees toward the parent company worked against them at that point.

Like many other Western Research alumni, Joe believes that the company did not survive the change in ownership because the difference in values was too great, which is exactly why he looks back to 1970 as the only occasion when he might have been able to do something differently that could have saved the company in the long run. If somehow he had managed to maintain his significant share in company ownership, or any ownership share at all, then every one of the changes after 1989 would have necessarily involved him. At the board level, he could have fought the changes with which he did not agree. He would have had the power to argue why the company needed the full spectrum of its activities, and why the high level of customer service was part of the winning package. Not having a share in ownership (after 1970), he could make the arguments in 1989, but no one was compelled to listen.

Although Western Research and Development is no longer the corporate entity it once was, the company legacy lives on. For the over 400 people who worked there, it lives on in memory. In Harold Paskall's *Capability of the Modified-Claus Process* and in the many technical papers delivered and published by the company's employees over the years, it lives on as intellectual property. It lives on in the many breakthroughs it pioneered for industry, and in the awards the company received in recognition of that work. At CETAC-WEST, Joe Lukacs's new company, where he regularly uses the history of Western Research as an example when aiding a new generation of entrepreneurs in the environmental area, Western Research lives on as a valuable case study. Finally, Western Research lives on in the pages of this book, where hopefully it will have its greatest influence yet.

In human terms, the knowledge, values, and influence of Western Research can be found the world over. From Malaysia to Montreal. From Frankfurt to New York City. The Western Research saga resides with some in well-earned retirement and with others who are still putting in the long hours of work that Western Research taught them was the normal way to do business.

Of greatest pleasure to Joe Lukacs, when he looks around himself today, is the way the people who grew up with him in Western Research have gone on to make their mark in a wide array of companies and business ventures, mostly in the environmental area. Through their achievements, they reprove every day what a powerhouse of teams within teams Western Research was during its heyday.

Finally, when you ask what was lost when Western Research burst like some object in space, the answer may be that more in fact was gained than was lost. All the technologies and

talents of which Western Research was composed have coa-
lesced into newer forms. They exist and shine, and have probably grown and multiplied, in the shooting stars that spun off
the original Western Research planet.

It is in celebration of those shooting stars that *The Last
Stack* continues.

❖ **What factors need to be considered when
selecting a new CEO for a company such as
Western Research?**

❖ **In chronological order, what were Western
Research's stages of growth?**

❖ **Do the stages you have identified have a
parallel in most small companies?**

V

The Shooting Stars

*When a big tree falls,
the light pours into the forest.
New plants can grow.*

*T*he culture and the expertise of Western Research did not die. For that to happen, all the Western Research alumni would have needed to retire or to change their careers so totally and completely that none of what they had learned at Western was applicable. In fact, the opposite would happen. The Western Research alumni went on to spawn new companies or enrich existing ones.

In this final section, twenty-four companies are profiled. What they have in common is either that they were started by people from Western Research backgrounds or that individuals or groups with Western Research pedigrees are important leaders within them. It is in these companies that the true, enduring spirit of Western Research resides. It is through them that Western's innovations, cultural, technological, and scientific, are maintained and extended. Here are the leaders of the environmental industry of today and tomorrow.

ANCORE INC.

perseverence and passion pay off

Eighteen and a half years after escaping Communist Poland, Andrew Kusmirek returned. In 1992, he landed in Warsaw to promote BOVAR technology and to begin negotiations for a sale of BOVAR analyzers. Officially, the Cold War was over, but as Andrew sat across the passport control desk from a Polish military officer who seemed to be perusing his passport forever, and going back to his computer to type in information far more often than was routinely necessary, Andrew began to sweat. He was remembering the letter he received in the period after his escape from this country, a letter from the State warning him that, if he was ever apprehended in Poland, he would face a jail sentence of at least five years. He was very much wishing he had never accepted this assignment from BOVAR.

Andrew Kusmirek

Finally, Andrew asked the soldier if it would be necessary for him to check in with the police once a week during his stay, which he knew had been the practice with visiting foreigners throughout the years. The soldier laughed and asked him how long it had been since his last visit. Told that it had been over eighteen years, the soldier declared that the era of that sort of thing was long over. Poland was a free country now.

Emboldened, Andrew asked what was taking so long with his passport. The soldier admitted he had been trying to locate a friend of his who worked at the airport who was also named Kusmirek. He wanted to see if the two were related. In fact they were, distantly.

By the time of this incident, Andrew Kusmirek had been working for Western Research (then BOVAR) for sixteen years. Because it was difficult to get recognition of his Polish master's degree in precision mechanics, he hid the fact of his being an engineer in order to get his first job at Western Research, as a draftsman. Over the years, however, his engineering skills became known and respected at the company, and he rose through the ranks to become supervisor of drafting and the machine shop (1987), then Instrumentation's manager of production engineering, and finally production manager.

Not long after the incident in the Warsaw airport in 1992, BOVAR Inc. offered Andrew a golden opportunity to open an office for the company in Warsaw. He decided to take it and, for the next two years, he worked a month in Poland, then a month in Calgary, on BOVAR's behalf. In charge of marketing and sales for Central Europe, he drove over 200,000 kilometres in that two-year period.

What Andrew swiftly learned was that Poland was a country of enormous economic opportunity. During the Communist era, Russia had more or less forbidden Poland to explore for oil and gas. That way, the country remained reliant on, and a market for, Soviet petroleum. After the fall of the Iron Curtain, Poland did begin to drill for oil and gas, and with great success. As well as petroleum, the country had some of the biggest power plants in the world: coal-fired plants producing 4,000 and 6,000 megawatts of electricity. One had a 400-metre stack. The country was investigating cleaner gas-fired power generation.

What the state of Poland's re-development meant to Andrew Kusmirek was that instrumentation sales opportuni-ties were only the smallest part of what could be done in that country. He began trying to interest BOVAR in moving its European manufacturing headquarters to Poland. One impetus was the fact that a fully equipped building was available for purchase at one-fifth of what a similar building would cost in the company's current manufacturing locale of Frankfurt.

Toward the end of his two-year contract, Andrew realized BOVAR did not intend to make this move. Nor was it likely to greatly extend its Polish operation in other ways. If that was to be the case, his interest in staying in Poland was not great, and he told BOVAR that he would like to exercise his option of returning to Calgary. Knowing that the Polish operation would likely collapse without Andrew Kusmirek in charge of it, BOVAR offered him another deal. What about taking over the Polish operation himself, and representing BOVAR as one of his contracts? Again the details of the proposal were very much in his favour, and Andrew decided to take it on. Another attraction was that several Calgary companies had already approached Andrew about becoming their commission agent in Poland, something that had been impossible as long as he was a BOVAR employee but which was perfectly possible now.

Andrew called his new venture Ancore Inc. That was the holding company, and it operated in Poland through a subsidiary called Ancore International Inc. The first few years of any new venture are often the highest-risk time, and Ancore was no exception. Even after he trimmed down to a one-man operation, Andrew was looking at US$250,000 a year to operate. One thing that was very much in his favour was that he had participated in two trade missions to Poland (one for Western Research and another for BOVAR) and would soon be taking part in a third such mission under his own company name. These missions had given him a network of highly placed contacts in his new/old country which was an absolute necessity for doing business at the level he intended.

The biggest opportunity Ancore Inc. pursued at this time was a major gas plant contract. While representing a Canadian design/manufacturing company, he hired another Canadian company, an engineering company, to assist in the bidding procedure, to prepare the technical specifications, and to eventually become project manager. What Andrew Kusmirek was doing was introducing a North American-style bid into the post-Cold War environment of Poland. Under the old Communist system, costing, financing, risk assessment, and even detailed budgeting had been rendered unnecessary by rigid central control of every project. But in a market-driven economy, the same items became of paramount importance. Poland had a lot of catching up to do, and Andrew's experience and present position put him in an excellent spot to help.

It took three and a half years of work, extraordinary hours, and no holidays, but Andrew Kusmirek's presence in Poland, his perseverence, and his passion for what he was doing finally paid off. The bid was successful. For the Canadian company he represented, Andrew Kusmirek had won a US$60 million contract.

From that excellent beginning, Andrew has continued to build his business in Poland. He has become a problem solver, finding out what is needed in the on-going rebuilding of post-Cold War Poland and bringing together the services necessary to accomplish it: a match-maker who supervises major projects from feasibility, through bidding and financing, to fruition. The model he uses is much the same as the one he decided upon in his first years of company life. He operates solo, accessing whatever amount of engineering expertise he needs through his connection with two engineering design companies. His advantage continues to be his knowledge of business acquired with Western Research. The Communist system tended to produce great scientists and engineers who were long on theory but lacking in understanding of North American business practices. Having both engineering design and production skill, plus business savvy, and functioning smoothly across the Polish/English language barrier, Andrew Kusmirek is a man comfortably and capably in the middle, bridging the gap between the two systems that will eventually, in many business ways at least, be one.

After not being in Poland for over eighteen years, Andrew Kusmirek has been back 85 times since 1992. Between then and now, one of the things he has learned to do is focus. Nowadays he does not chase every opportunity that comes up. He evaluates them, selects the ones he wants to pursue, and then: "I'm like a cobra. I strike when I'm prepared and the time is right, and my chances of succeeding are very good." The next evolution in his career he believes will be in the financial direction. Instead of bringing projects together in an engineering sense, he expects to be doing so more on a financial level. "Back in my engineering days at Western Research," he says, "I used to hate budgeting. But I guess I learned a lot doing it. Now it looks like it might be my future."

THE BRIMSTONE COMPANIES

failure is still not an option
for this hard-working team

The two Brimstone Companies were incorporated in 1992 by Ron Dimmer, Don Stevens, and Mike Anderson, all of whom are Western Research alumni. Brimstone Engineering Services, Inc., based in Colorado, began to do business immediately, while Brimstone Instrumentation Ltd., based in Calgary, performed market studies until entering an R & D phase in 1995. Brimstone Engineering Services, Inc., with Ron Dimmer as president, is owned by the three equal share holders: Ron Dimmer, Don Stevens, and Mike Anderson. Brimstone Instrumentation Ltd., with Don Stevens as president, restructured in 1995 and added more Western Research alumni to its group of owners. The company's major shareholders now include Don Stevens, Ron Dimmer, Mike Anderson, and Robin Rankine. Barry Glenn, Dennis Hnidan, and Terry Crooks hold minor share equities.

BRIMSTONE ENGINEERING
SERVICES, INC.

Brimstone Engineering Services, Inc. is a Colorado-based corporation, offering unique field testing and process evaluation services. It is active in the oil refining, gas processing, and chemical industries. The processes to which its services apply include amine treating plants, Claus sulfur recovery units, tail-gas treating units, thermal and catalytic incinerators, and other sulphur-related industrial processes. In addition, Brimstone offers highly specialized analytical testing of fuel gas, LPG, and hydrogen plant process streams.

Brimstone Engineering Services, Inc. was launched in May 1992 by Western Research alumni, Ronald Dimmer and Donald Stevens. In September of that year, Michael Anderson was added as an equal partner along with additional staff, all of whom were former Western Research employees. Operating out of Denver, Brimstone Engineering Services, Inc. is

Ron Dimmer

very much a technological and cultural continuation of the work Ron Dimmer did in the United States when he managed Western Research's U.S. operations. Considering his twenty-two years in plant testing and analysis with Western Research, and his eight years and counting with Brimstone, Ron Dimmer brings enormous knowledge and experience to Brimstone in the amine, sulphur, and tail-gas treating analytical testing areas. The company has perfected the process, pioneered at Western Research, by which a plant's process streams are sampled and analyzed, plant data is collected, and complete heat and material balances are calculated. From this information, detailed evaluations of the plant's operation are fashioned. Brimstone's experience allows its principals to derive expert trouble-shooting programs and operating recommendations from its studies. Improved plant operation and higher sulphur recovery efficiency are the rock solid benefits of this work: extremely important to an industry that faces ever more stringent sulphur emission standards.

While Ron Dimmer regards his company's main product to be process analytical information, Brimstone also supplies specialized analytical equipment and associated services to the industries it serves. With the advantage of having its own laboratory, Brimstone can create bench-scale pilot plants for client companies. This can help greatly in areas such as catalyst and process chemistry development. Brimstone Engineering also designs, fabricates and supplies specialized gas chromatographs for clients. The company also provides training and maintenance in their use. In cooperation with Alberta Sulphur Research Ltd., Brimstone manufactures and markets an analytical system for the measurement of H_2S/H_2S_x in liquid sulphur which is vital to the verification of performance in sulphur de-gassing processes and in the Quality Assurance checking of marketed sulphur.

Drawing on its reputation for excellence and expertise, Brimstone works with industry representatives to organize and host the world's only annual operational sulphur symposium. Each September, Brimstone Engineering Services, Inc. facilitates the Vail Sulfur Symposium in Vail, Colorado, which attracts sulphur process experts from the major oil and gas companies, engineering contractors, and industry consultants from around the world. The Vail Sulfur Symposium has gained recognition by industry as being the number one symposium of its kind in the world. Proof of this is the attendance record: 100 percent capacity in every year since its inception, six years ago.

Brimstone Engineering Services, Inc., with offices in Englewood, Colorado and Chino Hills, California, in association with its sister company in Calgary, Alberta, continues to expand on the network of industry contacts that Ron Dimmer and partners started building when they entered the industry as employees of Western Research in 1970.

BRIMSTONE INSTRUMENTATION LTD.

Also incorporated in 1992, Brimstone Instrumentation Ltd. has set out to expand the boundaries of UV spectroscopic technology in sulphur species analysis. The goal was to develop a new family of ultraviolet analytical instruments capable of measuring sulphur species concentrations in inlet acid gas, tail-gas, incinerator stack gas, and related sulphur process streams. The overall goal is to go beyond traditional single-point UV photometry and to come up with a spectroscopic analysis that encompasses the entire UV spectrum of interest.

At the same time, the new family of analyzers has been designed to increase accuracy and reliability, while reducing the complexity of operation and the expense of maintenance. These are tall orders by anyone's definition, but Brimstone has been successful in meeting them. Not only has the company met these initial objectives, but it has been able to do so while achieving a very competitive selling price. Brimstone Instrumentation has also eliminated some of the standard encumbrances associated with this type of instrumentation. The Brimstone instruments have no sample lines, nor do they require expensive climate-controlled shelters.

The commercialization of these products began in 1992 with a three-year program of market research, technology development, and product design. Don Stevens was in charge of the market research and planning, while Robin Rankine

led the technology development with his inimitable brand of inventiveness. Barry Glenn, Manager of Manufacturing and the company's principal engineer, provided the analyzer systems hardware and software designs. Other key members of the Brimstone Instrumentation staff include Dennis Hnidan, Cheryl Whyte, Gordon Ferguson and Janis Brigan, all well known as key contributors to Western Research in former times.

The first Brimstone-manufactured systems went into service in 1995. The first installation of its tail-gas (air demand) analyzer system was at the Texaco Wilmington Refinery in Los Angeles in December, 1995. In the same month, a second tail-gas analyzer system was installed in the Warren (now Dynegy) Sand Hills, Texas, facility. The next three years saw

Don Stevens with the first prototype of Brimstone's tail-gas analyzer, 1995.

gradual, controlled growth as the company proved its technology and built its reputation. The year 1999/2000 saw an extraordinary increase in sales. Sales expanded nearly four times, including international sales in Europe and Mexico. Thanks to an excellent product track record and a reputation for unparalleled customer service, business is booming.

To help Brimstone capture a share of the international market, another name, familiar in the pages of this book, has

Standing, left to right: Don Stevens, Janis Brigan and Dennis Hniden. Seated: Barry Glenn, Shannon (Stevens) Bader.

become part of the Brimstone story. Wilhelm Pier's prestigious German-based company, Pier Enterprises, is now a licensed manufacturer of the Brimstone Instrumentation Ltd. technology.

The Brimstone companies are a bright, successful continuation of the traditions its company founders helped establish at Western Research thirty years or more ago. The knowledge, know-how, and ability they once poured into Western Research, enhanced by further experience, have become the foundations upon which Brimstone Engineering Services, Inc. and Brimstone Instrumentation Ltd. will build and thrive.

ENTECH ENVIRONMENTAL

a company that climbed its way to success

In late 1990, John Jackson, Ross Jackson, and Tim Seedhouse, three senior staff members of the Western Research lab and field department, shut themselves in Ross's office and discussed forming a company of their own. Western Research was in the process of becoming BOVAR, with a consequent

Left to right: Jackie Hudson, Bill Wong, John Jackson, Ross Jackson.

change of ownership and management style, and the three wondered if it wasn't a good time to move on. A fourth lab and field stalwart, Bill Wong, was invited in on the deal, and, on a day other Western Research/BOVAR employees dubbed "Black Tuesday," the four announced their intention to leave the old company and start Entech Environmental Services Limited, an emission sampling, monitoring, and lab analysis company.

Entech began operation in January of 1991, working out of John Jackson's basement rec room. Buying a new computer, and setting it up beside a couple of old ones, they got a separate telephone line and proceeded to get the news out that they had changed address and were in business for themselves. Their target for the first year was quite conservative, and they had over half that much business lined up in a week. They took the next step, renting a single bay in a northeast Calgary building. At the beginning, John and Tim did the field work, while Ross took care of the reporting and the accounting. Bill got on with building the lab. The workload rose quickly, and more employees were taken on accordingly. Bob Mick and Frank Champion were the next two added, both from BOVAR.

Six months later, Jackie Hudson paid a visit to Entech. Since leaving Western Research in 1981, Jackie had held various jobs in the ambient monitoring area, but had been out of the ambient field for a while. She wanted back in, but she wasn't at Entech looking for a job. She wanted a piece of the action. This tallied with a desire on Entech's part to build an ambient department. Shortly, Jackie Hudson became one of the Entech partners, and another company was formed, Entech Environmental Monitoring. After running as a separate com-

pany for five years, Entech Environmental Monitoring merged with Entech Environmental Services.

The Entech team in the year 2000

The equipment the company needed was assembled in many ways from many sources. John Jackson likes to deal, and he had some good luck and made some good coups toward equipping the new company. One of the best was when Amoco, in the process of dismantling its Lone Pine Creek plant, cut him a deal on most of the contents of the plant's lab.

An early test of the company's ability to adapt fast and take on big projects came when Syncrude invited Entech to Fort McMurray to assess an electrostatic precipitator job. Ross and John went north, and, as the process engineer pointed out the desired test points, Ross was counting the heads he would need to accomplish the task. The total came to twenty-two, many times the payroll at Entech at the time.

Entech took it on and scrambled to assemble its crew. Several were former Western Research hands, and several more had to be brought in from the United States, after considerable dickering with Immigration Canada. Eventually the government was convinced that Entech couldn't do the job any other way. To give the multi-sourced crew a cohesive look, Entech ordered blue coveralls with the company name on the back and hats printed with the company ensignia. The crew was instructed to wear both the Entech coveralls and the Entech hats at all times. It was a solid idea but a little wonky on the execution. When the coveralls were handed out and unfolded for the first time, it was discovered that the company in charge of putting the names on had silkscreened across a crease. The result was:

EN   TECH
ENVIRON   MENTAL

The hats were another kind of problem. In the heat, the iron-on letters started to peel. Some wits on the crew peeled theirs so only the letters MENTAL remained.

But the important fact was that the work went off without a hitch: two ESP tests per day on eleven sources for fourteen days.

The air quality monitoring group had a similar start. The original plan was to stay out of the trailer rental business and to focus instead on the less capital-intensive consulting side. Again, an intensive mailer and phone call campaign was under way, and, within a week, a call came in from one of the nearby gas plants, asking for a meeting regarding an air quality monitoring project. John and Jackie drove up to the plant site. During the meeting, the client asked if the new air quality monitoring group had two fully equipped rental trailers available to start work in two weeks. Before Jackie could answer that Entech wasn't planning to offer that service, John jumped in and said it was quite possible. "We just have to check the status of the fleet." Back in the truck, Jackie asked, "What fleet?" After hours on the phone begging their bank manager and suppliers, the trailers were delivered, the first of many in the Entech rental fleet.

As Entech developed, it tended to leave the sulphur plant business to the competition, while pursuing markets in which companies like BOVAR were less comfortable: industries like power generation and pulp and paper. John Jackson was already well known in pulp and paper emission testing because of a Method Five stack sampling course he taught at Mount Royal College. Joe Lukacs had talked him into taking this on while he was with Western Research. Operators for both the power companies and the pulp and paper companies were required to take the course as part of their basic qualifications, but they tended not to do the work for their companies, despite having learned how. What they did instead was look for a company to do it, and who did they know better than John Jackson? When John started Entech, he called upon this extensive network of acquaintances and friends in those industries.

After a decade in business, Entech is a well-established, multi-disciplinary company, dedicated to supplying accurate and cost-effective environmental services to industry. Having their own lab allows them to yield quick results to clients, which is another bonus in out-pacing competitors. The heart of the business is still helping clients to comply with the conditions of the operating approvals issued by government. The six or seven stacks at a pulp mill, the three or four stacks at an average power plant, all need to be tested twice per year, and this is the company's bread and butter on the stack testing and analysis side. The corresponding air quality tests beyond the plants, also compliance-driven, support the air quality monitoring business. Started by Jackie Hudson, the air quality monitoring side is now managed by another ex-Western Research employee, Gary Cross. Jackie has put her analyzer expertise to use developing and managing a new group within the company that specializes in continuous stack emission monitoring, testing, and instrument stack surveys.

From the original focus on power plants and pulp and paper, Entech has branched out into sour gas plants, oil refineries, cement plants, fertilizer plants, waste incinerators, co-generation units, and compressor stations.

The Entech success story is based on many principles and practices that came to the company, along with its leaders, from Western Research. The philosophy that the "customer is your best friend" has served Entech well. Just as they did at Western Research, the leaders at Entech believe in treating every customer's problem seriously and working on it until it is solved.

As was the case with Western Research, Entech has invested in people. It has created a cohesive and long-lasting team. Open door management and making sure that families are happy with the choices of their breadwinners are other winning philosophies. Entech has been very successful in more than a decade of operation at creating a company culture that permeates the office and goes to the field. The company has grown from its four-man start-up to be the largest source testing company in Canada.

SULPHUR EXPERTS (WESTERN RESEARCH)
AMINE EXPERTS

the Sulphur Doctors live on

When John Sames left BOVAR in 1997, following a five-year assignment for the company in Germany, he bought his way out. He took with him so many parts of the company that were formerly key elements of Western Research that he incorporated Western Research into his new company name: Sulphur Experts (Western Research). He perceives Sulphur Experts to be a continuation of Western Research in its technology and methods, culture, and management philosophy. Sulphur Experts is also successful in the way that the older company was at its peak.

Sulphur Experts is a process engineering company with a special focus on the sulphur plant. The central element upon which the company was built was the Process Analytical Engineering (PAE) group that John Sames established at Western Research in 1980 under Don Colley's management, which he later purchased from BOVAR in 1997. Sulphur Experts markets gas plant and refinery testing, performance and optimization studies, sulphur plant efficiency tests, and incinerator optimization tests–all of which will sound very

Western Research alumni at Sulphur Experts: Bruce Klint, John Sames, Peter Dale, and Gerald Bohme

familiar to those who have read the balance of this book about Western Research. Many of the on-site sampling and on-site analytical techniques pioneered by Western Research are still used, or have been improved upon, by Sulphur Experts. Full engineering evaluations, delivering real improvements in plant performance, are the main focus of Sulphur Experts' service.

The data achieved through testing and analysis are evaluated using tools such as the commercially successful sulphur plant simulator Sulsim®, and proprietary in-house software programs INCWRD, Cauldron, and GComp, all of which were developed within Western Research and purchased by Sulphur Experts in 1997. Judy (Ritter) Arrizza, who originally programmed the software for Western Research, works for Sulphur Experts on contract from her home in the United States. She continues to improve and update the programming. Sulsim® is now in version 5, released in March, 1999. This comprehensive simulator of the sulphur plant process is popular worldwide, with only one commercial competitor.

The process engineering team that John Sames has assembled at Sulphur Experts has a strong Western Research character. Bruce Klint, Gerald Bohme, and Peter Dale have long Western Research histories and are co-owners in the new venture. Other Western Research alumni at Sulphur Experts are Brent Lloyd, Ruth Fike, Chuck Stephenson, Peter Seville, Jamie Swallow, Martin Miller, and Farsin Derakhshan. The company has grown since its break with BOVAR and now has eighteen employees located in four offices that reflect the worldwide nature of the company's business: Calgary,

Alberta; Oakville, Ontario; Tyler, Texas; and Heerhugowaard, Netherlands. The most recent additions to the company's cadre of professionals are Elmo Nasato and his wife Linda Nasato in Ontario, and Phil Olesky in Texas. All three are engineers with sulphur plant experience.

John Sames' management philosophy is to promote individuals as professionals in their own right, first, and as members of the collective Sulphur Experts, second. This is done by encouraging publication and seminar presentation, and keeping everyone in the public eye. John also believes in making sure his people are well equipped for the international nature of their business: the adventure of new cultures and exposure to different standards, regulations, and languages. Company personnel travel extensively, and it is important that all understand and relate to the cultures encountered.

Left to right: Brent Lloyd, John Sames, Peter Dale, Martin Miller, Jamie Swallow, Bruce Klint, Gerald Bohme, and Farsin Derakhshan

In addition to the process engineering group and the Western Research process software, John Sames also brought with him to Sulphur Experts the well-respected Western Research sulphur seminars. After John's arrival at Western Research in 1980, he and Harold Paskall were the two individuals charged with the all-important task of maintaining the company's technical image through the organization and presentation of seminars. Over the last twenty years, John has presented 127 seminars, from Kananaskis and Houston to Istanbul and Amsterdam, from India and Singapore to Indonesia and Uzbekistan–literally all over the world. He has been careful to maintain the no-selling, education-only traditions instituted by Harold Paskall on day one and has enjoyed the same surprising promotional benefits by staying technical and not promoting his company too strongly at these events. Through the seminars, Sulphur Experts has built its reputation as sulphur doctors. The process analytical consulting work and software sales naturally follow.

John Sames acquired the rights to Harold Paskall's 1980 textbook on the modified-Claus process (now in its sixth printing). The second sulphur text, co-authored by Harold Paskall and John Sames in 1988 and reprinted by Sulphur Experts, has become the standard text for the sulphur seminars. It is presented to all participants. Sulphur Experts inherited the sulphur doctor reputation from Western Research and has branded that identity into its company through its S_x logo: a visual pun on the medical prescription sign seen on pharmacies.

To say that John Sames has learned from Western Research and from father-figure Joe Lukacs is obvious understatement. He has closely followed the Western Research model in building his company into an international power in process analysis and process education. He has always understood that knowledge was the secret of Western Research's success. Joe Lukacs brought his own and Dr. Petrunic's knowledge of sulphur plants from Canadian Fina to Western Research. The Western Research team built on that knowledge until it was the best in the world. When John Sames decided to move upstream from the sulphur plant into the amine sour gas sweetening plant, something Western Research had talked about for years, he brought in true experts in the field in both Canada and Europe, in the persons of Mike Sheilan and Egbert van Hoorn, to enable the company to achieve the same standard of knowledge in the amine plant as it enjoyed in the sulphur plant.

Because he did not stop short of a total, ground-up, world-leading knowledge, the subsequently formed sister company Amine Experts has been a considerable success.

The most recent and exciting news for this globe-trotting company is in its software area. Long ago, Judy Arrizza's father Dr. Bob Ritter imagined an omnibus computer program that would simulate not only the sulphur plant but the associated amine plant and hyrocarbon processing that fed them. For some time now, the individual parts of that simulation have existed as separate business entities-curiously, all Albertan. Sulphur Experts had Sulsim® (sulphur plant); D. B. Robinson had Amsim® (amine plant), and AEA-Hyprotech had Hysim® (hydrocarbon processing), later called Hysys®. After a long period of negotiation, the three have come to agreement and are about to release a combined program, which will no doubt take the world of sour gas process simulation by storm.

Sulphur Experts (Western Research) and Amine Experts are truly the technological and cultural children of the old Western Research. They are in many ways the fulfillment of Joe Lukacs's dream and the promise of the older company: high-tech, hard working, and known around the world for quality and performance.

WILHELM PIER

the client's best friend

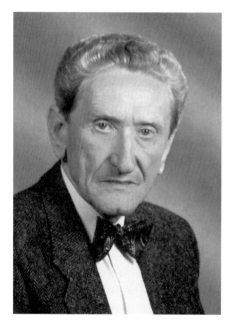

Wilhelm Pier

Y ou often hear of businessmen who started with nothing, but there may be no one of whom it is more true than Wilhelm Pier. In the ruins of post-war Germany, he scavenged bits and pieces from which to build his first saleable product: a saw operated by a sewing machine treadle. The market for his treadle saws was created by the shortage of metal. People were making their consumer goods from wood. When the Americans backed a new currency for post-war Germany, it became possible again to buy things. That was the end of the saw business.

His next venture was the construction of freight elevators that ran diagonally beside flights of stairs. There were no safety specifications for this type of elevator, but Wilhelm voluntarily built his to the safety specs that existed for vertical elevators. The quality of his workmanship got him a contract with the large German chemical company, Farbwerke Höchst, to work in their physical department. During that time, with the help of Höchst physicist named Dr. Hoffman, the idea of manufacturing infrared photometric analyzers was born.

Early in the 1950s, Wilhelm Pier got an order from Höchst for a small analyzer capable of measuring moisture in the drycleaning process. He developed a machine known as the Moisture Controller Höchst. Later, Höchst would start giving the machine away free as a means of selling dry-cleaning chemicals. At this point, they gave the machine to Wilhelm, and it became the Moisture Controller Pier. During the marketing of this analyzer, Wilhelm made great inroads into France. He had an office in Paris and became what he calls a "European German," a fact that was essential to his later success with Western Research.

In the 1960s, Wilhelm Pier became associated with the American company Anacon after an Anacon representative saw an analyzer he had created for measuring heavy water in nuclear plants. The result was a fifteen-year relationship, which came to an end because of Anacon's sale to Foxboro. It was at this point that Anacon's Larry Maley recommended that Joe Lukacs get in touch with Wilhelm Pier.

As detailed in Chapter 25 of this book, Wilhelm and Joe Lukacs met in the Frankfurt airport and agreed upon a business relationship within the three-quarters of an hour they had between planes. The trust between them was immediate. They shook hands, and Wilhelm became Western Research's European representative. Then Wilhelm rushed home to look up what a Claus plant was for.

Wilhelm prides himself on having attended more than twenty Western Research sulphur recovery seminars over the years. He did so in order to be able to talk intelligently with his clients on the subject. It took a few years for even Wilhelm to break through the European resistance to buying a western Canadian instrument, but he finally did so. Once started, he was able to sell to major engineering companies like Lurgi and to end users in refineries and coke oven plants. After several tough years, he displaced most of the Dupont analyzers which had been dominant in Europe prior to Western Research's entry into that market.

For ten years, Wilhelm bought tail-gas analyzers from Western Research (and, towards the end of the period, BOVAR), modifying the electrical connections to European standards. He produced and manufactured his own walk-in shelters for the analyzers, and, depending on the application, added electrically traced sample lines.

The market acceptance of Western Research analyzers was such that Wilhelm Pier was able to sell beyond Germany into much of the rest of Europe. In cooperation with German engineering companies, he sold into the Far East as well. In 1991, BOVAR responded by setting up a full Western Research operation in Hattersheim, Germany, under the name BOVAR GMBH/Western Research, with John Sames as manager. Wilhelm's position changed from client to sales representative for the important German market. The handshake understanding he had always had with Western Research was replaced by a formal written agreement and the new BOVAR/Western Research company was installed in a building owned by Wilhelm Pier and custom modified to Western Research's needs.

For the next several years, John Sames worked very closely with Wilhelm Pier and often witnessed the pleasure his old-world clients took in him. Wilhelm was famous for his sayings. Because his relationship with Western Research analyzers was such a foundation stone of his business, he would say his company "was born in the gas fields of Alberta." He has always liked things British, such as gin and tonic, which he insists "improves his English." John recalls that he used to call the drink "liquid Berlitz" in his honour. Wilhelm even drives a Rover Sterling.

On Wilhelm Pier's business card, the letters VDI appear. They stand for *Verein Deutscher Ingenieure*, a society of German engineers chosen by government to hold this rank. At the heart of Wilhelm's fine engineering career is the manufacture, adaptation, and sale of analyzers, both custom analyzers and product lines, most with a specialization related to the sulphur recovery industry and the modified–Claus sulphur recovery process. His inventive engineering has enabled him to solve many difficult sampling and analysis problems for his clients, one example being his automated solution for cracked gas stream sampling in ethylene plants. His computer-automated system cleans out the sample probe, using a high temperature retractable drill head and sample-conditioning system so that the gas chromatograph is never blinded, a problem which had prevented effective analysis in this area for years.

Wilhelm Pier has several companies. Pier Amaturen is his engineering company, specializing in the manufacture of safety valves and other equipment. He designed and installed the main safety valves for the first research nuclear power plant (MZFR) at Karlsruhe, Germany. His "absolute tightness" foil safety valves have been used in many nuclear power plants since that time.

Wilhelm Pier Process Analytical Services is the company through which he sold Western Research analyzers, and through which he still sells his Pier Cracked Gas Samplers worldwide.

Wilhelm Pier GmbH, another company, was landlord to Western Research and serves as landlord for the other Pier companies.

A new company, Pier Enterprises, co-run by Wilhelm's son Peter and Matthias Franz (BOVAR GmbH's former technical manager), specializes in putting a German face on the lines of Canadian instrumentation that the company represents in Europe.

Besides his acuity as an engineer, Wilhelm Pier is renowned for his absolute dedication to his clients. He can't imagine a businessman who would fail to put his home phone number on his business card. When a client calls, Wilhelm is *unterwegs* (on the way), and for however long it takes to solve the client's problem. His power as a representative of his own and other people's instruments comes in part from the fact that the profit motive does not rule him. He has always claimed, "This is not my job; this is my enjoyment." When BOVAR sold its analyzer manufacturing arm to AMETEK in 1998, Wilhelm's long-term association with Western Research analyzers came to an end. His greatest concern was not lost revenue but the fact that he would have no analyzers for them when his clients next called. This was, to him, an embarrassment.

Wilhelm Pier's current venture was established to fill the void left by the loss of the Western Research analyzers. Wilhelm has made links with at least three Canadian companies, Galvanic, Brimstone, and Unisearch, and in so doing has managed to continue to service the industry with UV, paper tape and TDL technologies for H_2S. He also represents E^2Technologies on their infrared temperature devices, while continuing to manufacture his Pier Ethylene Sampler, with which he serves a world market.

The long relationship between Wilhelm Pier and Joe Lukacs (and, hence, Western Research) is unassailable proof that values are not necessarily a matter of nationality, language, or culture (in the sense of ethnicity). When Joe Lukacs and Wilhelm Pier met, they soon knew they shared a belief about what was important in business. They shook hands on it, and, twenty-five years later, they remain the firmest of friends and allies.

JACQUES WHITFORD GROUP LTD.:

If you hire the best, opportunities for growth will never be a problem.

—Hector Jacques

Jacques Whitford is an employee-owned, multi-disciplinary group of companies headquartered in Dartmouth, Nova Scotia. Under the inspired leadership of Hector Jacques, it combines the talents of consulting engineers, environmental scientists, and risk consultants.

With eighteen offices in Canada, four in the United States, and several abroad (Trinidad, U.K., Russia, Argentina), the company employs over 700 people, 42 percent of whom are engineers and scientists, and 37 percent of whom are lab and field technicians. The map of its projects is the map of the world. Rather than having a set menu of skills and services available in each of these markets, the company philosophy is to adjust to local needs. The result has been a steadily increasing international market share and an extraordinary range of capabilities.

Company disciplines include: environmental engineering, environmental sciences and planning, occupational health and safety services, hydrology/hydrogeology, geotechnical engineering, materials testing and research, air quality/noise assessment, integrated risk management, and environmental management systems.

The original Jacques Whitford company began in 1972 in Halifax, when geotechnical engineers Hector Jacques (the company's present-day CEO and board chairman) and Michael Whitford got together to offer services in the earth sciences disciplines to Atlantic Canada. They opened their second office in Saint John, New Brunswick, in 1975. They continued to expand in the geotechnical area but, by the 1980s, had realized to what extent their geotechnical work was preceded or surrounded by complementary environmental work. Predicting that environmental work was a tremendous growth area, and able to envision a powerful synergy, Jacques Whitford began to provide environmental service in the Canadian

Maritime provinces in 1985. The combination of environmental work and geotechnical work has been every bit as successful as they thought it would be.

The Western Research connection at Jacques Whitford dates back to 1994, two years after the opening of the Jacques Whitford Calgary office. Douglas Leahey's close-knit meteorological group at Western Research had become restless owing to changes of direction and philosophy, and, together, they had begun to scout for new opportunities. Douglas Leahey and those who worked for him believed their strength was in their complementary skills and that it would be ideal if they could preserve their group by moving it into a different company. Various circumstances led them to Jacques Whitford and, once they became acquainted with that company and its dynamic leadership, they realized they had hit pay dirt.

Western Research alumni at Jacques Whitford. Left to right: Douglas Leahey, Ben Kucewicz, Martin Hansen, and Mike Schroeder

Douglas Leahey, Ben Kucewicz, Martin Hansen, and Michael Schroeder moved to Jacques Whitford, together, in 1994, after negotiating a deal that would maintain the cohesiveness of their group and allow it to share in the profits it generated for its new company. Not long after, Monique Coté and Rick Ciezki followed the original four from Western Research to Jacques Whitford.

This group acquisition of employees had almost immediate benefits for Jacques Whitford's fledgling Calgary operation. At Western Research, the group had been very well known, particularly in the Canadian oil patch, for its general expertise and complex modelling, and for Michael Schroeder's and Douglas Leahey's skill as expert witnesses in regulatory hearings. They brought name recognition and instant credibility, to say nothing of a following of clients.

At the time of the transition, Douglas Leahey graciously stepped down as the group's leader in favour of Michael Schroeder. Since 1994, the group has doubled to twelve. From 1997 to 1999, Michael Schroeder was vice-president of Air Quality for Jacques Whitford, with national responsibilities. He continues to manage the Calgary air quality group.

For this group, one of the factors that made the transition from Western Research to Jacques Whitford fairly simple and definitely successful was the similarity between Joe Lukacs and Hector Jacques. Both are strong, visionary leaders, with strong parallels in their style and philosophy. For example, with respect to hiring, Hector Jacques believes in hiring the best graduates from the best schools in good times and in bad, and that it doesn't matter if he has a specific project for them to go to. This is an almost eerie echo to similar statements made by Joe Lukacs when he was building his company in the 1970s. Likewise, the Hector Jacques philosophy with respect to the company's clients is almost precisely the same as that which Western Research lived by through its history. On the back of all Jacques Whitford employee business cards is a company credo, which begins: "Clients are the most important visitors on our premises. They are not dependent on us, we are dependent on them. They are not an interruption of our work, they are the purpose of it."

The values that were at the heart of Western Research (hard work, commitment to and friendship with clients, self-motivation, autonomy) are all present and accentuated in the Jacques Whitford group of companies. What was a winning formula at Western Research is a winning formula at Jacques Whitford, one of the fastest-growing engineering and environmental companies anywhere. What it proves is the degree to which shared values can be a source of loyalty, hard work, integrity, and ultimately success, in the fortunate companies that seek this in their employees and demand it of themselves.

HFP ACOUSTICAL CONSULTANTS

complex computer modelling in the acoustical area

HFP Acoustical Consultants Corporation has provided acoustical engineering services to major industrial, environmental, and architectural clients since 1979, completing over 1,800 projects in that timespan. Though the company started from a petroleum industry base, and still regards the petroleum industry (including pipelines and petrochemicals) as its primary niche, it works in most industrial sectors of the economy: power generation, compression, co-generation, pulp and paper, mining and manufacturing. Most industries have environmental noise pollution issues and occupational noise exposure issues that HFP can assist them with.

Les Frank

HFP has many non-industrial clients as well. Many of these are architectural clients. Urban sound issues also fall into this category of work.

The company started in 1979 after Les Frank decided to pull up stakes at Western Research where he had been in charge of the sound component of the company's consulting group. A native of New York with a master's degree in engineering acoustics from Pennsylvania State University, Les Frank was inspired by his own entrepreneurial instincts and the Western Research example to go out on his own. He found a partner and began the HFP acoustical engineering company. Later, Les would buy out his partner and become the sole owner of HFP. The timing for this venture was very good. In the 1970s, environmental noise pollution issues were rapidly becoming of concern, and Alberta was leading the way in Canada toward demanding that engineers, developers, and architects all deal with noise issues in their area. Les Frank at HFP was in an excellent position to take advantage, and the company has done so over its twenty years of doing business.

Les Frank believes that HFP was built on many of the same principles and practices that made Western Research a success. He aspired to the same high standard of client service, and he followed the path of "inventing out of nothing" that had led to so many profitable Western Research innovations. HFP grew rapidly and, when hiring, Les Frank went with an Elmer Berlie axiom that any prospective employee ought to be assessed first at the gut level. If the person feels good at that level, then and only then does Les Frank turn to his or her resumé. At present, HFP has nine people working in its Calgary office and six in its Houston office.

Today, 90 percent of HFP's work is environmental in nature. The remaining 10 percent deals with control of plant noise for the hearing protection benefit of workers. Helping clients satisfy noise regulations in the Environmental Impact Assessment process is a major component of the company's work. After doing most of the company's expert witness work for many years, Les Frank now empowers key employees to handle this role.

When asked to define HFP's competitive edge, Les Frank singles out the company's ability to do complex computer modelling in the acoustical area. Few others in North America can do this and only some in Europe. The company has driven that advantage to a dominant position in several markets, including the broadly defined petroleum industry in Western Canada and the U.S. gulf coast. In its primary petroleum industry niche, HFP does 80-90 percent of the noise work in the Canadian oil patch. Its share in the United States is 30-40 percent, and the international workload is growing.

As the company has matured, the amount of its work done at the design stage of projects has steadily risen. In the early years, the work available was largely retrofitting existing facilities, as companies worked to catch up to a new awareness about noise problems and the new regulations from government. As the older facilities were brought up to standard and as HFP became an industrial leader, more company time has been spent working with the designers of plants, buildings, and roadways to build good acoustical performance in at the outset.

Les Frank also credits the regulatory environment of his home province of Alberta for HFP's success. The pro-activeness of the Alberta government in environmental regulation used to amaze the company's American clients, facts such as that companies could be compelled in Canada to do $2 million worth of acoustical work to protect a single farmhouse from plant noise. At the same time, when a company could perform successfully in that strict environment, it was a great advertisement. As the acoustical regulations toughened in the United States, HFP's Canadian origins and experience stood the company in good stead.

REID-CROWTHER & PARTNERS LTD.

a long history of excellence

Bill Berzins joined Western Research in 1991 as the company's first full-time consulting services sales and marketing director. With two engineering degrees and experience with NuAlta, Earth Tech (in California), and Canadian Marine Drilling (island-building in the Beaufort Sea), he was eminently qualified. He recalls what an awesome reputation Western Research had at the time, "like a university campus" operating in Calgary's northeast light industrial area. It felt like he was joining an institution with a long history of excellence.

Bill Berzins

Six years later, in 1997, Bill Berzins joined another impressive Canadian institution, the venerable engineering company Reid-Crowther & Partners Ltd. He became the chief operating officer, with a mandate to improve the company's bottom line. What attracted Bill to Reid-Crowther was certainly its fine reputation for engineering, but he was also impressed by the many similarities to Western Research that he found. Like Western Research, Reid-Crowther was a company whose senior management "walked the talk." They got involved in problem solving for clients and took an active role in project delivery. Bill Berzins had seen this in action with individuals like Joe Lukacs and Don Colley and he had a strong desire to emphasize that attribute at Reid-Crowther. A high standard of service to clients and the maintenance of technical edges in the marketplace were other corporate values that the two companies shared. Bill Berzins was determined to perpetuate those values.

Reid-Crowther, like Western Research, is a company that concerns itself with the enjoyability of the workplace. It believes in creating both a challenging and a friendly work environment. Reid-Crowther is at present 95 years old. In addition to its other merits, it has the ability to survive.

After a few months at Reid-Crowther, Bill Berzins co-initiated a management reorganization that focussed the organization more squarely on client service delivery. Part of that reorganization was that he left the chief operating officer role in favour of becoming vice-president in charge of the company's exciting southern Alberta operating unit. As such, he is in charge of a staff of 150.

The company has a wide array of business areas including: water supply, waste water management, environmental management, transportation, buildings, and industrial engineering. Its world reputation in waste water management is similar to that enjoyed by Western Research's Process Analytical Engineering team. Recent projects for the southern Alberta group include oilfield waste management facilities, the Bonnybrook waste water facility, Calgary's LRT extensions, the Deerfoot Trail freeway extension, the Calgary Convention Centre, and the renovation of the Calgary International Airport.

HMA CONSULTING, INC.

turning some of the biggest buildings in the world into some of the smartest

HMA is a consulting engineering firm dedicated to making modern buildings intelligent, through the use of automated and integrated systems for everything from security and asset protection to fire protection/detection and communication.

Roger Mellor

The reputation HMA enjoys in this high-technology niche can be deduced from the prestige of its projects. HMA's experienced principals and staff designed the security systems for the two tallest buildings in the world, the twin towers in downtown Kuala Lumpur that were featured in the movie *"Entrapment."* They have major contracts on Canary Wharf and in Manhattan. Besides extensive work in North America, the company works literally around the world: France, Germany, Mexico, Malaysia, Taiwan, Hong Kong, and the United Kingdom.

The M in HMA is Roger Mellor, a PhD in chemical engineering and fuel technology from the University of Sheffield, England. He came to Calgary to work for Western Research in 1971, after employment with Pilkington Glass in Toronto. He came as a combustion expert who, among other duties, was responsible for destroying mustard gas at CFB Suffield in 1973, Western Research's first hazardous waste disposal contract. After leaving Western Research in 1975, Dr. Mellor enrolled in the MBA program at the University of Calgary. Upon completion of that degree, he teamed up with Geoff Sams, another Western Research alumnus, to form Techcord Consulting. At Techcord, the two applied the principles of industrial engineering and process control to buildings, developing their expertise in computer automation systems for major building projects. Mellor and Sams parted ways in 1995, after which Roger Mellor teamed up with John Hatcher to create the U.S. corporation HMA Consulting Inc. HMA's head office is at College Station, Texas (home of Texas A & M). The company has offices in Calgary, Seattle, and Toronto, as well as joint ventures in Malaysia and the Philippines.

The list of developments on which HMA has consulted is a Where's Where of world buildings: the Kuala Lumpur City Centre (twin 88-storey towers); Alberta Children's Hospital, Calgary; George Bush International Airport, Houston, Texas; The Shining Institute, Taiwan; major league baseball parks in Milwaukee, Wisconsin, and San Diego, California; the Prime Minister's Residence, Putrajaya, Malaysia; Owen-Corning world headquarters, Toledo, Ohio; Canary Wharf, London, U.K.; Enron headquarters, Houston, Texas; Sun Life Plaza, Calgary; Union Station, Kansas City, Missouri; USA Today headquarters, Washington, D.C.; Coca Cola headquarters, Mexico City, and many others. If you were to add HMA's projects together, it would amount to millions of square feet of the most elite architectural space in the world.

Asked how his company has established such market power, Dr. Roger Mellor replies that it is a credit to the power and dominion of the American architects and developers for whom his company works. HMA does not market itself development by development but goes where its client developers go. It says a lot for HMA, however, that it is the company these prestigious developers choose to imbue their buildings with new millennium intelligence.

COOPER AIR INC.

the ultimate entrepreneur

Cooper Air is a float plane charter business based out of Patricia Bay near the Victoria airport on Vancouver Island. It is owned by Western Research alumnus and tireless entrepreneur Richard Cooper. It is a fourteen-year-old company with a strong reputation and a faithful and still growing clientele.

Richard Cooper

Richard Cooper was a Western Research flying technician for four years, from 1974 to 1978. The story of how he came to leave the company and move to Victoria involves a flying holiday with two Western Research buddies that led them to Victoria via California. When Richard Cooper saw flowers blooming on Vancouver Island in February, he decided it was time to move on. He resigned from Western Research and moved west.

When he first arrived in Victoria, Dick Cooper lived on the water at Esquimalt. He ran a flying school out of his back door, which turned out not to be entirely legal. He was flying a Luscombe float plane and his interpretation of his warning from police was that, if he bought a different plane and started a limited company, he could carry on. He bought a Cessna 172, incorporated, and continued. Eleven months later, the same policeman came to his door with the same concern. This time, Dick joined an existing flying school and, under its legal umbrella, did both training and some float plane charter work.

How Dick Cooper started Cooper Air from that starting point is textbook Cooper entrepreneurism. A local float plane charter company was in financial trouble. Dick knew the operation because, when their planes broke down, which they often did, they would send their business to him. The owner offered to sell the business to Dick, but he felt the price was too high, especially given the tired state of its two float planes. He refused the offer and the company was folded up.

Given that the float plane company had been around for a decade, Dick Cooper got the brainwave of acquiring its phone number. The phone number turned out to be available except that a substantial bill was owing. Dick phoned the owner of the now-defunct company and made him a deal. Although Dick wasn't interested in his company, he was willing to pay off the phone bill in exchange for the number. Done.

With that, Dick founded Cooper Air, which by happy coincidence was a close rhyme to the name of the company whose phone number he now had. As Dick hoped would happen, the old company's return business calls started coming to him, and, because of the rhyming names, most of the customer didn't even know they'd changed companies.

A substantial fisheries contract helped Cooper Air to get moving. More wheeling and dealing with planes saw the Cessna 172 turn into two planes: A Cessna 180 and a 185. Cooper Air continued to do training work, but the growth in the charter business soon eclipsed the amount of time spent teaching people to fly. The company was officially incorporated in 1987.

Nowadays, Cooper Air runs five float planes, including three DeHavilland Beavers. While the main port of call is still Pat Bay, Cooper Air is also involved in the Victoria Marine Adventure Centre (directly in front of the Empress Hotel in Victoria Harbour). The work the company does is "everything imaginable": flying realtors, surveyors, mechanics, possible underworld types, repairmen, fishermen and other tourists. Makers of film and television are also among the "oddball assortment" of Cooper Air clients. When Dick Cooper's chief pilot Don Berends saw something in Finlayson Arm that matched the description of the waterbody's fabled sea creature, it prompted an episode of *Unsolved Mysteries*. Cooper Air did the flying for the show, working in formation while shooting video plane to plane.

Pilot Don Berends came to work with Cooper Air in an interesting way. When Dick Cooper bought an island farm, he had a tractor but nothing to pull. He went to the dairy farmer next door to see about renting some implements. There, he ran into a wheeler-dealer not unlike himself. The farmer bargained the farm equipment against Dick's giving his nephew a flying job. The nephew, Don Berends, had five hours of commercial flying under his belt at the time. He now has 10,000 hours and is a junior partner in Cooper Air, as well as being its chief pilot. Cooper Air has five other full-time staff. Dick Cooper, meanwhile, regards himself as semi-retired as of 1999–but take that with a grain of salt.

CANTOX ENVIRONMENTAL INC.

pioneers in environmental risk assessment

Cantox Environmental Inc. offers a highly scientific approach to the assessment of risks associated with chemicals. Health risk assessment involves the evaluation of potential risks to humans and the environment from chemical emissions. Cantox Environmental is the leading Canadian consulting firm in this business.

In the environmental field, health risk assessment is a relatively new approach that is used to assess risks resulting from chemical exposures to air emissions, water emissions, or from contaminated sites. The underlying basis involves determination of the chemical exposures resulting from multiple exposure pathways, including air, water, soil, fish, wildlife, and vegetation. Exposures are compared with chemical exposure limits derived from toxicology studies to determine whether risks exist. The approach includes assessment of risks associated with simultaneous exposures to chemical mixtures, as occur in the real world.

CanTox Inc. was formed over two decades ago by three PhD toxicologists in Ontario, all with experience in Health and Welfare Canada. Initially, their consulting company was an amalgamation of private practices that specialized in obtaining government approvals for clients in the food, drug, cosmetics, and agricultural areas. The group incorporated as CanTox Inc. in 1985. The composition of the company, as it grew, continued to emphasize a PhD level of expertise.

Gord Brown

In the late 1980s, CanTox underwent an important vision change. It imported toxicology, the science it relied on in the food and drug areas, into environmental work. Assessment procedures used in food and drug were adapted for environmental applications and were combined with complex environmental exposure pathways to come up with the company's sophisticated environmental risk assessment methods.

It was in this period that Western Research became involved with CanTox. Dr. Gordon Brown returned to Western Research after completing his PhD, and one of his first major assignments was to assist with "Project Swiftsure." The goal of Project Swiftsure was the safe destruction of chemical warfare agents stockpiled at the Canadian Forces Base near Suffield, Alberta. Gord Brown's job was to coordinate regulatory approvals necessary to proceed with the chemical warfare destruction at Suffield, something that interested both the provincial and federal governments. The project involved high-temperature incineration of the blistering agent mustard gas and the chemical neutralization of the nerve agent lewisite. It was immediately obvious to all involved that there was significant community opposition to the project, based on health concerns, even though the nearest major communities were 20 and 150 kilometres away.

Gord Brown called on Dr. Robert Willes of CanTox Inc. (now Cantox Environmental Inc.) to complete a human health risk assessment for the project, and to participate in public meetings to explain the results of the risk assessment. This information put the project risks into perspective. His findings showed that the public health risks associated with destruction of warfare agents in this project were in fact very low. Project Swiftsure went ahead, and Canada's stockpile of chemical warfare agents was permanently destroyed.

Shortly after this project, Cantox was again retained by Western Research and Chem-Security (Alberta) Ltd. to complete a human health risk assessment for the expansion of the Swan Hills Hazardous Waste Treatment Centre, another project viewed with considerable distrust by some. Once again, the risk assessment approach and its associated public consultation program served to allay the majority of public and regulatory concerns. The expansion was approved and built.

For Gordon Brown, working with Cantox had proven the effectiveness of the risk assessment approach. When Gord left

Western Research in 1993, he joined Cantox. Today, he is vice-president of Cantox's western region. The Calgary office has successfully applied risk assessment to many more high profile projects, including: Syncrude's oilsands operations; Cominco's smelter at Trail, British Columbia; Lafarge's cement manufacturing plant at Exshaw, Alberta; Weyerhauser's OSB and pulp mills in Alberta; a former gas plant in Okotoks, Alberta; and several oil and gas flaring projects.

The risk assessment/management approach is rapidly growing in the environmental industry. Cantox is maintaining its competitive edge in these areas by combining top scientists, state-of-the-art methods, and strategic alliances with other key consulting firms that provide supporting scientific disciplines (such as air quality modelling, hydrogeology, and environmental engineering). Through understanding and communication, Cantox is able to introduce solid, meaningful information on health risks associated with chemical emissions from industry to concerned stakeholders and regulators.

BOVAR INC.

owner and operator of Canada's only fully integrated hazardous waste treatment facility

B OVAR Inc. is a world leader in the challenging hazardous waste management business. Its Swan Hills Treatment Centre is the only fully integrated hazardous waste facility in Canada. As its owner-operator, BOVAR provides an essential service to a broadening community.

Graham Latonas

Hazardous wastes are industrial by-products that have proven injurious to human and environmental health. Many of these wastes are persistent organic pollutants (POPS), which accumulate in the tissues of animals and spread to remote areas through the food chain. They know no boundaries, certainly not provincial or national ones.

The safe disposal of, or treatment of, such wastes is BOVAR Inc.'s primary business. In 1985, BVRS (which became BOVAR in 1989) entered into an agreement with the province of Alberta to build the Swan Hills treatment facility, an operation that could effectively and wisely deal with the province's hazardous wastes. In the early years, BVRS (subsequently BOVAR) was partnered with an Alberta crown corporation. In 1996, BOVAR attained the province's 40 percent and became whole owner and sole operator of the facility.

BOVAR has a strong ancestral connection with Western Research. During the preparations for operation at the Swan Hills plant, Western Research carried out many of the background studies, and, of particular importance, designed the study by which the Von Roll rocking kiln was tested in a trial burn. Graham Latonas who was involved at Swan Hills as a Western Research employee at this time, returned there in 1990 to work directly for Chem-Security, BOVAR's subsidiary charged with the operation of the Swan Hills facility. Graham is now vice-president of environmental affairs in BOVAR's waste management division.

Besides the Swan Hills Treatment Centre, BOVAR has two major international involvements.

In Malaysia, BOVAR has a 23.75 percent minority interest in Alam Sekitar Malaysia Sdn. Bhd. (ASMA). ASMA is a private-industry provider of monthly air and water quality data to the Malaysian department of environment and other clients. By year-end, 1999, the system consisted of forty-six

air monitoring stations and ten water monitoring stations. This involvement dates back to the late 1980s, when the Western Research consulting group won a proposal competition to supply and co-own the service.

Swan Hills Plant

BOVAR's second international involvement is in the United States. Through its subsidiary, Chem-Security Ltd., the company is in the final stages of a project to design, build, and commission a chemical neutralization facility in Tooele, Utah. Using patent technology, developed on a similar project for the Canadian Armed Forces near Suffield, Alberta, BOVAR is neutralizing a stockpile of the nerve agent lewisite for the American army.

The Swan Hills Treatment Centre remains the heart of BOVAR's operations. Since 1988, the centre has treated over 225 million kilograms of toxic, flammable, corrosive, oxidizing, and otherwise hazardous waste from Canadian sources. The incineration system was designed to achieve "6-9" efficiency, meaning 99.9999% efficiency in its treatment of hard-to-destroy chemicals like PCBs. Because of the hazardous nature of these wastes, the centre is subject to the strictest of controls. Its systems for air, soil and water monitoring must likewise be the best available. Public concern necessitates complete openness about the operation and the results of its monitoring. Communication with stakeholders is an ongoing commitment. All this is as it should be, but it makes for expense and challenge for the operator.

But the greatest challenge BOVAR Inc. faces at Swan Hills is volume. For a variety of reasons, the volume of hazardous wastes arriving at the centre fluctuates considerably year to year. This necessitates occasional shutdowns of portions of the plant, an operational as well as financial challenge. Given that hazardous waste is a global problem, the decision has been taken to allow the importation of hazardous wastes into Canada and Alberta. This will improve the economics and the operations of the Swan Hills Treatment Centre.

The hazardous waste treatment industry is controversial by its very nature. The fact remains that hazardous wastes must be dealt with somewhere. Restricting their treatment to the most advanced, most scrutinized, and most safely run facilities in the world makes good sense, and so BOVAR proceeds.

SOUTHERN ALBERTA INSTITUTE OF TECHNOLOGY

serving the practical needs of students and their future employers

The relationship between Western Research and Calgary's Southern Alberta Institute of Technology (SAIT) dates back to Western's early years. First of all, a great many of the company's technicians were trained at SAIT. Secondly, several Western Research employees changed career at some point to become SAIT instructors. The first to make this move into teaching was CSEM developer Fred Waddington, who came to SAIT in 1975. Dan Violini, a Western Research air quality monitoring specialist, followed in 1979, becoming an instructor of industrial instrumentation technology. The photograph on the next page shows Western Research leader Joe Lukacs with Dan Violini and four others who have been employed by both Western Research and SAIT. They are posed with a Western Research-manufactured analyzer that Dan Violini bought for SAIT's training purposes in 1984.

SAIT is one of Canada's top post-secondary institutions, serving a national and international clientele. The institute was started by the Alberta provincial government in 1916 to meet the practical needs of both employers and students, a philosophy it maintains today. Heritage Hall, the institute's oldest building and centrepiece, was built in 1921 with a first-class view of downtown Calgary.

During World War II, the Canadian government took over the campus. While the regular students did their learning across town at the Stampede grounds, the SAIT campus graduated thousands of RCAF wireless operators for the Allied cause. Following the war, returning veterans boosted SAIT's enrolment enormously.

At the time of this writing, SAIT is in a major expansion and upgrading project. Part of the $145-million-dollar project is an architecturally designed blending of the old Heritage Hall with a new classroom and laboratory complex. The frontal

Joe Lukacs and the SAIT/ Western Research alumni, posed with a Western Research analyzer. Left to right: Mike Zelensky, Dan Violini, Gord Crowder, John McKee, Joe Brigan, and Joe Lukacs

view of Heritage Hall that so many identify with SAIT will remain the same, while, behind it, the old building expands into the modern complex. An Automotive Centre of Excellence and a new student's residence are also being added.

Over the years, SAIT has responded to the changing needs of students and industry. The earliest programs were in steam engineering and motor mechanics. Today, the institute offers applied degrees, diplomas, and certificates in engineering technologies, health sciences, applied arts, business, and apprenticeship trades. Continuing education and customized training are growing areas. Currently, SAIT provides education and training to 65,000 learners per year. Partnerships with industry are a fairly new method by which the college finances itself and guarantees that its programming is current and relevant.

Dan Violini is in his twenty-first year at SAIT. He served as associate dean from 1986 to 1997. When he started in 1979, industrial instrumentation technology was part of the power engineering department. Power engineering grew over the years to include chemistry, chemical engineering technology, petroleum engineering technology, and electrical engineering technology. Correspondence courses in gas-process operations and field-production operations were an enormous support to the Alberta gas processing industry.

When Dan Violini started in his department, he was one of fifteen faculty. That number has risen to 120. In distance learning alone, the department handles over 3,000 students per year, to go with the 1,000 on-campus students. In terms of industrial partnerships, the department is delivering custom courses for eighty oil companies in Alberta.

A great uniqueness of the department is its entrepreneurial activities, which are currently generating $5 million annually. Much credit for this goes to Owen Baker, dean of the department from 1979 to 1998. Long ago, Mr. Baker worked for Elmer Berlie at Texas Gulf Okotoks. Later, Mr. Baker worked at the Petrogras Balzac gas processing plant. Under his guidance, the power engineering department became a model of financial self-reliance. "In my area," says Dan Violini, "I don't get a cent from government. Half the department revenues come from business sources. It *is* a business."

ENVIROCHEM SERVICES INC./ ENVIROCHEM MANAGEMENT SYSTEMS INC.

going international with unique ISO-14000 software applications

Envirochem is a North Vancouver-based environmental engineering and scientific consulting firm, founded in 1984. In 1994, ex-Western Research chemical engineer Paul Beauchemin joined the company, and today he and Thomas Finnbogason, one of the company's founders, share owner-ship of the company. Envirochem employs eleven full-time staff and five associates.

Paul Beauchemin

Envirochem offers a wide range of services in the environmental area. From a starting point in the pollution prevention and toxic chemical management area, the company first evolved into a full environmental service provider. Many of the company's clients out-source their environmental work to Envirochem, so that the company essentially becomes their environmental department on either a retainer or fee-for-service basis. In this capacity, Envirochem could look after a client company's environmental audits, staff training in the environmental area, government regulatory liaison and permitting, environmental sampling, hazardous materials management, spill response planning, and pollution prevention planning. Whatever the client needs in the environmental area, Envirochem is able to offer either through its own resources or though project management and external liaison. The focus of the company is on implementing management systems that support proactive risk identification and minimization (pollution prevention) rather than reactive controls and clean-up after the fact. To support its environmental field work, the company maintains an in-house analytical laboratory.

The next evolution for Envirochem has been into the development and implementation of environmental management systems (EMS). The company has developed these systems based on the ISO-14000 international standard produced by the International Organization for Standardization in France. In the last decade, achieving and maintaining the world standard in environmental preparedness and practice has become an important factor in doing business beyond national boundaries. ISO-14000 is a way for companies and customers around the world to evaluate current suppliers and the companies wanting to do business in their country.

To improve access to its environmental management systems, Envirochem has taken the further step of developing software to guide companies in implementation and maintenance of their EMS, again designed to meet the ISO-14000 standard. Envirochem's software development program began shortly after Paul Beauchemin's arrival in 1994 and has made good use of his prior experience of developing a pollution source database for the Greater Vancouver Regional District (GVRD), a comprehensive software system that enabled the GVRD to inventory all industrial sources of air pollution.

Envirochem's major piece of commercial software is called EDICTS (Environmental Data Information and Compliance Tracking System), an easy-to-use but sophisticated computer-based EMS that systematizes environmental management, organizes data, and tracks compliance. It contains all the ISO-14000 elements. The software's versatility of application is such that it has been used for fish hatcheries and an air force base. The bulk of sales has been in the sawmill and other forestry areas. Envirochem is looking for a partnership arrangement that will allow the company to break out and market internationally.

Envirochem has also developed custom software for clients. For Vancouver's international airport, the company developed an environmental data-managing program. Another contract with the GVRD saw the company develop programming to manage all industrial effluents in the region. This program manages both monitoring data and permitting. Packaged for the marketplace, the system is called *e*PAS (electronic permit administration service).

Another product, *e*SAM (electronic self-audit module) does what the name suggests: it allows companies or consultants to conduct environmental audits for a large number of sites.

Working out of North Vancouver, with a second office on Vancouver Island, Envirochem is a company poised to make its move internationally. Paul Beauchemin sums up the company business plan this way: "to become recognized worldwide as the leading supplier of environmental management system computer software." Given the right partner, and a few breaks, the company stands an excellent chance of getting there.

MALDANER CROOKS

put a world of experience
behind your financial decisions

Maldaner Crooks, Chartered Accountants was formed in the spring of 1995 by combining the practices of Terry Crooks and Jim Maldaner, both past Bow Valley employees. While Maldaner Crooks, Chartered Accountants consists of the accounting practice, CMT Consultants Ltd., a sister company, is more directed toward financing, securities work, corporate valuations, and consulting on the purchase and sale of companies.

Terry Crooks

Maldaner Crooks provides clients with a standard suite of financial services. Often their clients are owner-managed businesses, and their usual beat is the city of Calgary and area. The two principals bring together a wealth of accounting and business experience, which includes the manufacturing, construction, and oil and gas sectors, as well as experience with large accounting firms. This breadth of experience enables Maldaner Crooks to advise clients on accounting, tax, and financial planning issues, as well as dispensing general business advice. Accounting services, preparation of financial statements, setting up and managing computerized accounting systems, preparing financial audits and statements, complying with tax and reporting requirements—all of these can be part of the service if clients want them.

Terry Crooks was Western Research's full-time accountant from April 1, 1975, to December 1, 1977, a crucial period in the company's history. When he first arrived, the company was in a financial crisis. It came very close to losing its research and development program, just as the air demand analyzer was approaching market readiness. By the time Terry left, the company was making good money, in significant part because of the sale of the air demand analyzer. After completing a restructuring of Western Research, Terry was taken away by BVRS. After a short stint as a trouble-shooter with Bow Helicopters, he was transferred to Edmonton to be in charge of three BVRS divisions and to function as a group controller under Don Thurston.

Later, Terry Crooks became the general manager of Northern Rig Lites Ltd. in Edmonton before returning to Calgary in 1982. During much of the 1980s, Terry worked installing and implementing computerized systems in the manufacturing and construction sectors. In the early 1990s, he returned to accounting work, solo at first, and, in that capacity, one of his first clients turned out to be none other than Joe Lukacs. Joe was putting together his new venture, CETAC-WEST, and he needed Terry's accounting services to help set it up. From that beginning as a sole proprietor, the organization has grown to the point where it has four professional staff, three sub-contractors, and one and one half administration personnel.

The growth of their company has allowed Terry Crooks and Jim Maldaner an opportunity to try out some of the Joe Lukacs skill set. From Joe, Terry learned about concentrating on people and core areas when building a business. He watched and learned as Joe moulded a diverse group of individuals into a team that could deliver the goals the company wanted to achieve. The way he did so always allowed sufficient personal freedom so that the company could grow.

WHITESHELL TECHNOLOGY INC.

practical and original high-tech solutions

Phil Harris calls himself a johnny-come-lately in the Western Research story. He arrived with the company as the senior scientist, from an R&D background with Atomic Energy of Canada, in 1993. He remained exactly five

years, by which time he was managing the company's research and development and all the engineering functions relating to instrumentation manufacture.

Phil and his wife Karin are both Winnipeg-born and raised. Both hold master's degrees from the University of Manitoba, Karin's in educational psychology

Phil Harris and Karin Harris

and Phil's in chemistry. Their bachelor's degrees were in computer science and physics, respectively. Karin Harris started Whiteshell Technology in June, 1998, as a project management consulting company, while Phil Harris was still with AMETEK (after their acquisition of BOVAR Western Research). As Phil puts it, Karin knew he was in need of a change, and, by starting her business, she lightened the financial load enough to make that easier for him to do. When he did leave AMETEK, he began consulting outside of Whiteshell but, the conditions of one of his contracts made it advantageous to move into the company, and he did. Karin Harris is the president of Whiteshell Technology.

Whiteshell Technology is a project management and project development company. In the millennium year, Karin contracted as quality manager for Enmax's Year 2000 upgrades, both to its mainframe computing system and on its process control systems. She also managed a large database project for Calgary Parks and Recreation.

On the product development side, the company provides

services in the areas of process analytical chemistry, spectroscopy, mechanical design, electrical engineering, and software engineering. Two sub-contractors, an electrical engineer and a mechanical designer, work with the company to round out its package.

In part, Phil Harris is continuing the work he did at Western Research, applying UV visible spectrometers to functions in the sulphur recovery industry. He is also broadening the applications, moving into sulphuric and nitric acid production, and various chemical processing plants (ethylene, syngas, coal gasification). He is also working with tunable diode laser spectrometers.

With Sulphur Experts and Galvanic Applied Services, Whiteshell Technology is using chemiluminescence to develop a sulphur specific detector for use in gas chromatographs.

Whiteshell contracted with Shell Canada to develop a process flow work sheet that allows plants and refineries to select the most suitable flame-detection system for each point along their processes, a study that changed awareness not only for the engineers and operators at plants and refineries but for the flame detection system suppliers as well.

Whiteshell is also pioneering a new gas-detection technology for the mud-logging systems on exploration wells.

Another area in which Whiteshell is enjoying near-perfect results is in guiding clients to government funding sources and helping them access those sources. By helping clients plan strategies for attainment and use of research funding, Whiteshell stimulates research and development efforts in which the company can be involved in other capacities.

Phil Harris feels that he imported many Western Research traditions into the basic design and practices of his new company. Experienced Western Research hands John Sames, Randy Hauer, and Len Edwards taught him a great deal about how to focus on clients; how to get to know them personally and how to find out their problems and solve them. In this way, Western Research was an essential transition from his previous huge employer/huge client situation at Atomic Energy of Canada to his future situation as owner/operator, with Karin, of their own small company.

AMAROK CONSULTING

top design and management in the air quality monitoring area

Kevin Warren became the manager of air quality monitoring (AQM) at Western Research in 1989. He held the position for ten years as the company changed in various ways around him. Throughout the period, the things that did not change were that it remained the largest AQM group in Canada and that it held the dominant market share in western Canada. A source of particular pride was the joint-venture air quality monitoring system that BOVAR brought to Malaysia in 1995. It involved fifty air quality monitoring stations.

In 1998, Kevin Warren's AQM group was sold by BOVAR to AGAT Laboratories. Kevin stayed on with AGAT for a year to supervise the transition, and then, in March, 1999, he left to start his own company, Amarok Consulting. Amarok is Inuit for wolf and the idea to name his company that came from his daughter who was studying the Inuit in school at the time.

Kevin Warren

The shape that Amarok acquired as a company was influenced by an earlier entrepreneurial opportunity. Kevin Warren was offered a chance to start an AQM group in an existing company, but he decided not to based on the high capital costs involved. A single air quality monitoring trailer cost $60,000 at that time, and that one station could serve only a single customer per month. To keep up with the demand of a healthy AQM group, several more trailers would be needed, amounting to a substantial financing need.

Instead of taking this capital-intensive approach, Kevin started Amarok as a consulting business, dedicated to the design and management of air quality monitoring programs. The major opportunity to which his company is responding is the shift within Alberta to a zone-based air quality management system that allows local stakeholders to design their own solutions to air quality issues, rather than relying on a province-wide approach. Amarok's first and largest client to date is the Parkland Airshed Management Zone (PAMZ), a multi-stakeholder, non-profit organization consisting of industry, local government, environmental organizations, and Alberta Environment. PAMZ was formed in 1997 in response to concerns about the air quality effects of projected industrial growth in the Parkland region. PAMZ is the third and most recent airshed management zone in Alberta. Twelve board members represent the four stakeholder groups and the board operates on the principle of consensus. It has been an eye-opening experience for Kevin Warren, who was raised in the often-rapid decision-making environment of private business.

When asked how Western Research affected him as an entrepreneur, Kevin Warren stresses the service orientation of his old company. At Western Research, he learned to shape his services to the client's needs, and to be available. Just as Wilhelm Pier has always done in his highly successful European businesses, Kevin Warren's business cards carry his home phone number. He stresses to clients that he is available twenty-four hours a day.

Another principle drawn from Western Research has to do with respect. "People say you have to earn respect," says Kevin. "I say, why not start off with respect and work from there." At Western Research, he felt respected from the outset. It gave him the confidence to go out into the field, and, if he made mistakes, to learn from them. He always felt free to share his thoughts and ideas. Recalling his experience with Western Research, Kevin Warren says, "In the morning, I was always happy to be going to work. I knew I was working with the best company and with the best people."

DAN HALL

engineering a successful career in law

Dan Hall credits his two years at Western Research with instilling in him a fascination with the law and a desire to practise environmental law. As a mechanical engineer working in the acoustical and noise control area, he was involved with environmental impact assessments and with administrative tribunals such as the ERCB and the NEB. He liked what he saw. Later, having been a Western Research employee would assist Dan again as a newly graduated lawyer looking for articles of clerkship with a law firm.

Dan Hall left Western Research in August, 1979, to begin his law degree at the University of Calgary. The timing was such that he graduated and re-entered the working world shortly after the introduction of the National Energy Policy and the total collapse of the Calgary oil boom. Like many other legal articling students, he was offering to do his articles for free, and was getting no takers. Knowing that the firm of Fenerty, Robertson, Fraser and Hatch (now Fraser Milner) did considerable regulatory work, he applied there. It turned out that the company was very familiar with Western Research, and the fact that Dan was from a Western Research background weighed heavily enough that partner Francis Saville invited him to article with them. Dan Hall proceeded from there to a successful legal career and has never forgotten Western Research's part in launching the process.

Dan began his career in law doing litigation. He moved to an oil company to get closer to corporate, commercial, and regulatory work, and this led him eventually to the legal department of BP. Dan spent many years at BP Canada and obtained wide-ranging experience in many aspects of oil and gas and mining law. He was also appointed Assistant Corporate Secretary of the BP Group of companies and worked extensively with the British Petroleum head office in London, England. Dan also worked as a commercial manager with BP Canada in acquisitions and divestitures.

Having worked for a major company, and having handled major company accounts, Dan was in a good position to set up his own practice, which he did in the early 1990s. His Calgary firm, which began as a sole proprietorship and then became associated with Britton & Hall, is over nine years old. The firm carries on a general law practice with emphasis on corporate and commercial matters, and oil and gas acquisitions. As well, it does extensive work in technology law (patents, trademarks, and licensing), real estate, and civil litigation.

Dan's most enduring touchstone from his Western Research experience is the confidence he obtained in his first career as a young environmental consulting engineer fresh from university. He carries that confidence with him today.

GLOBAL ANALYZER SERVICES LTD.

service first

At the time when Glenn Sabo was getting up in the night to answer Western Research and BOVAR trouble and maintenance calls, he did not realize it would one day be the source of his business as an independent entrepreneur, but that is exactly what came to pass. His seventeen years of involvement with Western Research and BOVAR analyzers meant that clients all over North America associated him with the maintenance of, and the solving of problems to do with, the analyzer systems at their plants. When he parted ways with BOVAR in 1996, that didn't change. Because of the nature of service at Western Research over the years, the clients had his home phone number. When he told them he no longer worked for BOVAR, they said, we know that, but our analyzer is not functioning, and we want you to fix it.

At the time of leaving BOVAR, Glenn Sabo thought he'd never look at another analyzer. But when those phone calls started coming, he recognized a golden business possibility and

Glenn Sabo

he acted quickly. In December, 1996, Global Analyzer Services Ltd. sprang to life. When a new continuous-emission monitoring (CEM) code became law in Alberta in mid-1997, the company's market was assured. As Glenn puts it, "The floodgates opened." He and one staff person have been working seven days a week ever since.

The new CEM code is a slightly reduced version of what is demanded by the Environmental Protection Agency in the United States. The old Alberta system that was satisfied with twice yearly checks on the functioning of a plant's continuous emission monitoring system has been replaced by a code that demands daily verification that the system is working. Numbers won't do any more. What the government is asking for is quality assured data. What this means in practical terms is daily calibration of the systems with gas and frequent testing. Relative accuracy test audits (RATA) are done on a regular basis, generating, as the saying goes, a lot of "RATA-data." Cylinder gas audits (CGA) test the linearity in the systems. Whereas it used to be common to test only the middle range where the emissions were concentrated, it is now necessary to test the system at very high and very low emission rates as well.

In addition to helping his clients with their assessments, evaluations, calibrations, and maintenance, Global's service also includes rebuilding, refurbishing, and updating the systems so that the needed regulatory results can be achieved. Global also functions as a representative for several analyzer product lines and is able to supply clients with whatever equipment they need in this way. But the company is service first, sales second. The latter supports the former, rather than the other way around.

All in all, the many trouble calls Glenn Sabo used to respond to, day and night, weekdays and weekends, in his Western Research/BOVAR days are paying off handsomely now. What it amounts to is over twenty years of experience building, servicing, and testing a variety of process control and source monitoring analyzers. For many in the gas processing business in Alberta and beyond, Glenn Sabo and Global Analyzer Services are the names to call for compliance and service needs.

CLEARSTONE ENGINEERING LTD.

a global vision of environmental improvement

David J. Picard is the principal of Clearstone Engineering Ltd., an internationally experienced, Calgary-based firm, specializing in air emissions assessments and industrial air pollution control. The company's marketplace is situated largely at the upstream end of the oil and gas industry, but does a significant amount of refinery and petrochemical work as well. The current staff of the company is eight, including Dave Picard as sole owner.

Dave did his bachelor's degree at the University of Alberta in mechanical engineering. He proceeded to do a master's in chemical engineering at the University of Calgary. His first industry involvement was in the oil and gas industry as a project engineer for O'Rourke Engineering Ltd. In 1985, he hired on with Western Research where, in four years, he did landmark work on major projects like the Swan Hills hazardous waste treatment facility. He is credited as the principal investigator on the ultra-rigorous trial burn protocols by which the Von Roll rocking kilns at Swan Hills were tested. When he left Western Research to start Clearstone in 1989, he combined his oil and gas training with his environmental experience to create a problem-solving company.

Dave Picard says of Clearstone, "Our goal is to help clients evaluate and resolve their air emission problems." The number of ways that Clearstone pursues this simple-sounding goal is amazing. The company offers emission estimation and measurement services and has the further capability to design, procure, and construct emission-control systems. Odour assessment and control is another company service that sees Clearstone involve itself in the client's plant or field, solving problems.

Beyond the control of planned emissions, the company also deals in fugitive emissions, the unintentional side of air pollution, where it is a leading authority on assessment and control methods. Fugitive emission sources include leaking equipment, pond evaporation, flares, and storage losses.

In addition to the services it provides, Clearstone has

software applications that enable clients to take control of their own air pollution management. For example, Clearstone has software for companies to use in managing and reporting their own leak detection and repair programs. A major piece of Clearstone software, titled EnviroPro, manages emissions data for oil and gas companies (assessment, management, and reporting). EnviroPro is used by five of Canada's ten largest oil and gas producers. In a joint-venture with a major multi-national oil company, Clearstone developed software that uses statistical inventory reconciliation to detect leaks, calibration problems, and poor fuel inventory accounting procedures at retail gas stations.

Clearstone also pursues its involvement in the air pollution industry by publication and through involvement in government and international task forces. While David Picard was with Western Research, he co-wrote and published a number of articles on his work. With his own company, he has continued to publish steadily and to involve himself in professional organizations like the Air and Waste Management Association.

As Joe Lukacs always stressed to his employees, publication is perhaps the best method of bringing your work to the attention of your industry. In Dave Picard's case, it has led to environmental, scientific, and engineering involvements of ever-broadening scope. At home, he is often called upon as an expert witness for NEB and EUB hearings. Internationally, he is assisting with the largest environmental initiatives on the planet. For the United Nations Framework Convention on Climate Change 2000, Dave prepared a background paper on methodological options for estimating fugitive emissions in the fuels sector. With the International Panel on Climate Change (IPCC), he was one of the original co-authors of the section on oil and gas systems in the IPCC publication Guidelines for Developing National Greenhouse Gas Inventories. Through the World Bank and CIDA, he has done considerable work abroad. He has made several trips to China, training in matters such as setting up systems for environmental data management and environmental monitoring. In 1994, Clearstone prepared air quality and emission-monitoring guidelines for the Peruvian oil industry.

This summary of Clearstone Engineering's work is short of the mark in terms of accurately representing the company's activities. For an eight-person company, it is involved in a striking number of contracts and initiatives all over the world, and it is hard to do it justice in a small space. In the fugitive emissions area alone, the company lists eighteen projects, all with major pipeline, oil company, and hazardous waste treatment clients. It is hired by other top-notch environmental companies and major engineering firms, which is always a sign of the high standard of its work, and the high regard it enjoys in the greater community.

MIKE ZELENSKY

can do the job,
whatever it happens to be

Mike Zelensky

Mike Zelensky is one of a small number of ex-Western Research employees who can say they worked for the company twice. He was part of the company's consulting engineering group for five years (1979-84). After leaving to pursue other opportunities (including two years of instructing at SAIT), he hired on eventually with Concord Scientific (which became Concord Environmental), a company BOVAR bought in 1994. Mike was right back with the same company he had started with, albeit with a new name and new ownership.

Just before BOVAR Environmental was sold to Conor Pacific in 1997, Mike Zelensky jumped ship to become his own boss. He has been a busy and successful sole proprietor engineering consultant ever since.

Mike is originally from Edmonton and his first degree was from the University of Alberta. He was the gold medal student in mechanical engineering. He continued his education at the California Institute of Technology in Pasadena, where he completed a master's in mechanical engineering with options in combustion and dispersion. Mike's best man, Dan Hall, was working at Western Research when Mike came on the job market. Before departing for law school, Dan Hall led Mike to Don Colley at Western, and Don hired him as a project engineer for his group.

During his stay with Western Research, Mike Zelensky became one of three patenters of a waste gas incinerator design that launched a profitable line of products, which are still on the market today. He also worked on emission inventories and many EIAs and learned a great deal that he would apply later in his career.

At Concord Environmental, Mike worked with Mervyn Davies whom he had met at Western Research. At that time, he finalized a public safety model for Alberta's Energy and Utilities Board (EUB) that is still in use today. The model is used by the EUB and by Jacques Whitford Environmental senior scientist Dr. Douglas Leahey, among others. Mike continues to apply it in his own consulting practice.

Mike Zelensky describes his consulting business as part public safety management and part air quality management. He works with clients in the sour gas industry on public safety issues, including risk assessment and management, emergency response strategies, and incident mitigation, mostly with respect to accidental releases of hydrogen sulphide. Dispersion modelling is a central tool of his trade, which allows him to quantify risks associated with such accidental releases. In air quality management, he deals again with hydrogen sulphide, but also with the effects of sulphur dioxide. The sulphur dioxide work includes stack-top temperature reduction studies. Here, Mike works with Sulphur Experts in applying modern computing power to the principles Harold Paskall established in the 1970s on behalf of Western Research.

Part of the work on stack-top temperature studies is helping clients get government approval for the change of operating practice that will achieve the fuel savings and reduce greenhouse gases. Other regulatory work includes securing government approval for such things as well-test flaring and applications for new facilities, also changes to existing operating approvals. Mike has also had major contracts with the EUB.

When Mike Zelensky thinks back on his Western Research days, he particularly remembers the "can-do" philosophy of the company. The attitude was, "We know we can do it. We just haven't done it yet." Joe Lukacs, Elmer Berlie, and Don Colley were leaders who placed great confidence in their people. They took on whatever came along and, when young engineers like Mike Zelensky solved the clients' problems, it was a confidence boost throughout the company. It fostered a self-assurance that is central to Mike Zelensky's work to this day. He is never afraid to take on a new kind of job in his field of expertise. He knows from experience that he can do it, whatever it happens to be.

ACCESS ANALYTICAL LABORATORIES INC.

accessible and defendable solutions

Access Analytical is a brand new environmental laboratory company, the newest company profiled amongst these shooting stars. At the same time, it is old in experience. The principals and core staff of the new venture combine for 150 years of industry experience in the oil, gas, pipeline and industrial plant environments.

The analysis services offered by Access Analytical include hydrocarbon assessment/interpretation, testing for BTEX, volatile industrial solvents, PAHs, amines, glycol, and heavy metals, to name a few. The company also analyzes for salinity in soil, potable water, and the constituents of waste water. The data is accessible electronically and in a timely fashion.

Access Analytical is a joint venture between Western Research/BOVAR alumni Bob Corbet and Trevor Ahlstrom and WSH Laboratories, a company widely known in the Calgary area for water testing and waste water solutions.

From 1987 to 1993, Bob Corbet worked in the laboratory of Western Research, first within BVRS and then

Bob Corbet

BOVAR. He arrived in the midst of the excitement of trying to develop lab analyses and standards that would fulfil the considerable needs and demands of the Swan Hills hazardous waste treatment facility. The unprecedented intensiveness of the audits, and the fact that the facility was responsible for dealing with such a wide range of hazardous wastes meant that Bob Corbet and his group within Western Research developed rare and marketable expertise. Trevor Ahlstrom joined the company and the lab in 1990, during the first expansion at Swan Hills, when the lab group was parlaying its new expertise into other cutting-edge projects around the country and abroad.

Bob Corbet left BOVAR in 1993. Initially, he went into independent consulting, and then he was asked to develop a new laboratory for Norwest Labs in Calgary. Trevor Ahlstrom joined Bob at Norwest, and, together, over the next six years, they grew the company and broadened its services to the point where it was a multi-million dollar enterprise.

Entrepreneurship represents the next level for the team of Corbet and Ahlstrom, and they have specific philosophical and practical goals for Access Analytical Laboratories. The plan, already in place, is to provide a project-oriented set of services that goes beyond the traditional analytical staple of "just numbers." Clients are given results they can trust, plus access to the meaning of the data in relation to their application, be it process or regulatory in nature. This includes applications such as site assessment, soil remediation, and licencing.

There is a link between Corbet's and Ahlstrom's goal in their new venture and their Western Research experience. It was at Western that they learned that the client was their best friend. It is their present goal to meet and establish relationships with the clients of their laboratory so that they can go beyond the providing of data to the solving of actual client problems.

Bob Corbet sees himself as carrying other Western Research codes and cultural assets into Access *Trevor Ahlstrom* Analytical. At Western Research, he learned that work could be enjoyable through challenge every day and that a work environment could be both exciting and supportive.

CETAC-WEST

the shooting star machine

After twenty-seven years of running Western Research, Joe Lukacs knows a thing or two about commercializing new technology. Making money as a primary goal does not interest Joe that much, but founding smart and profitable businesses that solve client problems, deliver value to the society, and compete effectively nationally and internationally, does remain a passion for him.

Joe Lukacs

Joe Lukacs went into the management-mentoring business full time in 1994, two years after leaving BOVAR Inc. At that time, he accepted the opportunity to become founding president and CEO of the Canadian Environmental Technology Advancement Corporation (CETAC-WEST). An initiative of Environment Canada's Green Plan, CETAC-WEST helps small and medium-sized enterprises succeed in the business of solving technological problems in the environmental area. CETAC-WEST is a non-profit corporation created with funding from federal and provincial sources. To date, it has helped over one hundred entrepreneurs to develop and manage their businesses.

The fifty to sixty client companies who come to CETAC-WEST in a year tend to be longer on technological acumen than on business savvy. Often, they have a product concept or technological idea they believe does or can work. What they do not know is how to go about assessing its commercial viability, financing its testing and production, getting it into the marketplace, and, most importantly, securing the financing and expertise needed to attain their goals. CETAC-WEST takes these clients on a step-by-step journey that may last anywhere from two to five years. If the technologies have the legs to run that course, they will likely be successful.

The process at CETAC-WEST begins with a business case evaluation. An analyst investigates the product or technology to make sure that it is unique and has a potential market niche. That research often includes discussion with potential end-users and competitors. Beyond this point, the entrepreneur is coached to produce a business plan and a compelling argument in favour of his/her product or technology. At this point, Joe Lukacs contacts his network of mentors who join the client-entrepreneur and the CETAC-WEST team in a round-table discussion, usually over lunch. The entrepreneur presents the compelling argument and the mentors discuss and challenge that vision. After this opportunity, CETAC-WEST helps the entrepreneur re-tool the plan until it is market ready, until it has the combination of common sense, marketability, and appeal that will make it fly in the real world.

Once CETAC-WEST has coached the entrepreneur to this point, it is time to find the financing, and perhaps the strategic alliances, that will allow for development and commercialization. Here, CETAC-WEST adds the role of matchmaker to that of analyst and coach. The company introduces the client-entrepreneur to the "angels" who have the wisdom and financial power to help the vision become a reality.

Many of the concepts and methods used by Joe Lukacs and his team at CETAC-WEST were first pioneered and applied by Joe at Western Research. The prominent and successful seminars used by Western Research to brand the company and prove its expertise prompted Joe to use the seminar and workshop method to teach clients as a group, while at the same time creating a network among them. *The Entrepreneur to CEO Workshop*, an annual event lasting a week, exposes the client entrepreneurs to the fundamentals of building and growing successful companies. It also generates excitement and synergies as the entreprenueurs meet one another and share their problems, solutions, strategies, and passions. The success and popularity of this workshop has led to demand for it in other jurisdictions.

CETAC-WEST has a growing file of success stories. Some of the innovative projects with which the company is involved include: a well-plugging technology developed by Steelhead Reclamation to prevent leakage from abandoned oil and gas wells; an economical oil-sand cleaning technology that made millionaires out of a husband and wife entrepreneurial team; and an airborne leak-detection technology for pipeline application (Inventus Technologies).

At the centre of this successful mentoring and management enterprise, Joe Lukacs is once again orchestrating a challenging and exciting—and at times explosive or hilarious—work experience for his CETAC-WEST team. He is, as ever, constantly on the go and always excited by each new business day. Joe's infectious passion for business and excellence, which ignited Western Research into existence and then into prominence, continues to produce results at CETAC-WEST. By distilling the wisdom of his own experience, and of the mentors he gathers around him, Joe Lukacs has manufactured in CETAC a "shooting star machine," a reliable way of honing entrepreneurial talent and aiming it at the heart of the market.

Index